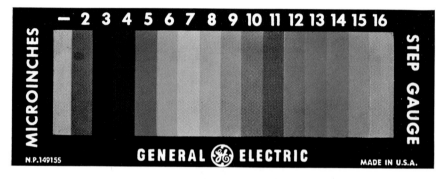

Step gage observed by reflection of
sodium light. (See discussion on
page 178.)

C. L. Andrews

Chairman, Department of Physics
College of Education
State University of New York

Optics

OF THE

ELECTROMAGNETIC

SPECTRUM

Prentice-Hall, Inc.

Englewood Cliffs, New Jersey

1960

To my wife

Preface

This textbook is prompted by the twentieth-century renaissance in physical optics. Optical methods are extending from x-rays to radio waves. The radially accelerated electrons in the synchrotron provide a continuous source of polarized electromagnetic waves from x-rays to the infrared with which to study optical properties of matter. The best measurements of the velocity of electromagnetic waves are no longer made with light but with microwaves. Interference filters are built to order. The interference pattern of a Michelson's interferometer is being used to guide the engines that rule diffraction gratings, and the resolving powers of gratings have increased another order of magnitude. The century-old attempt to observe beats of short duration between primary sources of light has been solved, opening the field of experimental study of the duration of radiation from individual atoms.

No less stimulating are the new devices and methods for studying the principles of wave optics. Microwaves with wavelengths of convenient length provide interference and diffraction patterns that can be spread out on the laboratory table and measured on a meter stick. Thin films are plates of glass and brick walls. Diffraction patterns in the apertures and near the edges of screens can be measured for the first time. The analysis of classical far field diffraction patterns becomes easier if we treat them as part of the whole diffraction pattern including that in the aperture itself. Microwave lenses and prisms of artificial dielectrics made of metal dipoles provide a concrete picture for understanding dispersion by real dielectrics.

The first part of Chapter I lays a historical background for an examination of the contributions of contemporary wave physics. In Chapter II the vibration spiral is introduced at the same time as complex notation for representing amplitude and phase. Throughout the book the algebra of wave superposition is accompanied by plots of vibration spirals on complex coordinates. The introduction of new topics is most frequently inductive and experimental. For instance, in Chapter II the radiation of tangential fields by accelerated electrons is treated first by construction methods. Interference patterns are introduced by construction of superposed waves. The cross sections of cylindrical and plane waves are constructed to give a family of parabolas as an interference pattern. This pattern is checked by measuring the interference pattern produced by the reradiation of cylindrical waves from a metal rod radiated by a plane wave of microwaves. The method finds application later in the study of the total diffraction pattern of a straight edge.

The diffraction of longitudinal waves is treated in Chapter XI by the classical Fresnel-Kirchhoff methods. The diffraction of transverse waves is treated in Chapter XII as unfinished experimental work. Simple empirical equations employing the concepts of Thomas Young are used to describe the present experimental results. This chapter includes work of the author and his students. As the elusive boundary conditions are cornered experimentally the treatment of diffraction will become a part of electromagnetic theory. Maxwell's equations are derived in Chapter XIII from the elementary laws of Gauss, Ampere, and Faraday. No previous course in electromagnetic theory is assumed. The prerequisites are a course in general physics and one in elementary calculus.

The author is indebted to Mr. W. C. White and Mr. E. D. McArthur, who supported and gave ideas for the development of educational microwave equipment, to Dr. Katherine Blodgett for reading Chapter VIII on interference in thin films, Dr. Frank Studer and Dr. Dudley Marple who read Chapters X–XII in diffraction, and Mrs. Winifred Wilson who constructed the drawings, all of whom are from General Electric Research Laboratory. He is also indebted to Dr. Henry Breed of Rensselaer Polytechnic Institute who read the manuscript, to the author's students who made helpful contributions and criticisms, to his son Merrill L. Andrews who criticized the manuscript as a student, and to his wife Kathlyn C. Andrews who typed the manuscript, criticized the style, and read proof.

C. L. ANDREWS

Contents

v

SUPERPOSITION OF WAVES (*Continued*)

CHAPTER IV

THE VELOCITY OF LIGHT   76

CHAPTER V

STANDING WAVES   92

CHAPTER VI

INTERFERENCE OF WAVES FROM TWO SECONDARY SOURCES   108

CHAPTER VII

MICHELSON'S INTERFEROMETER   135

DISPERSION (*Continued*)

CHAPTER XVI

POLARIZATION   388

CHAPTER XVII

DOUBLE REFRACTION   428

CHAPTER XVIII

ELLIPTICAL POLARIZATION   449

chapter I

The Electromagnetic Spectrum

Part I. Historical Introduction. Secs. 1.1–1.5

1.1 Electromagnetic Waves

The expansion of the science of physics during the past century includes a spread of the spectrum of light to encompass, on the long wavelength side, infrared and radio waves and, on the short-wave side, ultraviolet, x-rays, and gamma rays. This expanded spectrum is revealing the extremes of nature, the structure of galaxies and atoms. From the larger spectrum are developing the medical sciences of radiography and radiotherapy, and the engineering sciences of communications and crystallography.

This expansion of the electromagnetic spectrum may seem to complicate physics with topics too numerous to be encompassed by one profession. However, nature provides a simplifying compensation. The waves are identical in every respect except frequency and wavelength. The optics of electromagnetic waves is concerned with the properties of wave motion that are common to the whole spectrum.

1.2 Optics

The word *optics* originally pertained to the eye and the sense of vision. With the development of lenses and combinations of lenses to form telescopes, the word was extended to include aids to vision. Although the study of light rays is as old as astronomy and geometry, the explanation of image formation by systems of lenses in terms of light rays was made by Galileo. By his use of the telescope to study the planets, Galileo initiated the use of optical systems in scientific investigations.

The study of the optics of rays, or geometrical optics, has since become divorced from the eye. To avoid treating the image formed on the retina of the eye, the concept of *virtual image* was developed. A diverging cone of rays from a point source coming through an optical system to the eye is treated as though it diverged from the vertex of the cone, and is called the *virtual image of the point source.* The virtual image exists by virtue of the eye. An observer interprets a diverging cone of rays entering his eye as originating at the vertex of the cone.

Confronted with the problem of correcting chromatic aberration in the refracting telescope, Sir Isaac Newton made a series of observations of the effects of passing white light through prisms and explained the separation of white light into the colors of the spectrum in terms of geometrical optics. On the basis of measurements with the few samples of glass available, Newton concluded falsely that the angular dispersion of colors was proportional to the deviation of the beam and as a result that chromatic aberration could not be corrected by systems of lenses.

Of equal importance for the next hundred years were Newton's queries on whether light radiation consisted of waves or corpuscles. Newton's *Opticks* was written in three books. The first two described his observations and measurements. As Newton found his work frequently interrupted and knew that he could not complete his experiments, he wrote the third book as a series of 30 numbered questions preceded by the statement, "I shall conclude with proposing only some queries, in order that a further search be made by others."[1]

Far from exciting further measurements by others, Newton's queries, which showed a leaning toward the corpuscular theory, were accepted as evidence that light radiation was corpuscular.

So dazzled had the physicists become by the authority of Newton, that it remained for two men outside the field of physics, one an English physician and the other a French engineer, to examine the nature of light critically.

Thomas Young, a medical doctor who was studying vision, turned to the study of light itself. In 1801 Young presented a paper before the Royal Society "On the Theory of Light and Colors." He announced the principle of interference. On the basis of Newton's measurements of the thickness of air films necessary to produce the several colors, Young calculated the wavelengths.

In a subsequent paper Young explained the diffraction pattern of a

[1] Sir Isaac Newton, *Opticks, Book III.*

straight edge as simply an interference pattern between the incident wave and wavelets reradiated from the edge. The calculated wavelengths obtained for the colors in the diffraction patterns agreed with those calculated from the interference pattern produced by thin films.

Not one physicist in England would listen to the idea of interference. Young's work was berated in the journals. His treatment at the hands of his fellow scientists seemed as cruel as the treatment of Galileo by the scholars of the church. These modern inquisitors did not quote the Bible. They quoted Sir Isaac Newton's *Opticks*. Not that they had read Newton's *Opticks* very well. If they had they would have read his 30 queries or suggested experiments whereby it might be learned someday whether light radiation was wave or corpuscular. It was easier for the teachers of optics for 100 years after Newton to teach the leanings of Newton than to perform measurements such as he had suggested.

Young tried again. Using two pinholes as secondary sources he did the experiment now performed in every elementary laboratory of physics. He observed the interference pattern, a family of hyperboloids, and measured the wavelength. Young had succeeded in explaining three different color patterns on the basis of the principle of interference: (1) colors in thin films, (2) diffraction colors by a straight edge, and (3) colors produced by overlapping of light from two secondary sources. Each pattern yielded the same wavelength for any given color.

For seven years Young's work on interference of light waves received the same rebuff. The Rosetta Stone had recently been discovered and Young turned to the less controversial work of translating hieroglyphics.

Fourteen years after Thomas Young discovered the principle of interference, a French engineer Augustus Fresnel independently showed that diffraction patterns, formed when light passed through apertures or by objects, could be explained by assuming light to be wave motion. Fresnel employed Huygens' principle and added to it the concept of phase.

Fresnel's mathematical formulation of Huygens' principle for light waves was in such usable form that it served to predict diffraction phenomena previously unobserved. Simeon Poisson pointed out to Dominique Arago that Fresnel's theory led to the absurd conclusion that a bright spot could be found in the middle of the shadow of a small opaque disc. Arago looked and found the "absurd" bright spot and thus became the first physicist to be converted to the wave theory. Arago sent the memoir of the French engineer to the English physician. Young found a needed audience in Arago and Fresnel. He returned to a problem that had long bothered him in optics, that of explaining polarization. After six years an idea came. Young wrote to Arago that polarization might be explained by assuming that light is a transverse wave. Fresnel clinched the idea by showing experimentally that pencils of light polarized at right angles to each other did not interfere.

Thus an English medical doctor and a French engineer began the study of the wave nature of light known as *wave optics* or *physical optics*.

It is to be noted that Young's and Fresnel's theories of diffraction were different. By Young's theory the diffraction pattern of an aperture in a screen is the interference pattern between the direct unperturbed wave and Huygen's wavelets reradiated from the edges of the screen. By Fresnel's theory the diffraction pattern of the aperture is the interference pattern of all the Huygen's wavelets from every position in the aperture. The edge had no effect other than to bound the radiating area.

Fresnel's idea was expressed with such mathematical clarity and pedagogic pictures that it has been, with refinement by Gustav Kirchhoff, the sole explanation of diffraction in all textbooks of physical optics for over a century.

Until recently Young's theory of diffraction has been of only brief historic interest. However, with the development of sources of hand-sized centimeter waves it is now possible to measure diffraction patterns near and in the plane of the aperture itself. Such patterns are calculated more easily on the basis of Young's theory of diffraction.

1.3 The Discovery of Electric Oscillations

In 1842 Joseph Henry, a professor of natural philosophy at Princeton University, was studying the discharge of a Leyden jar capacitor. He tried discharging the jar through a coil of wire in which he had placed some sewing needles. As he had anticipated the needles became magnetized, but, although he always charged the Leyden jar in the same manner, the needles were left magnetized sometimes in one direction, sometimes in the opposite. After repeated tries he concluded that the discharge did not consist of a current from one side of the jar to the other, but a series of diminishing currents first in one direction and then the opposite, in other words a damped oscillation. This observation followed naturally from Henry's earlier discovery of self-induction in electric circuits. Felix Savary had drawn the same conclusion from experiment 15 years earlier. However, Henry's independent discovery of electric oscillations as a continuation of his investigation of inertial effects in electric circuits had more influence on the electromagnetic theories that were to follow.

Henry concluded his paper by suggesting that electric oscillations might give rise to waves. Since Henry gave no experimental evidence of such waves, this suggestion was of little importance except that it was typical of the way in which physicists of the time were searching for relationships between the fields of physical science. The discovery by Hans Christian Oersted of the magnetic field around a current-bearing wire had united the two previously unrelated subjects of electricity and magnetism. Faraday and Henry had shown that electric "currents" were induced in a circuit by change of linkage between the circuit and magnetic lines of force.

The question of the day was, "Could not other fields of natural science be related?" Thus for 20 years Michael Faraday of the Royal Institution in London searched for effects of electric fields and magnetic fields upon light with a long series of negative results. Every time a stronger magnet was available he searched for any possible effect on a beam of light. Finally in 1845 he observed that when a beam of plane-polarized light was passed through a piece of lead glass in a direction parallel to the lines of force of the magnetic field, the plane of polarization was rotated. Other liquids and solids were found that gave the same results. Faraday had made the first observation of a relation between magnetism and light.

1.4 The Discovery of Electromagnetic Waves

The discovery of the Faraday effect resulted from a direct search for an effect of a magnetic field on light. The discovery by James Clerk Maxwell that light is a wave of electric and magnetic fields originated without any thought of light. Maxwell's sole purpose was to express in rigorous mathematical form the known laws of electricity and magnetism, employing Faraday's concept of electric and magnetic lines of force. Maxwell expressed Faraday's law of induced electromotive forces in terms of fields. A time rate of change of magnetic field gives rise to a space rate of change of electric field. Likewise, broadening the concept of current to include the time rate of change of electric field, Maxwell expressed Ampere's law entirely in terms of fields. A time rate of change of electric field at a point is accompanied by a space rate of change of magnetic field at that point.

Combining these field forms of Faraday's and Ampere's laws, Maxwell showed that electric and magnetic fields do not spread out in space at infinite speed as had been previously assumed, but with a velocity in a vacuum equal to the number of electrostatic units of charge in an electromagnetic unit of charge. Maxwell noted with surprise that this fundamental constant in electricity was, within the limits of existing measurements, equal to the velocity of light. Thus he concluded that light was an electromagnetic wave.

Maxwell read his paper on "A Dynamical Theory of Electromagnetic Field" in 1864. Although the electrical constant had been measured by Wilhelm Weber and Rudolph Kohlrausch eight years earlier and the velocity of light by Leon Foucault two years earlier, no one had noted that the two constants of nature were equal. The discovery of electromagnetic waves was a victory of theory. The fields of light, electricity, and magnetism had been joined in one. Faraday, in his search for a relationship between light and magnetism, could scarcely have imagined how close the relationship was.

Maxwell's electromagnetic waves were transverse as Young and Fresnel had shown light to be. It was no longer necessary to imagine an elastic medium to propagate the waves. The necessity of an "ether" with density less than that of our best vacuum and shear elasticity greater than steel had been the remaining objection to the wave theory of light.

The immediate effect of Maxwell's discovery was to stimulate more precise measurements of the velocity of light and also the number of electrostatic units in an electromagnetic unit of charge. In 1882 Albert Michelson measured the velocity of light as 2.998×10^{10} cm/sec and in 1907 E. B. Rosa and N. E. Dorsey measured the electrical conversion factor to be 2.997×10^{10} cm/sec.

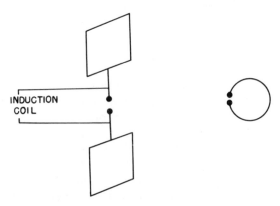

Figure 1. Hertz's oscillator and detector.

Of greater popular appeal than the measurement of another significant figure in the two constants of nature was the discovery by Heinrich Hertz of electromagnetic waves radiated by an electric discharge. Hertz employed Henry's discovery of electric oscillations. He used an induction coil to cause repeated breakdown between two balls. The frequency of the damped oscillation could be adjusted by changing the size of the two coplanar metal sheets attached to the balls of the spark gap. The metal sheets served as a capacitor. (See Fig. 1.) Using a single resonant loop and spark gap as detector, he allowed a beam from a parabolic cylinder to be incident normally on a plane reflector. He detected standing waves and measured a wavelength of 5.4 m.

The waves were polarized. The loop revealed waves when the line between the balls of the detector was parallel to the line between the balls of the transmitter, and none when they were perpendicular. Hertz studied polarization by reflection from a wall of paraffin and measured Brewster's angle. That is, he found the angle of incidence for which reflection occurred when the electric field was parallel to the plane of incidence. Hertz's experiments were repeated in physics laboratories over the world. Every experiment concerned with the wave nature of light was repeated with Hertzian waves, ten million times the length of light waves.

1.5 The Expansion of the Spectrum

In contrast to Hertz's discovery of electromagnetic waves ten million times as long as light waves was the slow pushing back of the boundaries of the spectrum on each side of the visible range. Three new detectors, the photographic plate, the thermopile, and the bolometer, exceeded the range of the eye. Macedonio Melloni found rock salt to be transparent in the infrared and A. C. Becquerel showed that quartz was transparent to ultraviolet. Lenses and prisms were made of rock salt and quartz to extend the spectral range.

In the last half of the nineteenth century there was developed a new intensive branch of physics, spectroscopy. The recording of the wavelengths of spectra of gases and vapors of the elements was a task of pure science which could compare only with the cataloguing of the stars. These data of series of spectral lines of the elements were the basis in the next century of determining the structure of the atoms of these elements.

The greatest contributions to a particular field of science may come from workers in a different field. Maxwell was working with electricity and magnetism, a field seemingly foreign to light. Likewise Wilhelm Konrad Roentgen, when he discovered x-rays, was studying electric discharge at low pressure. The study of cathode rays as the pressure in the tube was steadily lowered made a popular pastime and colorful demonstration in college laboratories.

Roentgen's discovery was scarcely an accident. In the hope of producing cathode rays of such energy that they might penetrate the glass wall, he had developed an unusual vacuum technique and applied higher potential differences across his tube. That he might detect any possible cathode rays escaping from the tube, he covered it with black paper. Nearby he had a paper screen which he had washed with barium-platino-cyanide, a coat which would fluoresce if cathode rays impinged upon it. The surprising new radiation that caused the screen to glow was not cathode rays penetrating the tube but a radiation emanating from the spot where the cathode rays struck the glass. Targets of metals of heavy elements were more efficient emitters of x-rays. If Roentgen's discovery could be called an accident, it was the kind of accident that occurs only to people who are searching for something.

Using slits less than 0.01 mm wide, H. Haga and C. H. Wind found that x-rays were diffracted by a single slit and calculated that the wavelength must be of the order of 10^{-8} cm. The finest ruled gratings were too coarse for the measurement of such wavelengths. Max von Laue made the ingenious observation that x-ray wavelengths are of the same order as the separation of the atoms in crystals and that the regular array might serve as a grating. Two of his students, W. Friedrick and P. Knipping, performed the experiment. It worked.

Nature had provided the gratings for measurements of x-ray wavelengths. Within two generations the discovery of x-rays has yielded branches of medicine, radiology, radiotherapy, and crystallography. The uses of this new patch of the electromagnetic spectrum may be summarized: (1) taking of shadow pictures of the interior of bodies opaque to light, such as bones and organs of the human body and flaws in metal castings; (2) destruction or alteration of cells of living organisms, reduction of cancerous growths, and production of mutations in plants and animals; (3) the determination of the structure of crystals through the study of the diffraction patterns that the crystals produce in a beam of x-rays; (4) the determination of the structure of atoms by measuring the wavelengths of x-rays which the atoms emit and absorb.

The expansion of the spectrum from the low-frequency end toward the infrared has been the history of electrical engineering. One may object that transmission-line engineering is far afield from optics. However, the methods of the transmission-line engineer have been extended to portions of the electromagnetic spectrum which are distinctly optical. Thus to an electrical engineer the study of interference of light in a soap bubble is a transmission-line problem.

Although Hertzian waves from damped electric discharges had been employed in wireless telegraphy, the continuous waves of radio were made possible by electronics. Electronics has been defined as the control of the motion of electrons in evacuated tubes. This definition must now be broadened to include such semiconducting solid-state devices as transistors. One of the means of removing electrons from metals is to raise the kinetic energy of the electrons by increasing the temperature of the metal. In 1904 J. A. Fleming made use of the one-way flow of electrons from a hot filament as cathode to a cold plate as anode to rectify the high-frequency alternating currents produced in wires by Hertzian waves. The rectified current could be measured by a galvanometer or detected with an earphone. Two years later Lee de Forest added a third electrode, a grid of parallel wires between the cathode and anode. By adjusting the electric potential of the grid relative to the cathode he could control the electron stream to the anode. With this triode tube he was able to relay and amplify a high-frequency signal at the expense of energy from a local battery.

An electronic oscillator was now possible. By feeding back some of the amplified high frequency to a tuned circuit on the input side of the amplifier, a continuous oscillation could be maintained. At frequencies of less than a few megacycles per second the frequency of the tuned circuit is determined by lumped inductances and capacitances.

$$\nu = \frac{1}{2\pi\sqrt{LC}}$$

where ν is the frequency in cycles per second, L is the inductance in henrys, and C the capacitance in farads.

Tube and circuit engineering have yielded continually higher radio frequencies as indicated by the language of radio communications. First our radio dials were marked in kilocycles per second and then in megacycles per second. Now television employs h-f, high frequency of hundreds of megacycles per second. The cross-country television relays use u-h-f, ultrahigh frequency of thousands of megacycles per second. Radar uses v-u-h-f, very ultrahigh frequency of tens of thousands of megacycles per second. It appears that the communications engineer will run out of adjectives in another decade. The ultrahigh-frequency waves are known also as *microwaves*. If

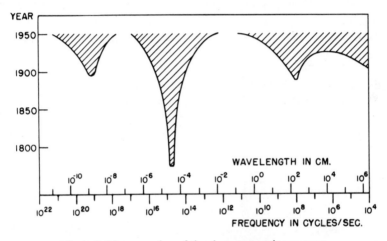

Figure 2. The expansion of the electromagnetic spectrum.

they had been named by workers approaching from the infrared they might have been called megawaves. These higher frequencies are no longer expressed in terms of lumped capacitances and inductances, but in the elementary terms of dimensions of tuned cavities or transmission lines expressed in wavelengths.

The expansion of the electromagnetic spectrum may be represented by Fig. 2. Such a chart must have room for expansion by the reader. Two pincers movements are noted, one between x-rays and the ultraviolet and the other between infrared and radio waves.

Part II. Generation and Detection of Electromagnetic Waves. Secs. 1.6–1.7

1.6 Sources of Electromagnetic Waves

The spectral ranges of the primary sources of electromagnetic waves are indicated in Fig. 3. The shortest measured waves are the gamma rays emitted by atomic nuclei. Line radiation emitted from excited atoms includes x-rays, ultraviolet, visible light, infrared, and microwaves. Molecular spectra extend from the visible through the infrared into the microwave region. Triode tubes in special circuits may be made to produce electromagnetic waves of any frequency from 1/sec up to 10^{10}/sec.

In the visible spectrum line radiations are emitted by excited vapors or gases. In the x-ray spectrum the characteristic lines of the atoms are emitted by solids bombarded by electrons. These lines are superposed on a continuous x-ray spectrum. The continuous spectrum is emitted by decelerated electrons of the cathode stream. A hot solid emits radiation which extends over a

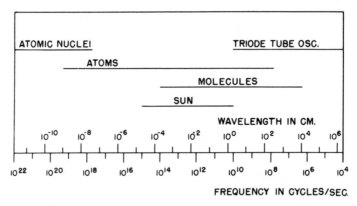

Figure 3. Spectral ranges of sources of electromagnetic waves.

continuous range of frequencies. Figure 4 is a graph of the energy distribution against wavelength for tungsten at 2000°K. The energy distribution curve for any body must lie below that of a black body at the same temperature. Figure 5 shows a plot of the energy distribution through the spectrum for black bodies at three temperatures. Note that the curve approaches zero asymptotically on the long wavelength side.

The lines in Fig. 3 which indicate the measured frequency range from each of the sources may be extended by the reader as new observations are made. Nuclear gamma-ray spectroscopy is a new science. That line is expanding in both directions. The greatest current activity in measurement of molecular spectra is in the microwave region. With the use of large microwave telescopes the black-body radiation curve will extend soon to microwaves.

Most of the demonstrations and experiments described in this book require only simple sources available in laboratories of elementary physics. Three narrow ranges of spectrum will suffice for demonstrations of the principles of wave optics: (1) x-rays of wavelength 8.3 × 10^{-8} cm, that is the K_α and K_β lines of aluminum; (2) the visible spectrum expanded to include the near-ultraviolet lines of mercury and the near-infrared lines of cesium; (3) microwaves of wavelengths 3 cm and 12 cm.

The 8.3 A x-ray line of aluminum has been chosen for simplicity. Less than 2000 volts is required to excite the line. A mechanical pump with a dry

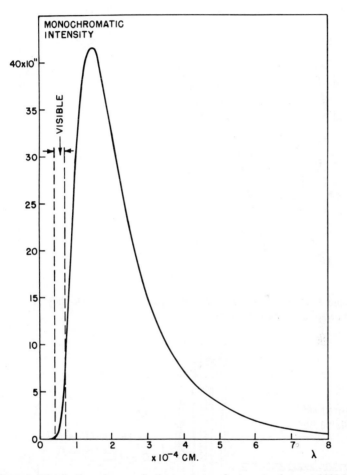

Figure 4. Distribution of energy in the spectrum of a tungsten lamp at 2000 K.

ice and alcohol trap will give sufficient vacuum. Figure 6 is a diagram of an x-ray tube designed for this soft x-ray range. Three line sources in the visible and near visible will serve as samples: (1) a sodium arc lamp with its yellow doublet provides a source for the measurement of wavelength differences by use of interferometers; (2) a mercury arc provides the famous green line and sources in the near ultraviolet; (3) a cesium lamp has two intense lines in the near infrared.

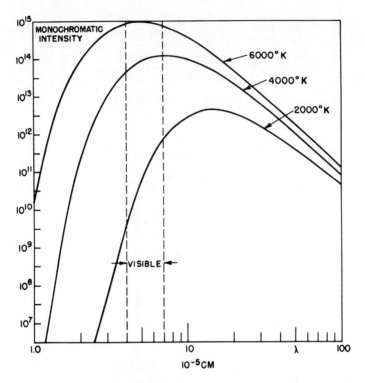

Figure 5. Distribution of energy in the spectrum of a black body at various temperatures, plotted on a logarithmic scale.

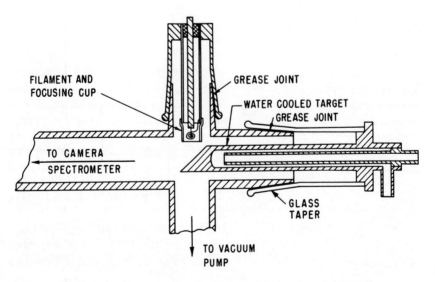

Figure 6. A tube for soft x-rays with replaceable target and filament.

Linear sources of white light and point sources may be obtained by illuminating slits or holes with the image of the positive terminal of carbon arc. Much simpler for illumination of a slit is a straight coiled tungsten filament such as shown in Fig. 7. For many purposes an auto headlight serves as a point source. Figure 8 is a diagram of a zirconium arc. It is the smallest point source available and requires no pinhole in front of it.

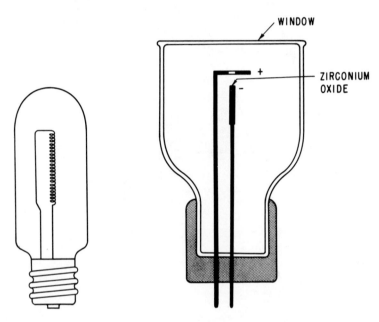

WINDOW

ZIRCONIUM
OXIDE

Figure 7. Straight coiled   Figure 8. Zirconium arc.
tungsten filament.

The simplest source of microwaves is a triode tube designed to fit as an integral part of two coaxial resonant cavities. Figure 9 is of a microwave triode known as the *lighthouse tube*. Figure 10 is a cross-sectional diagram of a microwave oscillator with the tube withdrawn. Figure 11 shows the oscillator. The plate supply is of 200 v, 60 cycles/sec. Oscillation takes place during about $\frac{1}{4}$ cycle when the potential of the plate is sufficiently high. During that time there are about ten million oscillations, so the wave may be considered continuous as far as any studies of interference are concerned. The frequency is 2450 megacycles, assigned by the Federal Communications Commission for educational purposes.

Microwaves have for man a unique place in the electromagnetic spectrum. Their wavelengths are the length of a man's hand. The interference and diffraction patterns may be spread over the laboratory table and measured on

Figure 9. Lighthouse triode tubes. (Courtesy of General Electric Company.)

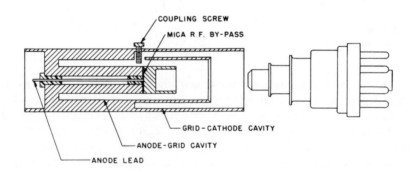

Figure 10. Cross section of a microwave oscillator cavity.

an ordinary meter stick. Thus microwaves serve as an introduction to the other waves of the spectrum.

Figure 11. Microwave transmitter. (Courtesy of Central Scientific Company.)

1.7 Detectors of Electromagnetic Waves

The spectral ranges of some of the common detectors of electromagnetic waves are indicated in Fig. 12. The human eye has the narrowest range of these detectors, namely 4000 to 7000 A. Even in the visible range, the eye is replaced by more quantitative devices for comparing intensities of spectral lines and interference patterns.

The spectral range of the photographic plate is from gamma rays to 14,000 A in the infrared. The effect of radiation of any given frequency on the photographic emulsion is cumulative. Thus by long time exposures faint spectral lines and interference patterns may be recorded.

When some materials absorb electromagnetic waves they re-emit electromagnetic waves whose frequencies are characteristic of the absorber. This phenomenon is called *fluorescence*. As expressed by Stokes' law, the frequency of the reradiated wave is always less than that of the incident wave. For instance, in fluorescent lamps the ultraviolet of a mercury arc is absorbed in the fluorescent coat and re-emitted as visible light of longer wavelength.

X-ray photographic plates are sometimes backed by a fluorescent coat to increase their speed.

If the reradiation continues for some time after the exposure, the reradiating substance is called *phosphorescent*. A way of circumventing Stokes' law in detecting infrared by visible radiation is to expose screens coated with certain phosphorescent solids to ultraviolet. If those screens, while still glowing, are exposed to infrared, they will glow even more brightly.

A simple sensitive device for detecting gamma rays, x-rays, and ultraviolet is the electroscope of the elementary laboratory. These radiations ionize

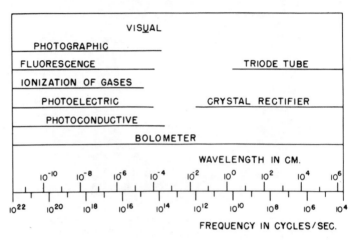

Figure 12. Spectral ranges of detectors of electromagnetic waves.

the air making it conductive. The rate of discharge of the electroscope is a qualitative measure of the intensity.

A refinement of the electroscope is an ionization chamber indicated in Fig. 13. The potential difference between the wall of the metal chamber and the electrode is of the order of 50 v. For measuring intensities of soft x-rays of about 10 A, the ionization chamber may be filled with dry air. The potential across the chamber is slowly increased until the current is saturated, indicating that all the ions which are produced by the x-rays reach the electrodes before they have time to recombine to form neutral molecules.[2] The ionization current is then proportional to the intensity of the x-ray beam. The window is of cellophane, aluminum, or beryllium. For more rapid measurements, electronic circuits have replaced the electrometer.[3]

The photoelectric effect may be used to detect radiation ranging from the

[2] A. H. Compton and S. K. Allison, *X-rays in Theory and Experiment:* Princeton, N. J., Van Nostrand (1934) p. 8.

[3] L. A. DuBridge and H. Brown, *Rev. Sci. Inst.*, **4**, 532 (1933).

highest gamma-ray frequencies to the infrared. We shall confine the word photoelectric to the phenomenon of removal of electrons from metals by impinging photons. The electrons thus removed may be drawn to a collector by an electric field and thence complete a circuit through a resistor. The potential drop across the resistor may be applied to a linear amplifier. If the photocell is evacuated, the photoelectric currents will be proportional to the light intensity.

X-rays produce photoelectrons from all metals. The alkali metals with their loosely bound electrons are sensitive in the visible. Peaks in sensitivity

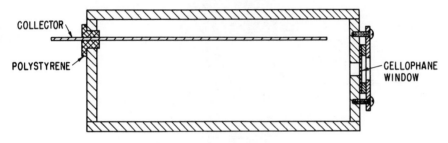

Figure 13. Ionization chamber for soft x-rays.

for the alkali metals occur in the near ultraviolet. Sensitive and insensitive metals have been mixed to increase the upper wavelength limit of the photoelectric cell to 10,000 A in the infrared. Most commercial photoelectric cells now have a sensitive plate of cesium-oxygen-silver alloy.

Figure 14 is a cross section of a photomultiplier tube. Photoelectrons from the first plate are accelerated to the second plate through a potential difference of about 100 volts where they may knock out about ten electrons. Each succeeding plate is at a higher potential so that each plate and corresponding circuit amplifies the current ten times, giving a total current amplification of a million. Such photomultiplier tubes are useful in quantitative scanning of low-intensity diffraction patterns of light and x-rays.

Cells used in intensity meters for light serve the double role of photoelectric cell and rectifier. They are called *barrier layer* or *photronic* cells. In the cell of Fig. 15 a layer of copper oxide is deposited on a copper disc and a thin layer of silver evaporated on top of it. Light passing through the silver drives electrons from the copper oxide into the silver leaving the copper at higher potential than the silver. Figure 16 is a cross section of the photronic cell. The sole source of energy is the light beam. The greatest sensitivity of photronic cells is in the range from 3000 to 7000 A.

Certain semiconducting crystals display an increase in conductivity when exposed to radiations from portions of the spectrum. Selenium cells, sensitive to radiation from 4000 to 14,000 A, were the first in general use.

Figure 14. Photomultiplier tube. (Courtesy of Radio Corporation of America.)

Figure 15. Photronic cell. (Courtesy of Weston Electrical Instrument Corporation.)

Cadmium sulfide crystals are being produced commercially with impurities less than one part in several million. They are sensitive to a spectral range all the way from gamma rays to 70,000 A in the infrared. They may serve as point detectors in qualitative x-ray spectroscopy

The simplest detector of radio waves is the crystal rectifier consisting of a sharp wire pressed against a sensitive spot of certain crystals such as silicon, germanium, or galena. Figure 17 is a typical plot of current against potential difference across the crystal. If the currents are sufficiently small, that is of the order of 100 μa or less, the rectified current is closely proportional to

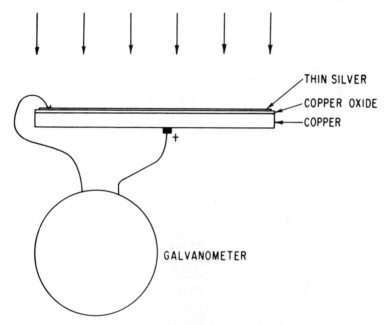

Figure 16. Cross section of photronic cell.

the square of the potential difference across the crystal. Thus the micro-ammeter reading is proportional to the power received and therefore to the intensity of radiation. Figure 18 is a cross-sectional diagram of a simple intensity meter made by attaching a silicon crystal to a microammeter. Figure 19 is a photograph of a commercial intensity meter for use at micro-wave frequencies.

It is often desirable to measure the absolute intensity of radiation in watts per square centimeter or in calories per square centimeter per second. The problem is to transform all the radiant energy to heat and measure the rate of producing heat. For x-rays the absorber may be a block of lead of sufficient thickness. For microwaves it may be a termination of a wave guide matched

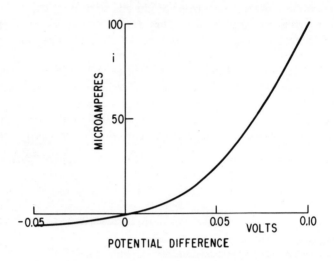

Figure 17. Plot of current against potential difference across a silicon crystal.

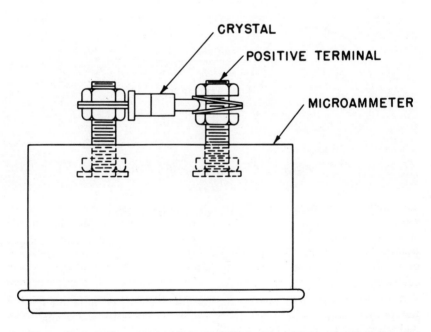

Figure 18. Intensity meter made by attaching a crystal to a microammeter.

to absorb all the wave energy and transfer the heat to a water line. These methods are applicable only if the intensity is higher than a few watts per square centimeter.

In spectroscopy it is important to measure the power of spectral lines and in astronomy intensities of the images of stars. The bolometer was devised by Samuel P. Langley in 1880 for measurement of the intensities of fine lines and

Figure 19. Intensity meter for microwaves.

points. Langley's bolometer consists of two fine platinum strips forming two arms of a Wheatstone's bridge. Platinum is chosen for its high thermal coefficient of resistance. The strips are blackened on one side and one of them shielded from radiation. The art of making bolometers for various parts of the spectrum, particularly the ultraviolet, visible, and infrared, is described by Aldrich of the Bureau of Standards.[4]

[4] W. E. Forsythe, ed., *Measurement of Radiant Energy:* New York, McGraw-Hill (1937).

Part III. Properties of Electromagnetic Radiations
Secs. 1.8–1.11

1.8 Electromagnetic Waves

Electromagnetic waves require no medium for their propagation. They are unique for their extreme range of frequencies. Frequencies have been studied from one to over a billion billion cycles per second. The velocities of all these waves are identical in a vacuum. In common with all waves the frequency of an electromagnetic wave remains unaltered as it passes through different media, or, as far as is known, as it travels through astronomical distances. Only radio and microwave frequencies may be measured directly. All other frequencies are calculated from wavelength and velocity measurements from the expression $v = \nu\lambda$ which applies equally well to a train of waves or a train of railroad cars, where v is the velocity, ν the frequency, and λ the wavelength. Chapter IV of this book will be devoted to the measurements of the velocity of light.

Although it would be possible to measure the length of a water wave by running alongside the wave with a meter stick, such a method would be inconvenient with sound waves and impossible with light waves. The only means we have of measuring the lengths of light waves is to divide the wave into two or more parts and let the secondary waves interfere with each other. The simplest case of interference is between waves traveling in opposite directions along a string to produce standing waves.

Two principles of superposition determine the resulting wave motion when two or more electromagnetic waves cross each other. (1) The effect of each of the superposed waves is the same whether it acts alone or with other waves. (2) The resultant electric field strength E at any time and place is the vector sum of the electric field strengths of the independent component waves. Likewise the magnetic field strengths H are added vectorially.

The first principle has been checked for light under the most extreme conditions. If two light beams cross each other and are studied beyond the region where they overlap, no change in one beam has ever been observed to alter the amplitude, phase, or polarization of the other. This independence of the component waves gives rise to simple wave equations. Sound waves and water waves exhibit this independence only if their amplitudes are sufficiently small. Theory indicates that scattering of electromagnetic waves by electromagnetic waves is too small to be observed by present methods except for high-energy gamma rays.

Stationary interference patterns of waves on the surface of water are used as an elementary demonstration of the second principle. By using two sources of the same frequency and constant phase difference such as two prongs attached to a vibrator and oscillating vertically in the water, we may produce two interfering circular waves. Two vibrating straight edges may be used to produce two interfering plane waves on the surface of the water.

Figure 20 indicates a construction method of determining the interference pattern of two plane waves of the same frequency in a region where they cross obliquely. If they are water waves, the solid lines indicate crests and the broken lines troughs at an instant. Circles indicate points of *destructive interference* where crests and troughs meet. Crosses indicate positions of *constructive interference* where two crests meet to form a higher crest or two

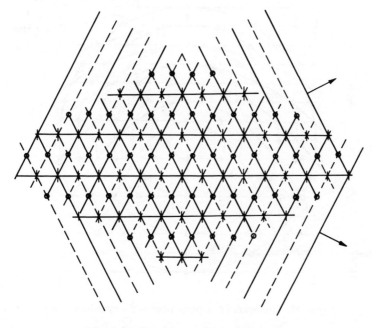

Figure 20. Interference of two plane waves.

troughs to form a deeper trough. Note the path that the resultant double crest or double trough will follow during a half period. The heavy lines connecting crosses are lines of maximum wave motion. In the process of interference the total wave energy is conserved.

Figure 21 indicates a construction method of finding the interference pattern of a plane wave and a cylindrical wave of the same frequency. The crosses and circles indicate points of constructive and destructive interference, respectively. The heavy lines are the paths of constructive interference along which the cross points of crests and of troughs move. They are parabolas along which the plane wave and cylindrical wave are in phase.

Similarly, the interference pattern of two cylindrical waves of the same frequency is constructed in Fig. 22. The paths of like phase are a family of hyperbolas. This is the interference pattern in the historic experiment by which Thomas Young proved that light was wave motion.

As proposed by Young and proven by detailed experiments of Fresnel, light waves are transverse. Much of what we know about the polarization of light by reflection from dielectrics and double refraction in crystals was quantitatively predicted and checked by Fresnel on the basis of the theory that transverse light waves were propagated by an elastic ether.

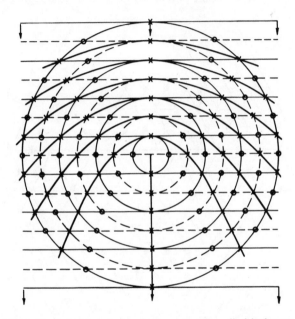

Figure 21. Interference of a plane wave and a cylindrical wave.

With the development of the electromagnetic theory of light much of classical optics has been altered only to the extent of substituting an electric wave for Fresnel's wave in an elastic solid. If we are concerned solely with rehashing old information we may frequently ignore the magnetic wave.

However, if we wish to attack such current problems as the diffraction patterns of electromagnetic waves near wave-sized objects or the behavior of the waves in the new nonconducting magnetic materials called ferrites, we must be prepared to measure and treat the interdependent electric and magnetic waves.

In Chapter XIII we shall treat optics as a branch of electricity and magnetism based on the laws of Ampere, Faraday, and Gauss. We shall at that time develop Maxwell's proof that the time rate of change of magnetic field is accompanied by a space rate of change of electric field and likewise that a time rate of change of electric field is accompanied by a space rate of change of magnetic field. In the meantime we may carry a picture of interdependent oscillating electric and magnetic fields. Figure 23 shows the radiating waves from an oscillating electric dipole such as the half-wave dipole

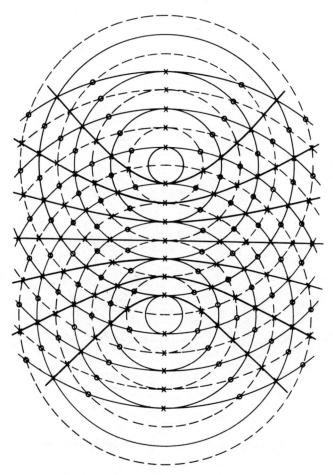

Figure 22. Interference of two cylindrical waves.

of a microwave antenna. The loops represent electric fields, the dots represent outward magnetic fields, and the crosses indicate magnetic fields into the page. The magnetic lines are circles about the axis of the dipole. Outside the first loop the wavelength measured radially outward is closely that of a plane wave. If we swing the fingers of the right hand from the direction of the electric field at any point to the direction of the magnetic field the thumb points radially outward in the direction of propagation. The intensity of radiation at any point is proportional to either the square of the electric field strength or the square of the magnetic field strength. The field strengths are indicated by the density of lines of force. We note that in this traveling wave the electric and magnetic fields are in phase.

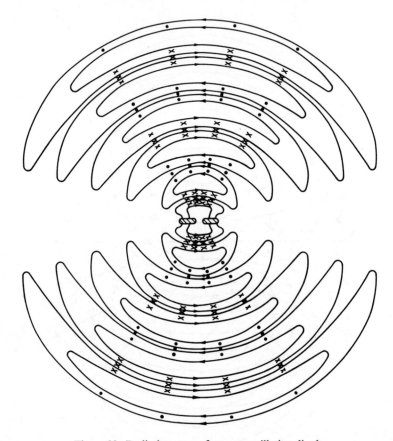

Figure 23. Radiating waves from an oscillating dipole.

1.9 The Doppler Effect

The discovery of the effect of speed of the source or observer of a wave upon the frequency observed had to await the age of the speed of railroad trains. Christian Doppler discovered the effect in 1842. There is still no classroom demonstration of Doppler effect as good as the observation of the higher frequency of a train whistle or jet plane as it comes toward the observer and the lower frequency as it goes away.

The circles of Fig. 24 are snapshots of the crests of a water wave or compressions in a sound wave observed when the source is moving at constant velocity v to the right. Points 1 and 2 are positions of the source one and two periods after passing O. The largest circular crest originated at O, the next at 1, and the smallest at 2. A crest is about to leave point 3 at the

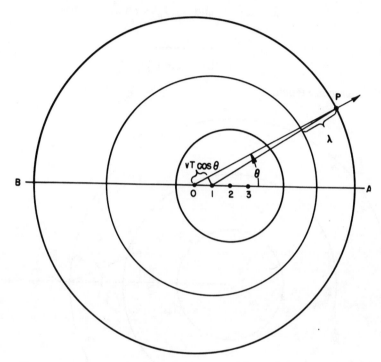

Figure 24. Doppler effect. Source moving relative to medium and observer.

time the snapshot is taken. If the position P of the observer is a large distance from the source compared to the distance the source moves in a period, then with good approximation we may assume that two successive crests are moving in the same direction as they pass P. If v is the velocity of the source in the direction OA then the source moves a distance vT in one period T. In one period the source comes closer to P by the amount $vT \cos \theta$, where θ is the angle between the direction of velocity of the source and the line from the source to the detector at P. Now λ_0 is the wavelength and ν_0 the frequency when the source is at rest; λ is the observed wavelength and ν the observed frequency when the source is in motion. Because of the motion of the source the wavelength received at P is reduced by $vT \cos \theta$.

$$\lambda = \lambda_0 - vT \cos \theta. \tag{1.1}$$

If c is the velocity of the wave, $T = \lambda_0/c$, then

$$\lambda = \lambda_0 \left(1 - \frac{v}{c} \cos \theta\right). \tag{1.2}$$

But $\qquad\qquad \lambda = c/\nu \qquad$ and $\qquad \lambda_0 = c/\nu_0,$

therefore $\qquad\qquad\qquad \nu = \dfrac{\nu_0}{1 - \dfrac{v}{c} \cos \theta} \qquad\qquad (1.3)$

for the source in motion.

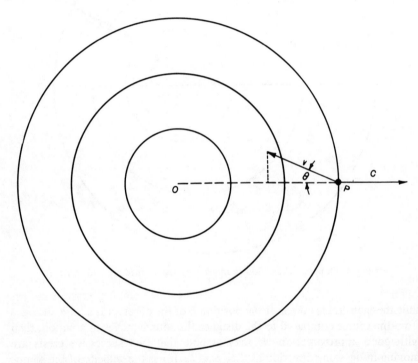

Figure 25. Doppler effect. Observer moving relative to medium and source.

In Fig. 25 the source is at rest relative to the medium that propagates the wave, but the observer at P has a velocity v with respect to the medium. The velocity of the wave relative to the observer is equal to the vector sum of the velocity of the wave relative to the medium and the velocity of the medium relative to the observer. In Fig. 25, c is the velocity of the wave and v the velocity of the observer relative to the medium. Let λ_0 be the wavelength, ν_0 the frequency of the source, and ν the frequency received by the moving observer. The radial velocity of the wave relative to the observer is $c + v \cos \theta$ so that

$$\nu \lambda_0 = c + v \cos \theta. \tag{1.4}$$

For an observer at rest the frequency is $\nu_0 = c/\lambda_0$. Substituting for λ_0 in Eq. (1.4), we obtain

$$\nu = \nu_0 \left(1 + \frac{v}{c} \cos \theta \right) \tag{1.5}$$

for the observer in motion.

Note that in each case the only velocities that affect the frequencies are components along the line between source and observer. If v is small compared to c, then Eq's. (1.3) and (1.5) are nearly alike. For convenience in comparing the two equations the right-hand side of Eq. (1.3) may be expanded in an infinite converging series so that

$$\nu = \nu_0 \left(1 + \frac{v}{c} \cos \theta + \frac{v^2}{c^2} \cos^2 \theta + \cdots \right). \tag{1.6}$$

The preceding treatment has been concerned with waves moving relative to a medium. By a postulate of relativity the velocity of light is the same relative to all observers and can involve no reference to motion of the observer through an ether. The theory of relativity yields the frequency

$$\nu = \nu_0 \frac{\left(1 + \frac{v}{c} \cos \theta \right)}{\sqrt{1 - \frac{v^2}{c^2}}} = \nu_0 \left(1 + \frac{v}{c} \cos \theta + \frac{1}{2} \frac{v^2}{c^2} + \cdots \right) \tag{1.7}$$

in which $v \cos \theta$ is the component of either the velocity of source toward the observer or the velocity of the observer toward the source. The two cases are indistinguishable.

Applications of the Doppler effect constitute a large portion of astrophysics. By comparing the spectrum of a star with a laboratory spectrum of some of the elements found in the star, the astronomer computes the velocity of the star toward or away from the earth. In the solar system itself it is used to measure the velocities of the edges of the sun moving toward or away from us.

The components of velocities toward and away from the earth for the principal stars of our galaxy have been recorded. The spectral lines of some stars are found to be doublets which periodically come together and separate again, indicating that the light comes not from one star but from two stars revolving about a common center of gravity. Many such spectral binaries and their periods have been catalogued.

The spectra of other galaxies indicate that all of them are moving away from us with velocities as high as one-sixth the velocity of light. In 1929 Hubble found that the velocities of the galaxies away from us were approximately proportional to their distances from us. This would be exactly so for any observer in a system that was expanding uniformly. Thus the astronomer speaks of an expanding universe. Because of the high velocities computed, some astronomers question whether the shift of the spectrum toward the red can be entirely Doppler effect. This is one of the problems for the 200 in. telescope at Palomar.

One hundred years after its discovery the Doppler effect is finding application outside the field of science. If a microwave beam is reflected from a moving mirror, such as a person or automobile, we may think of the image as a source which is moving with twice the velocity of the mirror. Since the speed of automobiles is small compared with the speed of light, only the first two terms of Eq. (1.7) need be considered. If $v \cos \theta$ is the component of the velocity of the automobile toward the source, then

$$\nu = \nu_0 \left(1 + \frac{2v}{c} \cos \theta \right).$$

Direct frequency measurements can not be made to enough significant figures to distinguish ν from ν_0. However, if the two frequencies are combined they give beats or the difference frequency

$$\Delta \nu = \nu_0 \frac{2v}{c} \cos \theta. \tag{1.8}$$

A receiver will detect the beat frequency and serve as a motion detector, or, if the output of the detector is fed to a frequency meter calibrated in miles per hour, the instantaneous velocity of the moving object can be determined at a distance.

Still more simply, the reflected wave mixes with the transmitted wave in the oscillator of the motion detector and the beat frequency will be observed as an oscillation in the plate current of the triode tube. In other words, the single triode tube and cavity oscillator serve both as transmitter and as local oscillator in a superheterodyne receiver. The beat frequency is the intermediate frequency of radio parlance. Since the transmitter and receiver are one, there is but one parabolic reflector for directivity thus eliminating the difficulty of pointing two reflectors in the same direction.

Equation (1.8) may be derived in another way. Every time the reflector moves a half wave closer to the source-detector combination the phase difference between transmitted and received wave completes a cycle. Thus the beat frequency equals the number of half waves which the mirror moves per second.

The same phenomenon of beats may be observed with light. If one of the mirrors of a Michelson interferometer, Chapter VI, is moved at constant speed, then the frequency with which dark bands pass the cross hair is the difference in frequency of the two waves.

1.10 Quantum Nature of Electromagnetic Radiations

We no longer speak of a controversy between the wave and corpuscular theories of light. Both the wave and quantum nature of electromagnetic radiation are quantitatively established. The wavelengths have been measured throughout the spectrum except for the shortest gamma rays. The quanta of radiant energy or photons have been measured all the way from the most energetic gamma-ray quanta to the microwave quanta involved in molecular spectroscopy.

If one has a Geiger counter and a lighted match, he may listen to the random patter of ultraviolet quanta. On the other hand, if one has a simple triode microwave oscillator, a pie plate for mirror, a foot ruler, and a crystal detector, he may measure electromagnetic waves as easily as sound waves.

When light beams interfere, their wave nature is exhibited. When electromagnetic waves are radiated or absorbed by matter, the quantum nature is shown. All exchange of energy between matter and electromagnetic waves is in increments of $h\nu$, where h is Planck's constant 6.624×10^{-27} erg sec and ν is the frequency of radiation.

Just as electromagnetic radiation has both wave and particle properties, so matter in motion has both particle and wave properties. The quantum nature of electromagnetic radiation is most readily observed for quanta of high energy $h\nu$ associated with the high frequencies of x-rays and gamma rays. The wave nature of matter in motion is most readily observed for small particles with high speed. C. Davisson and L. H. Germer first observed the wave nature of moving particles when they reflected a beam of electrons from a crystal of nickel to a photographic plate on which they found a diffraction pattern similar to that produced by reflecting x-rays from the crystal. The diffraction pattern could be explained only by assuming that the moving electrons had wave properties.

The complementary wave and particle aspects of electromagnetic radiation and of matter are quantitatively united in the indeterminacy principle formulated by Werner Heisenberg in 1927. According to classical mechanics, if we could measure precisely the simultaneous position and momentum of every particle in a system such as an isolated box of gas, we might predict the future positions and momenta of all those particles. The study of individual x-ray quanta and high speed electrons brought an increasing recognition of fundamental limitations in the measurement of exact positions and momenta of photons and particles. If Δy is the indefiniteness of the y position of a photon on Cartesian coordinates and Δp_y is the necessary corresponding indefiniteness in the y component of the momentum, then Heisenberg has shown that

$$\Delta p_y \, \Delta y \geq h.$$

For example, if electromagnetic radiation passes through a long narrow slit in Fig. 26 of width Δy, then the y position can not be determined more closely than Δy. If the slit is made narrower, the y position of the quantum passing through the slit is determined more closely. However, as the slit becomes narrower the beam will spread through a wider angle as will be shown in Chapter VIII. Thus the component p_y of the momentum parallel to the y dimension of the slit will have a greater indeterminacy Δp_y.

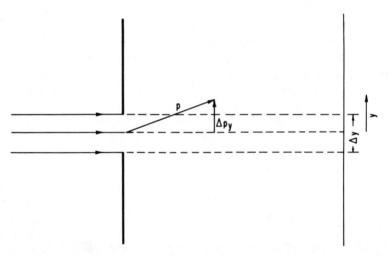

Figure 26. Illustration of indeterminacy principle.

This single illustration is inadequate to give understanding of the scope of the indeterminacy principle. The topic is introduced at this time so that the reader may be alert throughout the study of wave optics to the fundamental limitations in measurements of position and wavelength. There are no focal points or point images formed by waves, but only focal regions whose sizes are of the order of a wavelength. The indeterminacy principle has given added importance to such concepts of physical optics as minimum angle of resolution of optical instruments, the chromatic resolving powers of instruments of spectroscopy, and inherent finite widths of spectral lines.

In Sec. 14.4 we shall note how A. H. Compton was able to describe the scattering of x-rays quantitatively by treating the simultaneous equations for conservation of momentum and conservation of energy when an x-ray quantum collides with an electron. Otherwise this book will be confined to the wave aspect of electromagnetic radiations. The quantum aspect is treated in books of atomic and molecular physics.

1.11 The Unity of the Electromagnetic Spectrum

Isolated portions of the electromagnetic spectrum have been developed by men of different interests using different tools.

Currently x-ray spectroscopists and ultraviolet spectroscopists make skirmishes into the region of the spectrum between 10 and 100 A. If the waves are formed when cathode rays hit a target, they are called x-rays. If they are formed in a spark by an ultraviolet spectroscopist they are called ultraviolet. Actually they are the same waves. Only the tools are different.

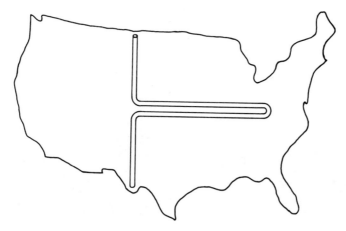

Figure 27. A half-wave dipole designed to radiate the frequency of 60 cycles.

The student of light and the communications engineer with their diverse tongues and tools are meeting in a no man's land between infrared and microwaves. An electrical engineer and the author came upon a "magic T" for microwaves. The one called it an a-c Wheatstone's bridge, the other a Michelson's interferometer. The argument continued. The next morning each came to the other to announce that a Michelson's interferometer and an a-c Wheatstone's bridge were the same thing.

Bragg diffraction of x-rays by crystals may be demonstrated on the lecture table in a man-sized analogy by scaling the crystal and x-rays upward 1 billion times. Wooden balls coated with silver paint simulate the atoms and 12 cm microwaves replace the x-rays.

If the earth were our footstool we could mark off the lengths of waves of 60 cycles/sec between our fingers. We could bend a wire like the half-wave dipole antenna in the parabolic reflector of Fig. 11 scaled upward 40 million times, and lay it down upon the United States as in Fig. 27. The dipole would be 1500 miles long and the wire 50 miles in diameter. It would be as good a radiator for waves of 60 cycles/sec as the 2 in. antenna is for waves of 2.5 billion cycles/sec.

This book is concerned with the properties of wave motion that are common to the whole electromagnetic spectrum. Gamma rays, x-rays, light, and microwaves are all the same waves differing only in wavelength and frequency. They are named by the devices used to produce or detect them. As the different devices are used over wider overlapping portions of the spectrum some of the names for the waves will have only historic meaning.

chapter II

Wave Propagation

2.1 Radiation from an Accelerated Charge

Hertz proved experimentally that a damped oscillation of electricity produces electromagnetic waves. We now ask, what kinds of motion are necessary for a charge to radiate electromagnetic waves?

To visualize how transverse electric fields are radiated, we shall add a third property to Faraday's lines of force. In order to explain experimental observations of action of charges on each other, Faraday endowed electric lines of force with two properties: (1) they repel each other laterally if they extend in the same direction; (2) they are under tension along their lengths. In order to explain radiation of the observed transverse waves we shall add a third property: (3) the electric lines of force from a charged body are constantly moving out with the velocity of light independently of the velocity of the moving charge. If a charge is at rest, then the line density and therefore the energy density of electric field at any point in space remains constant even though the lines are moving out. There is no radiation of energy.

If we make constructions of electric fields on the basis of this third property of electric lines of force, we can predict the conditions for radiation.

Figure 28(a) is an instantaneous picture of the electric field of a charge which is moving with constant velocity to the right. At that instant the charge is at O_2. For construction purposes we may tie convenient knots in Faraday's electric lines of force at regular time intervals as they leave the charge. The knots lying on the smaller circle left the charge when it was at point O_1. They are equally distributed angularly about O_1. Likewise the points on the outer circle are equally distributed angularly about point O from whence they originated. By this simple construction we find that, if a charge is moving with constant velocity, the electric lines of force are straight lines extending radially from the charge.

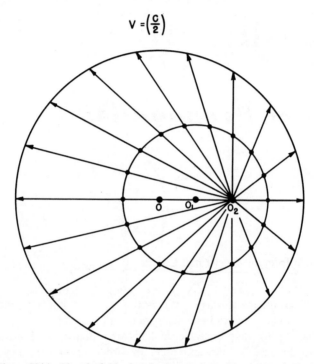

Figure 28(a). Electric field of a charge moving with constant velocity.

The treatment of moving charges in advanced theory may be found under the topics *retarded fields* and *retarded potentials*.[1,2] For our purpose the simple construction methods will suffice. Figure 28(b) is a construction of the electric lines of force around a charge moving at the velocity of light. Since the particle can never have the velocity of light in a vacuum, we shall consider the charge moving through a medium of index of refraction n. The velocity of the electromagnetic wave is c/n.

Figure 28(c) shows the charged particle moving with twice the velocity of light in the medium. At velocities higher than that of an electromagnetic

[1] W. R. Smythe, *Static and Dynamic Electricity:* New York, McGraw-Hill (1939), Secs. 13.25, 14.11.

[2] J. A. Stratton, *Electromagnetic Theory:* New York, McGraw-Hill (1941), Sec. 82.

wave in the medium the particle forms a conical wave front like the shock wave of a projectile traveling faster than sound or the bow wave of a boat traveling faster than surface water waves. If a large number of circles are drawn to indicate points on lines of force that originated when the charge was at positions between O and O_2, they will form a conical Huygens' envelope. The direction of motion of the "shock" wave is perpendicular to the conical

$$V = \left(\frac{c}{n}\right)$$

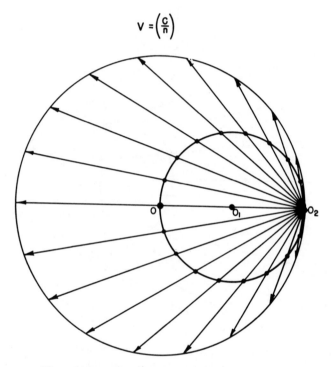

Figure 28(b). Charge moving with velocity of light.

surface. It is a transverse wave. The direction of the electric field at a point on the wave front is always along a line through that point and the vertex of the cone. If the medium is dispersive, that is, the velocity of the wave varies with frequency, then the direction of the slower waves will make a larger angle with the direction of motion of the charged particle. Electromagnetic shock waves are called *Cerenkov radiation* after the discoverer who first observed the light from high-speed electrons moving through water.[3,4] Cerenkov radiation, as visible light, is used to count cosmic rays and high-speed charged particles.[5]

[3] C. R. Cerenkov, *Acad. Sci. U.S.S.R.*, **8**, 451 (1934).
[4] C. R. Cerenkov, *Phys. Rev.*, **52**, 378 (1937).
[5] J. Marshall, *Phys. Rev.*, **86**, 685 (1952).

Figure 28(d) is a construction of the electric field of a charged particle moving with constant linear acceleration to the right. Points O, O_1, O_2, O_3, and O_4 are positions of the charged particle at equal time intervals. The electric lines of force emitted from an accelerated charged body are curved, unlike those from a charged body moving with constant velocity.

$$V = 2\left(\frac{c}{n}\right)$$

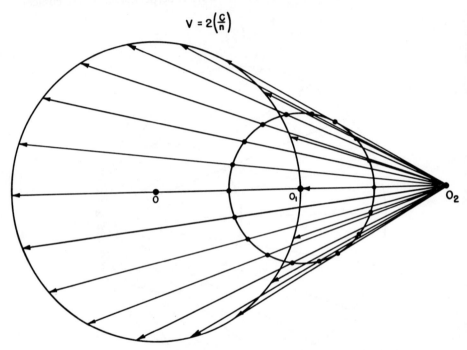

Figure 28(c). Charge moving with twice the velocity of light in the medium.

Figure 28(e) shows the electric field of a particle that has been at rest at O for a length of time, was accelerated from O to O_1 for an equal time at the end of which it had a velocity half that of light, and then moved with constant velocity for the last third of the time. The field emanating from a charge at rest or moving with constant velocity is radial. The field that emanates while the charge is accelerated is curved and has transverse components.

As the pulse of curved field of Fig. 28(e) moves out, the distance between circles remains constant. However, the tangential linear separation of the dots increases with time so that, as the pulse moves out, the curved field approaches a straight line and the ratio of the tangential to the radial component of the field increases. At large distance the pulse or radiation from the accelerated charge may be treated as entirely tangential.

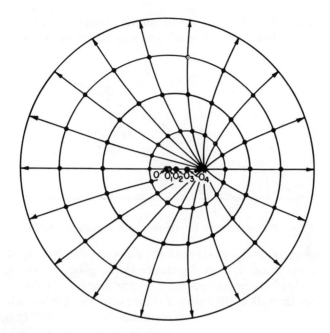

Figure 28(d). Charge moving with constant acceleration to the right.

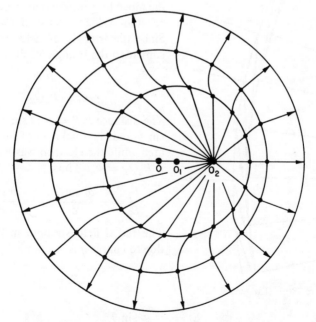

Figure 28(e). Charge accelerated for an interval of time.

If the pulse of Fig. 28(e) has moved out for a long time and O_1O_2 is much larger than OO_1, then a single line of force may be indicated as in Fig. 28(f).

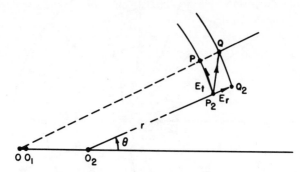

Figure 28(f). Geometry for determination of the ratio E_t/E_r.

In this diagram O_2 is the position of the charge at the time the diagram is drawn, r is the distance from the charge to the pulse, E_t and E_r are the tangential and radial components of the electric field in the pulse, and θ is the angle between the path of the charge and the radial line of force. The velocity of the charge v is small compared to the velocity of light; t_a is the length of time the charge was accelerated and t the much longer time that it moved with constant velocity between O_1 and O_2. Since the triangle of field strengths is similar to the triangle of distances,

$$\frac{E_t}{E_r} = \frac{P_2P}{P_2Q_2}.$$

The distance $P_2P = -vt \sin \theta = -at_a t \sin \theta$ and the thickness of pulse generated while the electron was accelerated is $P_2Q_2 = ct_a$. Thus

$$\frac{E_t}{E_r} = -\frac{at \sin \theta}{c} = -\frac{ar \sin \theta}{c^2}.$$

The radial field strength in free space due to charge q is

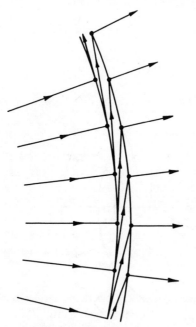

Figure 28(g). Tangential field.

$$E_r = \frac{q}{r^2}.$$

Therefore

$$E_t = -\frac{aq}{c^2 r} \sin \theta. \tag{2.1}$$

The tangential component of the electric field varies as the inverse first power of r while the radial field varies as the inverse square of the distance. When we are so far from a charge that we cannot detect the static radial field we can still detect the radiated transverse field. Figure 28(g) shows how the tangential field strength, as indicated by number of lines per unit area taken at right angles to the lines, becomes greater than the radial field strength.

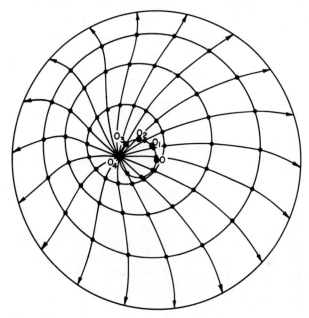

Figure 28(h). Charge moving with constant speed in a circle.

As seen from Fig. 28(e) and Eq. (2.1), the linearly accelerated charge radiates a maximum tangent field at right angles to its acceleration and zero along the line of acceleration. This is observed with x-rays. The continuous x-ray spectrum has a maximum intensity at right angles to the line of the electron stream that is stopped by the target.

In Fig. 28(h) the same construction method has been used to show the field of a charge that is moving with constant speed in a circle and thus always accelerated radially inward. Again the lines of force are curved. The accelerated charge radiates.

In 1947 visible light was obtained from high-energy electrons accelerated at right angles to their velocity as they traveled in a circle in a 70 Mev synchrotron. This was the first time that man had observed visible light from artificially accelerated electrons.[6]

[6] F. R. Elder, A. M. Gurewitsch, R. V. Langmuir, and H. C. Pollock, *Phys. Rev.*, **71**, 829 (1947).

2.2 Simple Harmonic Motion

We have noted that accelerated charges radiate energy by way of transverse electric and magnetic fields. In optics we shall restrict our considerations to radiation by sinusoidal waves, that is, waves whose electric and magnetic fields vary as the sine or cosine of time and position. The source is an electric charge undergoing simple harmonic motion and the fields in every point of the wave are changing in a simple harmonic manner. Complex vibrations will be resolved into a number of simple harmonic motions.

We shall review and define the terms of simple harmonic motion. Although simple harmonic motion is usually defined geometrically, it is such a common motion in nature that we shall first define it in physical terms and then show that this definition is consistent with the general geometrical one.

If a body is distorted within the limits of Hooke's law by external forces that displace the particles along straight lines, and then released, the body will vibrate with simple harmonic motion. Figure 29 shows a bob on the end of a steel ruler clamped in a vise and displaced slightly. If f_r is the internal elastic restoring force in the system and x is the displacement, then by Hooke's law

$$f_r = -kx,$$

where k is a physical proportionality constant known as the *spring constant* of the system. By Newton's second law

$$f_r = ma,$$

Figure 29. Bob on the end of steel ruler.

where a is the acceleration of the bob and m is a proportionality constant for the bob, expressing its linear inertia, commonly known as *mass*. Combining these two laws of nature,

$$a = -\frac{k}{m} x. \tag{2.2}$$

From this physical point of view, *simple harmonic motion is motion in which the acceleration is always proportional and opposite to the displacement.* The proportionality constant always contains an inertial factor and an elastic factor. We may extend the concepts of inertia and elasticity to include inductance and capacitance of an electric circuit.

Having introduced simple harmonic motion as a physical phenomena, we may now turn to the general geometrical definition. *Simple harmonic motion is the motion of the projection of a point moving with constant speed in a circular path upon any straight line in the plane of the circle.* For convenience let the line be the vertical diameter of the circle in Fig. 30, where y is the displacement of point P from the position of equilibrium O, and ω is the angular velocity of the reference particle moving in the circle, and measured in radians per second. Here P, the point undergoing simple harmonic motion,

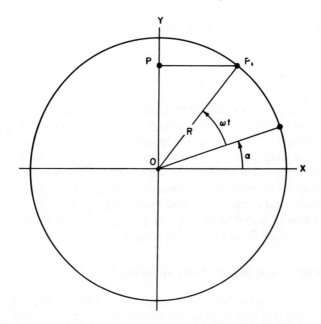

Figure 30. Circle of reference for description of simple harmonic motion.

makes one complete vibration when P_r on the circle of reference makes a complete revolution. The frequency ν is the number of vibrations per second and also the revolutions per second of the reference point. Thus $\omega = 2\pi\nu$. The period T or time for one vibration is the reciprocal of ν. Here α is the angular displacement of P_r from the zero position when we start to measure time; α is called the phase constant, and $(\alpha + \omega t)$ is the instantaneous phase of point P. Since we could as well start our clock when P_r is on the positive x axis, α may seem superfluous. However, if we are considering two simple harmonic motions which are not in phase, we can start the clock when the phase constant is zero for only one of them. The radius R of the circle is the maximum displacement of P and is called its *amplitude*.

From the geometry the displacement of P is

$$y = R \sin (\omega t + \alpha), \tag{2.3}$$

the velocity

$$v = \frac{dy}{dt} = R\omega \cos (\omega t + \alpha),$$

and the acceleration

$$a = \frac{dv}{dt} = -R\omega^2 \sin (\omega t + \alpha).$$

Substituting from Eq. (2.3), we obtain

$$a = -\omega^2 y$$

and

$$a = -(2\pi\nu)^2 y. \tag{2.4}$$

The general geometrical definition yields the same results as our earlier special physical definition. The acceleration is proportional and opposite to the displacement. By equating the proportionality constants of the two equations one may find the natural frequency or period in terms of the physical properties. The reader may recall having found by this method the natural periods of gravitational pendulums, magnetic pendulums, ballistic galvanometers, and circuits with pure inductance and capacitance.

We are now prepared to describe the passage of simple harmonic motion from point to point along the path of a wave.

2.3 Graphical Description of Simple Harmonic Waves

Before expressing the general wave equation we shall describe graphically the special but important simple harmonic wave. For concrete physical reference we may think of a transverse wave along a string, where y is the transverse displacement of a point on the string. More generally, y may be any physical disturbance such as a transverse electric field, density of air, or density in an electron cloud. The particles of the string undergo simple harmonic motion about their equilibrium position. Only the physical disturbance moves through the medium. We name the wave by the physical disturbance, a wave of displacement, a wave of pressure, or a wave of electric field.

The displacement y is dependent on two independent variables: (1) the time, (2) the position of the particle on the string. Thus a three dimensional graph is needed to describe the displacement of a particle at any point along the string at any time. It is often convenient to fix one of the variables and note how the displacement varies with the other. In our thinking we may fix the position x along the string from the origin merely by putting a screen with

a vertical slot in front of the horizontal string and observing how the displacement varies with time. Likewise we may fix the time by taking an "instantaneous" flash picture of how the displacement at that instant varies with

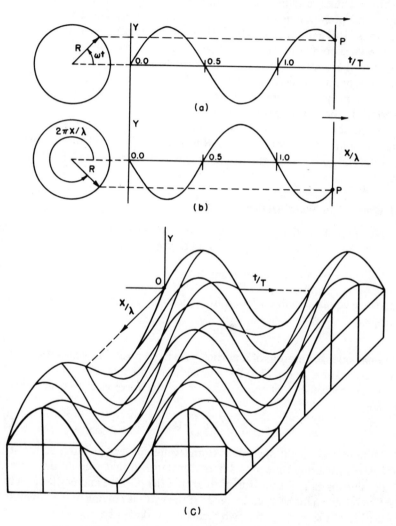

Figure 31. Dependence of displacement on time and position.

position along the string. Figure 31(a) is a graph of displacement against
time t for a given particle, 31(b) is a graph of displacement against position x
along the string at a fixed time, and 31(c) is a three dimensional plot which
gives the displacement of any particle at any time. For convenience we shall

express time in fractions of a period by t/T and the positions along the string in fractions of a wavelength x/λ.

The displacements are simple harmonic with respect to both time and position. Thus, recalling the definition of simple harmonic motion, we employ the point moving in a reference circle. The axes of time and position of graphs 31(a) and (b) extend from the center of the circle. The projection of the reference point is made upon a line parallel to the displacement axis which moves in the positive direction of the abscissa with constant velocity. The projected point P generates the graph. For one revolution of the reference point the projected point P sweeps out one period and one wavelength, respectively, on graphs 31(a) and (b).

In problems of wave motion we shall use a rotating vector instead of a rotating point. The rotating vector R is a radius directed from the center to the rotating point. Thus the displacement y is a projection of the rotating vector.

2.4 Equation of Wave Motion

We shall show that the graphical description of motion of a sinusoidal wave in Fig. 31(c) may be expressed algebraically by

$$y = R \sin 2\pi \left(\frac{t}{T} - \frac{x}{\lambda} \right). \tag{2.5}$$

The wave equation will be found in other forms. Since $\omega = 2\pi/T$,

$$y = R \sin \left(\omega t - \frac{2\pi x}{\lambda} \right). \tag{2.6}$$

If we consider the motion of a particle at a fixed position, then $-2\pi x/\lambda$ is the phase constant α in Eq. (2.3) for simple harmonic motion.

Since the velocity of the wave $v = \lambda \nu$, the wave equation may also be written

$$y = R \sin \frac{2\pi}{\lambda} (vt - x). \tag{2.7}$$

Note that we might measure x from a different zero position on the string and start measuring time at a different instant, so that y could be expressed as a cosine instead of a sine function or that the positive and negative signs of the two terms might be interchanged. If the wave is moving in the direction of increasing x, the signs of the two terms must always be opposite.

We shall show that Eq. (2.7) describes the wave completely. The wave equation must show that the shape of the string is moving unaltered to the right. After a time Δt the displacements y must have all moved to the right a distance $\Delta x = v \, \Delta t$. At any position x_1 and time t_1,

$$y_1 = R \sin \frac{2\pi}{\lambda} (vt_1 - x_1)$$

as indicated in Fig. 32. At the end of time $t_1 + \Delta t$ the vertical displacement at $x_1 + \Delta x$, which we shall call y_2, will be

$$y_2 = R \sin \frac{2\pi}{\lambda} \left[v(t_1 + \Delta t) - (x_1 + \Delta x) \right].$$

Since $\Delta x = v \, \Delta t$

$$y_1 = y_2. \tag{2.8}$$

Therefore Eq. (2.7) describes an unaltered shape of a sinusoidal wave moving along the string in the direction of increasing x.

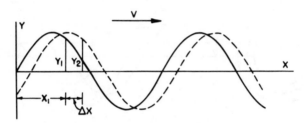

Figure 32. Propagation of waves.

2.5 Vector Representation of Amplitude and Phase

Much of the optics of waves is concerned with superposition. When two waves are superimposed the displacement at any point is the resultant of the displacements of the two waves. The effect of each wave is independent of the presence of the other.

Figure 33(a) shows a graph of displacements against time of two transverse waves polarized in the same direction and passing the same point. If the waves have different frequencies, there are no short cuts. We must add the displacements instant by instant along the time axis to find the resulting complex wave. The sum of two simple harmonic functions of the same frequency is another simple harmonic function of that frequency. As seen from Fig. 33(a) the vector sum of the two rotating vectors that generate the component waves is the rotating vector that generates the resultant wave. This vector construction serves in lieu of analytic proof. If we know the amplitude of the resultant wave and its phase relative to one of the components, there is no more information to be gained. The rotating vectors give that information. In Fig. 33(a) the resultant wave lags wave A by 37° and leads wave B by 53° as seen either from the graphs on the time axis or the rotating vectors. In solving problems we need not draw the sine curves but only the rotating vectors that generate them.

The phase of a wave is meaningful only when expressed relative to another wave. We shall take one of the waves as reference and its rotating vector as reference vector. In all problems of superposition the reference vector should be indicated. It is usually drawn horizontally. In sweeping out the waves the tails of the rotating vectors will be together, but in vector addition it will be convenient to use the continuous polygon method shown in Fig. 33(b).

In the use of rotating vectors to represent simple harmonic waves, we have expanded the meaning of the word vector. In elementary mechanics a vector has magnitude and direction. The rotating vectors which we shall treat have magnitude and phase. For instance, if we had been treating sound waves

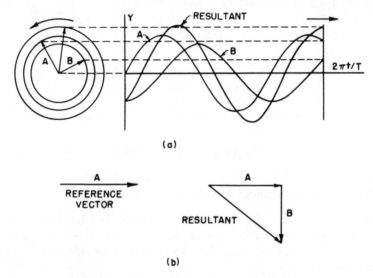

Figure 33. Addition of waves of the same frequency.

instead of transverse waves in a string, pressure would have been plotted as ordinate instead of transverse displacement y. Pressure is not a vector quantity. However, a rotating vector may be used to represent the amplitude and phase of a pressure that is varying in a simple harmonic manner.

We shall next consider another time-saving method, the representation of vectors by complex numbers.

2.6 Complex Numbers. A Simple Representation of Vectors

A review of the graphical representation of complex numbers will reveal that the treatment of vectors in two dimensions and complex numbers is the same.

Graphical representation of the "complete" number system requires two dimensions. The square root of a negative real number is called an *imaginary number* and may be expressed as a real number times the square root of minus one which is represented here by the letter j. For example the imaginary number $\sqrt{-4} = 2j$. A "complete" number may contain both real and imaginary terms such as $3 + 2j$ and is called a *complex number*.

As a scheme for plotting all the numbers in the system on Cartesian coordinates, the real term of any number is plotted as abscissa, and the coefficient of j in the imaginary term is plotted as ordinate. For example, the point representing the number $3 + 2j$ is indicated in Fig. 34. The complex number $3 + 2j$ may be used to represent a vector drawn from the origin to the point.

Real numbers are used to describe scalar quantities. Complex numbers are used to describe vector quantities. A first course in physical optics provides an introduction to the use of complex numbers as a simple representation of vectors.

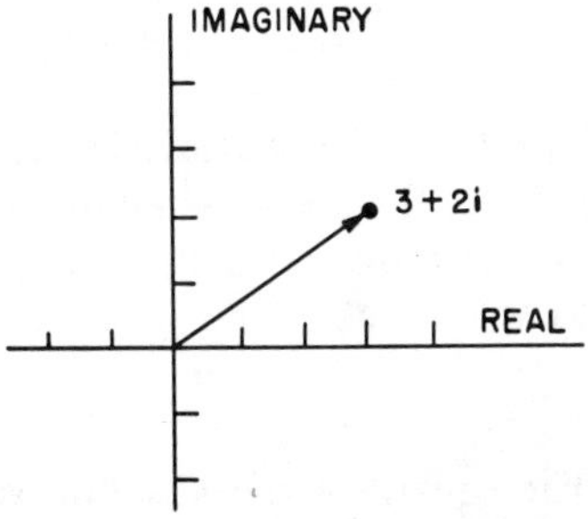

We also may use polar coordinates to represent complex numbers. If ϕ is the phase angle measured from the positive x axis to the vector and u is the magnitude or length of the vectors, then

$$x + jy = u \cos \phi + ju \sin \phi = ue^{j\phi}, \quad (2.9)$$

Figure 34. Graphical representation of complex numbers and vectors.

where e is the Naperian base. The second of the two Eq's. (2.9) may be found by series expansion of the three functions of ϕ.

If the amplitudes are represented by the letter u, we shall call the x,y plane the u plane. The same letter is often used to represent the vector. To distinguish between the amplitude u and the vector u, the vector quantity is often expressed with a bar over it in handwriting or with bold type in printing. In physical optics the vector is sometimes spelled out "the complex amplitude u," meaning a quantity with both amplitude and phase.

Thus we may write complex $u_1 = x_1 + jy_1$, and complex $u_2 = x_2 + jy_2$. The equation complex $\mathbf{u}_1 = $ complex $\mathbf{u}_2$ implies that $x_1 = x_2$, $y_1 = y_2$, and $\phi_1 = \phi_2$.

We may review two rules of algebra of complex quantities.

I. *In addition, the components of the vector (complex) sum are equal, respectively, to the sum of the components.*

For example,

$$(x_1 + jy_1) + (x_2 + jy_2) = (x_1 + x_2) + j(y_1 + y_2).$$

II. *In multiplication, the amplitude of the vector (complex) product is equal to the product of the amplitudes, and the phase angle of the product is equal to the sum of the phase angles.*

For example,

$$(u_1 e^{j\phi_1})(u_2 e^{j\phi_2}) = u_1 u_2 e^{j(\phi_1 + \phi_2)}.$$

In addition of vectors the Cartesian form is most convenient. In multiplication the exponential polar form is used.

The *conjugate* of a given complex number $\mathbf{u} = x + jy$ is another complex number $x - jy$. In polar form we may express the complex number and its conjugate by $x + jy = u \cos \phi + ju \sin \phi$ and $x - jy = u \cos \phi - ju \sin \phi$. Multiplying the two equalities, we obtain

$$x^2 + y^2 = u^2,$$

where u, which we have let represent the amplitude of a wave, is the *absolute value* of the complex number $\mathbf{u}$. The absolute value of a complex quantity is indicated by enclosing the complex quantity between two vertical lines. Thus we may write

$$u = |\mathbf{u}| = \sqrt{x^2 + y^2}.$$

The square of the absolute value is equal to the product of the complex quantity and its conjugate,

$$|\mathbf{u}|^2 = (x + jy)(x - jy).$$

Using the exponential form, we obtain

$$|\mathbf{u}|^2 = (ue^{j\phi})(ue^{-j\phi}).$$

2.7 Intensity of Radiation

Electromagnetic waves are a means of transmitting energy. The flow of power per unit area at right angles to the direction of radiation is the *intensity of radiation*. The intensity at a point is the limit of the power per area as the area approaches zero.

In the field of physical optics the word intensity always means intensity of radiation. In electricity the electric field strength is frequently called *electric intensity*. In this book, where optics and electricity meet, we shall not use the word intensity alone but shall specify electric intensity E or intensity of radiation I.

We wish to show that the intensity of radiation of a wave which involves motion of particles in an elastic medium is proportional to the square of the amplitude. If a particle of an elastic body which is taking part in wave motion is displaced to a maximum, then, as in the case of the bob on the steel ruler in Fig. 29, all its energy is elastic potential energy. A quarter period later it is all kinetic energy if the wave is undamped. If the particle is displaced within the limits of Hooke's law, the work stored as elastic potential energy is

$$\text{P.E.} = \int_0^u f_a \, dy,$$

where f_a is the external applied force required to hold the particle in the displaced position and is equal and opposite to the force of restitution f_r. From Hooke's law $f_r = -ky$, where k is the spring constant.

$$\text{P.E.} = k \int_0^u y \, dy = \tfrac{1}{2}ku^2,$$

where u is the amplitude of vibration.

For a plane wave traveling through an elastic medium the energy per volume is proportional to the square of the amplitude. If we consider a cylinder of unit cross section perpendicular to the direction of propagation and length v along the direction of propagation which is the distance the wave travels in unit time, the total energy in the cylinder travels through the end face in unit time. Thus the intensity of radiation equals the product of the energy density and the velocity. Since the velocity is a constant *the intensity of radiation is proportional to the square of the amplitude*. Thus the intensity of radiation is proportional to the square of the absolute value of the complex amplitude which in the preceding section was shown to be equal to the product of the complex amplitude and its conjugate.

2.8 Velocity, a Function of the Physical Properties of the Medium

We have observed that the natural period of a body undergoing simple harmonic motion is determined by the inertial and elastic properties of the system. The velocity of a wave through a medium also depends on the inertial and elastic properties of the medium.

We shall derive the expression for the velocity of a wave in a string in terms of the physical properties of the string. For convenience we shall employ a farm scene which disappeared in the early twentieth century. Threshing machines were driven by means of belts to steam engines 50 ft away. The operator adjusted the tension in the belt until, when he hit the moving belt with a crowbar, the dent or pulse made in the belt would move very slowly or even stand at rest. In this latter case the velocity of the wave relative to the belt was equal and opposite to the velocity of the belt relative to the observer. Thus the pulse remained at rest relative to the observer. Actually, when the belt was struck, a pulse traveled in each direction but the one moving in the same direction as the belt had a velocity twice that of the belt and could scarcely be seen. The operator claimed that this adjustment preserved the belt. In any event it amused the boys and, if they showed appreciation, he would give the belt one or two extra blows to produce some complex wave forms. The lacings in the belt could be seen moving over the stationary pulses repeatedly until the wave finally damped out. Christensen[7] has improved this demonstration for the classroom by using rubber tubing filled with sand as a belt.

We may now derive the velocity of the wave the magnitude of which is the same as the speed of the particles that travel over the stationary hump. Figure 35 shows such a pulse. A short section of belt Δl long which we have

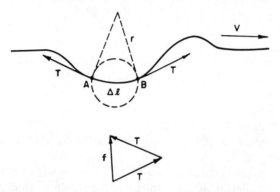

Figure 35. Radially accelerated element of string.

isolated by a dotted line is traveling over the top of the pulse. For any real wave pulse, Δl will approach a circular arc in the limit as Δl approaches zero. If the speed is constant, the short piece of belt is being accelerated toward the center of the circle with a magnitude v^2/r, where v is the velocity of the wave relative to the belt and r is the radius of curvature of element Δl. The force that accelerates the element of the belt is the vector sum of the two forces T due to tension acting at the points A and B. In the limit as Δl approaches zero the weight of the element of belt becomes negligible compared to the tension. The distance triangle made up of cord AB and the radii is similar to the force triangle so that

$$\frac{f}{T} = \frac{\text{cord } AB}{r}.$$

In the limit as Δl approaches zero the length of cord approaches the length of the arc. If ρ_1 is the mass per length of the string, then the mass of the piece is $\rho_1 sl$ and by Newton's second law

$$f = \frac{\rho_1 \, \Delta l v^2}{r}.$$

[7] F. E. Christensen, *Am. J. Phys.*, **16**, 248 (1948).

If we substitute for f in the previous equation, we obtain

$$v = \sqrt{\frac{T}{\rho_1}}. \tag{2.10}$$

Expressions for velocities of other waves take similar form. For longitudinal waves in a liquid

$$v = \sqrt{\frac{B}{\rho}},$$

where B is the bulk modulus of elasticity and ρ is the mass per volume or "volume density" not to be confused with the "length density" in the expression for a string. For transverse waves in a solid

$$v = \sqrt{\frac{n}{\rho}},$$

where n is the shear modulus of elasticity and ρ the density.

By definition of a solid, only solid media may transmit transverse waves. Thus the historical "ether" is a solid which, if it has a shear modulus of elasticity no less than steel, must have a density less than that of our best vacuum in order to transmit transverse waves with the speed of light.

In Chapter XIII we shall derive Maxwell's equations from the elementary laws of electricity and magnetism and show that the velocity of electromagnetic waves is

$$v = \frac{1}{\sqrt{\epsilon\mu}}, \tag{2.11}$$

where ϵ is the electric permittivity and μ is the magnetic permeability of the medium expressed in rationalized mks units.

2.9 Reversibility of Waves

If there is no absorption of a wave, the wave motion is reversible. For mechanical waves this is a special case of the principle of reversibility in mechanics. If the velocities of all the particles in a system are instantaneously reversed, the mechanical motion of all the particles will be re-enacted in reverse.

The interchangeability of the positions of object and image in elementary geometrical optics is an application of the principle of reversibility.

The field patterns of a given radio or microwave antenna are the same whether the antenna is used as a transmitter or receiver. Figure 36 is the plot of the field pattern of a particular microwave antenna taken in the electric plane, that is, the plane containing complete electric lines of force. The plot is of intensity of radiation, taken at large distances compared to the size of the antenna, against angle on polar coordinates. A television receiver antenna is rotated about a vertical axis until its main lobe is pointed into the beam that is to be received.

Microwave radar employs the principle of reversibility effectively by using the same antenna as transmitter and receiver. If the antenna is a parabolic reflector many wavelengths in diameter, most of the power is concentrated in one narrow lobe. It would be difficult to point a separate transmitter and receiver in the same direction. How-

ever, if the same antenna is used alternately as transmitter and receiver, then at any instant that an airplane lies in the main lobe of the transmitter it also lies in the main lobe of the receiver. The demonstration of the Doppler effect in Sec. 1.9 also employs the same antenna as transmitter and receiver.

Figure 36. Field pattern of a microwave antenna.

For later use we shall employ the principle of reversibility to find the relationship between the amplitudes of the incident, reflected, and refracted wave when a ray is incident from any angle in air upon the surface of a dielectric. In Fig. 37 u is the amplitude of a wave incident in air, r_{ad} is the fraction of the incident amplitude in the reflected wave when the incidence is from air to the dielectric, and t_{ad} is the fraction of the incident amplitude in the transmitted amplitude.

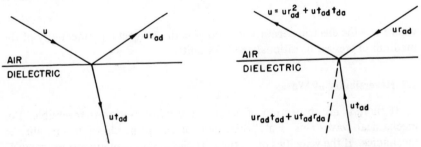

Figure 37. Principle of reversibility applied to reflection and refraction.

The principle of reversibility may be applied whether the medium is absorbing or not. Since the percentage of absorption depends upon distance traveled in the dielectric, we may employ a sufficiently short path in the dielectric that the absorption losses are negligible.

The reversed rays of amplitudes ur_{ad} and ut_{ad} will both be divided at the boundary between reflected and refracted waves. If reversal is exact, then the resultant of the refracted ur_{ad} amplitude and the reflected ut_{ad} amplitude along the dotted line must be zero. The resultant of the reflected ur_{ad} amplitude and the transmitted ut_{ad} amplitude must equal u. Algebraically

$$\begin{cases} ur_{ad}t_{ad} + ut_{ad}r_{da} = 0 \\ ur_{ad}^2 + ut_{ad}t_{da} = u, \end{cases}$$

where r_{da} is the fraction of amplitude reflected for incidence from the dielectric to air and t_{da} is the fraction of amplitude in the refracted ray when the incidence is from dielectric to air. It is seen that the percentages of reflected and refracted amplitudes is independent of the amplitude of the incident wave.

$$r_{ad} = -r_{da}. \tag{2.12}$$

The fraction of amplitude reflected is the same in each case. Note that the two cases do not involve the same angle of incidence. One of the two waves undergoes a 180° phase change upon reflection as indicated by the negative sign. Lloyd showed experimentally that it is the wave incident from the air on the dielectric that reverses phase upon reflection. Lloyd's mirror will be treated in Sec. 6.6. From the second equation,

$$r_{ad}^2 + t_{ad}t_{da} = 1. \tag{2.13}$$

We shall find this expression useful in the treatment of multiple reflections in thin films.

PROBLEMS FOR CHAPTER II

2.1.1. Plot the electric lines of force in the neighborhood of an electron that has decelerated at a constant rate from the velocity of light to rest in a distance of 4 cm.

2.2.2. From the physical and geometrical expressions of simple harmonic motion in Eqs. (2.2) and (2.4), derive the frequency of the bob on the ruler in terms of the physical properties of the system.

2.3.3. From the graph of Fig. 31(c), what is the displacement y at a point on the string a half wave from the origin and three-quarters of a period after the clock was started?

2.4.4. Solve problem 2.3.3. from the wave Eq. (2.5) and check with the previous graphical solution.

2.5.5. Plot graphically on coordinates of displacement and time two super-imposed waves of the same frequency and polarization, one of amplitude 2 cm and the other of 3 cm lagging 60° behind it. Plot the resultant wave point by point and determine its amplitude and phase. Solve the same problem by use of rotating vectors and compare the time required for the two solutions.

2.6.6. Plot the complex number $-3 + 5j$ graphically in complex space. What is the magnitude of the vector it represents? What is the direction of this vector relative to the positive real axis?

2.6.7. By expanding each term in a Maclaurin series, prove that

$$\cos \phi + j \sin \phi = e^{j\phi}.$$

2.6.8. Prove that $e^{j\pi/2} = j$.

2.6.9. Show that multiplying a vector by j rotates the vector through $\pi/2$ radians.

2.6.10. By constructing the real and imaginary components of two vectors and of their vector sum, illustrate rule I for addition of vectors.

2.7.11. In Fig. 33 what are the relative powers transmitted down the string by the three waves? What is the relation between the power transmitted by the component waves and the power transmitted by the resultant wave?

2.8.12. The grid wires of a disc-seal triode tube such as that of Fig. 9 are mounted within a few thousandths inch of the cathode. They must be under tension of 80% of tensile strength when they are at room temperature in order that they will not sag at the temperature of operation. The grid wires are stretched and welded across a metal washer which is the disc seen near the middle of the lighthouse tube. The technician who welds the grids of experimental tubes is seen to look through a microscope at the grid which is clamped to a magnetic vibrator driven by an audio oscillator while she turns the frequency dial of the oscillator. As she clamps and dials she throws approximately half the grids in the wastebasket. What elementary experiment in physics is she performing in order to improve the quality of tubes? What data are needed to compute the tension in the grid wire?

2.8.13. A grid wire of tungsten used in an experimental disc-seal triode is 0.2 cm long and 1.0×10^{-3} cm in diameter. When stretched across the grid washer and welded, the wire is observed to have a natural frequency of 100,000 cycles/sec. The density of tungsten is 19 g/cm³. What is the tension in the wire?

chapter **III**

Superposition of Waves

3.1 The Principle of Superposition

The principle of superposition may be stated in two parts:

(1) *The displacement caused by a wave passing a point at any instant is independent of other waves passing that point.* (2) *The total displacement at any point is the resultant of the displacements of all the waves.*

This principle does not apply to sound waves when the displacement is too large.

Part (1) has been tested many times for light. If a light beam is passed through an aperture and another beam made to cross it in the aperture, no change is ever detected in the frequency, intensity, or polarization of the first beam beyond the region where they cross.

Part (2) is more difficult to test except for special cases. Sound waves, whether continuous or damped, may be recorded both as component and resultant waves on an oscillograph. A simple demonstration of superposition is that of beats between two sound waves of small difference in frequency. Beat frequencies are also obtained between continuous electromagnetic waves produced by mechanical alternators and vacuum tube oscillators. The superheterodyne radio receiver combines the received radio wave with that from a local oscillator in the receiver to form a difference frequency or beat frequency.

Beat frequencies may be observed between two secondary sources of monochromatic light. For instance, if one of the mirrors of Michelson's interferometer of Fig. 90 is moving with constant velocity, then the dark bands move across the field of view with a beat frequency which is the difference between the frequency of the primary source and the Doppler frequency of the virtual secondary source. The secondary source moves with twice the velocity of the mirror.

In 1951 Ewen and Purcell[1] detected emission of the 1420 megacycle/sec line from hyperfine levels of interstellar hydrogen with a superheterodyne receiver. This was an observation of beats between an atomic emitter and an electronic tube oscillator.

In 1955 Forrester, Gudmundsen, and Johnson[2] proved the second part of the principle of superposition experimentally by observing beats between two primary sources of light. The difference frequency was only one ten-thousandth of the frequency of either component so that the beats were in the 10^{10} cycles/sec microwave region. This historic discovery was the end of a century-long search for beats between primary light sources. We may expect the continued study of beats between primary sources to give an experimental measure of the duration of the damped waves emitted by individual atoms.

3.2 Superposition of Waves of the Same Frequency

In the following chapters on interference and diffraction of waves we shall limit our thinking largely to the special case of superposition of waves of the same frequency from a common primary source. The secondary sources are sometimes produced by mirrors as in Michelson's interferometer, or by slots in a grating. The superposition of waves of the same frequency is generally called *interference*.

Young's principle of interference and Fresnel's extensive use of the principle of interference in solving problems of diffraction employed as a first step the concept of Huygens that *every point on a wave front may be considered as a source of secondary wavelets which combine to form succeeding wave fronts*. Using this principle, Huygens constructed secondary circular wavelets that had traveled outward for the same length of time from evenly spaced points on a wave front. He showed that their envelope was a new wave front on the side away from the source. He did not explain why the same wavelets did not propagate to the rear. As shown by construction methods in elementary textbooks of physics,[3,4] Huygens was able to explain

---

[1] H. I. Ewen and E. M. Purcell, *Phys. Rev.*, **83**, 881 (1951).

[2] Forrester, Gudmundsen, and Johnson, *Phys. Rev.*, **99**, 1691 (1955).

[3] E. Hausmann and E. P. Slack, *Physics*, 3rd ed.: New York, Van Nostrand (1948) Secs. 354–355.

[4] F. W. Sears and M. W. Zemansky, *University Physics*, 2nd ed.: Reading, Mass., Addison-Wesley (1955) Secs. 40–1, 40–2.

the equality of the angle of incidence and reflection and, from given velocities of wavelets in two media, to explain refraction of a wave at a boundary between the media. By his construction method Huygens indicated that waves should bend around corners, but he could give no indication of the structure of a diffraction pattern.

Fresnel retained Huygens' concept that every point on a wave front was a secondary source, but did not attempt to construct new wave fronts. Instead he concentrated on one point P of observation in space, and determined by superposition the resultant amplitude and phase of continuous wavelets from every point on the wave front as they passed point P.

The remainder of this chapter will be concerned with the methods of treating superposition of waves.

3.3 Composition of Simple Harmonic Motions

If two sinusoidal transverse waves of the same frequency and polarization pass the same point, the motion of the particle may be treated as the resultant of two simple harmonic motions.

We may plot graphs of the displacement due to each wave against time and find the resultant displacements at each instant, point by point as in Fig. 33, or we may add the rotating vectors to obtain the same information concerning the amplitude and phase of the resultant vibration.

We shall represent the complex amplitudes on complex coordinates. The expression complex amplitude, we recall, includes both amplitude and phase. Here $\mathbf{u}_1$ and $\mathbf{u}_2$ are the component complex amplitudes and $\mathbf{u}$ the resultant.

$$\mathbf{u} = \mathbf{u}_1 + \mathbf{u}_2.$$

The vector sum is indicated on complex coordinates in Fig. 38. If u_1, u_2, and u are the amplitudes and ϕ_1, ϕ_2, and ϕ are the phases of the two component motions and the resultant, respectively, then the complex amplitudes may be expressed in polar form.

$$\left\{ \begin{array}{l} \mathbf{u}_1 = u_1 \cos \phi_1 + j u_1 \sin \phi_1 \\ \mathbf{u}_2 = u_2 \cos \phi_2 + j u_2 \sin \phi_2 \\ \mathbf{u} = u \cos \phi + j u \sin \phi. \end{array} \right.$$

We wish to solve for the amplitude u and the phase ϕ in terms of the amplitudes and phases of the components.

The complex expression $\mathbf{u} = \mathbf{u}_1 + \mathbf{u}_2$ implies that the sums of the real terms on the two sides of the equation are equal and the sums of the imaginary terms on the two sides are equal. Therefore,

$$\left\{ \begin{array}{ll} u \cos \phi = u_1 \cos \phi_1 + u_2 \cos \phi_2 & (3.1) \\ u \sin \phi = u_1 \sin \phi_1 + u_2 \sin \phi_2. & (3.2) \end{array} \right.$$

Squaring and adding Eqs. (3.1) and (3.2) yields

$$u^2 = u_1^2 + u_2^2 + 2u_1u_2(\cos \phi_1 \cos \phi_2 + \sin \phi_1 \sin \phi_2).$$

By a trigonometric identity,

$$u^2 = u_1^2 + u_2^2 + 2u_1u_2 \cos (\phi_1 - \phi_2). \tag{3.3}$$

Dividing Eq. (3.2) by (3.1) gives

$$\tan \phi = \frac{u_1 \sin \phi_1 + u_2 \sin \phi_2}{u_1 \cos \phi_1 + u_2 \cos \phi_2}. \tag{3.4}$$

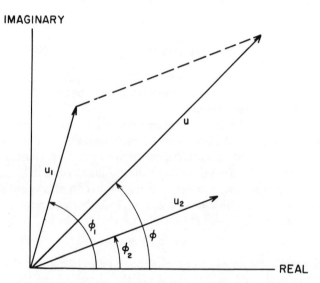

Figure 38. Vector sum represented on complex coordinates.

3.4 Incoherent Sources

A large number of sodium atoms in a vapor give out waves of the same frequency but the atomic oscillators are electrically isolated. Their phases are entirely random. Such sources of random phase are said to be *incoherent*. A large number of violin strings in an orchestra, all sounding the same frequency, have random phases. They are incoherent sources.

The amplitude and phase of the resultant of N wavelets is indicated in Fig. 39. If **u** is the complex amplitude of the resultant and $\mathbf{u}_1, \mathbf{u}_2 + \cdots + \mathbf{u}_N$ are the complex amplitudes of the components, then

$$\mathbf{u} = \mathbf{u}_1 + \mathbf{u}_2 + \cdots + \mathbf{u}_N = \sum_{k=1}^{k=N} \mathbf{u}_k. \tag{3.5}$$

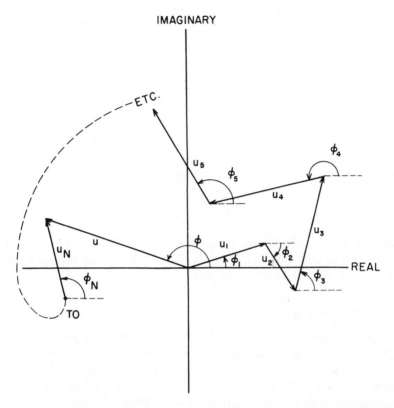

Figure 39. The resultant of N waves of the same frequency and random phase.

The complex amplitudes may all be expressed in polar form:

$$
\begin{cases}
\mathbf{u} = u \cos \phi + ju \sin \phi \\[2mm]
\mathbf{u}_1 = u_1 \cos \phi_1 + ju_1 \sin \phi_1 \\[2mm]
\mathbf{u}_2 = u_2 \cos \phi_2 + ju_2 \sin \phi_2 \\[2mm]
\quad \cdot \\[1mm]
\quad \cdot \\[1mm]
\quad \cdot \\[1mm]
\mathbf{u}_N = u_N \cos \phi_N + ju_N \sin \phi_N.
\end{cases}
$$

We wish to solve for the amplitude u in terms of the amplitudes and phases of the components.

The sums of the real terms on the two sides of Eq. (3.5) are equal and the sums of the imaginary terms on the two sides are equal. Therefore

$$u \cos \phi = \sum_{k=1}^{k=N} u_k \cos \phi_k \qquad (3.6)$$

$$u \sin \phi = \sum_{k=1}^{k=N} u_k \sin \phi_k. \qquad (3.7)$$

The process of squaring and adding Eqs. (3.6) and (3.7) yields two sets of terms, the square terms and the cross products. If the phase is random and N is large, there will be approximately as many positive as negative cross-product terms, thus leaving only the square terms. Thus for sufficiently large N

$$u^2 = \sum_{k=1}^{k=N} u_k^2. \qquad (3.8)$$

That is, the resultant intensity is equal to the sum of the intensities of the individual waves. If the amplitudes are all equal, the resultant intensity is N times the intensity of a component wave.

3.5 Coherent Sources

If some means is used to drive N violin strings with the same frequency and such that all N waves will be in phase and have the same amplitude at a point, then the resultant intensity will be N^2 times the intensity of one wave. This is not a contradiction of conservation of energy. If the N strings are separated by distances small compared to a wavelength, the device that drives a given string will have to do work at a rate N times as great to maintain the same amplitude when it is in synchronism with the other $N - 1$ strings. The waves go out from a common center.

If the N violin strings are sufficiently separated to be independent of each other, then the energy is not radiated equally in all directions. There is constructive and destructive interference in different directions in space. If there is a point at which all N waves arrive in phase, the intensity at that point will be N^2 times as great as from one source. The distribution of intensity in space has been altered by separating the sources.

If the N strings are not in phase but always maintain the same phase difference relative to each other, there will be a fixed interference pattern in space. The N sources are said to be *coherent* sources. Actually it would be impossible to drive N coherent strings by N separate sources of power. To perform such an experiment one would drive all N strings from a common alternator such as a 60 cycles/sec generator. The common source of power is called the *primary* source, and the driven strings are *secondary* sources. Two or more sources are absolutely coherent only if they are secondary sources.

3.6 Superposition of Perpendicular Simple Harmonic Motions

In Sec. 3.3 we considered the passage of two transverse waves of the same polarization past a point. We shall now treat the more general case in which two waves of the same frequency, each polarized in any direction, pass the same point. The particle at the point is undergoing two simple harmonic motions. The plane of the two intersecting lines of vibration is the plane of vibration. It will be convenient to divide the vibrations into two components at right angles to each other and express the displacements by y and x. If we start measuring time when the y displacement is zero,

$$y = Y \sin \omega t,$$
$$x = X \sin (\omega t + \alpha),$$

where Y and X are the amplitudes of the y and x vibrations and α is the phase of the x vibration relative to the y vibration. We may obtain the polar form by the transformation

$$x = r \cos \theta$$
$$y = r \sin \theta$$

in which r is the variable displacement from the origin and θ is the variable angular displacement from the positive x direction. Equating the real and imaginary terms, we have

$$r \cos \theta = X \sin (\omega t + \alpha),$$
$$r \sin \theta = Y \sin \omega t.$$

We may solve the two simultaneous equations for the displacements r and θ in terms of the independent variable t.

$$r^2 = X^2 \sin^2 (\omega t + \alpha) + Y^2 \sin^2 \omega t \tag{3.9}$$

and
$$\tan \theta = \frac{Y \sin \omega t}{X \sin (\omega t + \alpha)}. \tag{3.10}$$

These are the equations of an ellipse with center at the origin. Special cases will be treated in the problems.

The combination of simple harmonic motions at right angles to each other may be treated by the elementary method of geometrical construction. In Fig. 40, section (a) indicates a vertical vibration; (b), (c), and (d) indicate horizontal vibrations leading (a) in phase by $0°$, $45°$, and $90°$. The circles of reference are marked in $45°$ steps for each of the four simple harmonic motions. We are treating the special case in which the two vibrations are of the same amplitude.

The two lines which project the points moving in the reference circles upon their diameters at any instant may be extended until they intersect.

The intersection indicates the position of the vibrating particle. The position at the end of every eighth period is indicated by numbers. The resultant vibration is elliptical, the circle and straight line being special cases. We shall treat elliptical polarization of electromagnetic waves in later chapters.

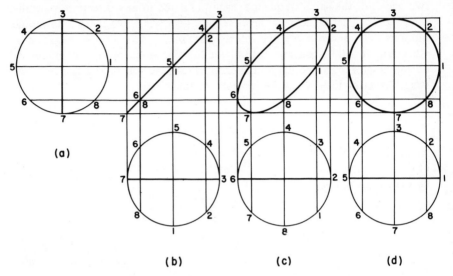

Figure 40. Superposition of perpendicular simple harmonic motions.

3.7 Compound Waves

Sound waves from an organ pipe or a string are usually composed of a fundamental note and overtones whose frequencies are integral multiples of the frequency of the fundamental. The resultant wave shows a complicated form on the oscilloscope. Sound analysis consists of finding the frequencies, amplitudes, and phases of the component sinusoidal waves.

The analysis of waves is based on a theorem of J. B. J. Fourier (1767–1830) that any periodic function may be represented by a sum of sine and cosine terms of the form

$$y = A_0 + A_1 \sin \omega t + A_2 \sin 2\omega t + A_3 \sin 3\omega t + \cdots$$
$$+ B_1 \cos \omega t + B_2 \cos 2\omega t + B_3 \cos 3\omega t + \cdots, \quad (3.11)$$

where y is the displacement at any time, A_0 is a constant, and the A and B factors are the amplitudes of the component waves.

One who is interested in analysis of simple sound waves may become rapidly acquainted with forms by attaching two electronic audio oscillators with amplitude and frequency controls to a cathode ray oscilloscope as indicated in Fig. 41. One will learn to recognize at a glance which of the first

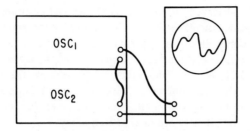

Figure 41. Demonstration of compound waves on an oscilloscope.

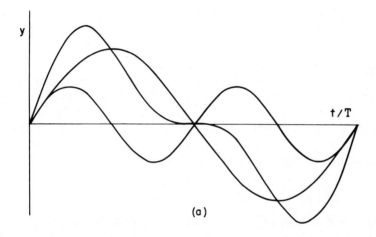

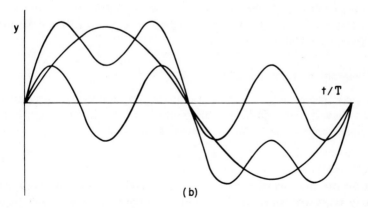

Figure 42. Composition of waves. (a) first and second harmonics. (b) first and third harmonics.

five harmonics is observed. Figure 42(a) shows the combination of a first and second harmonic, and 42(b) the combination of a first and third harmonic.

In practice, compound wave forms are analyzed quantitatively with mechanical or electric wave analyzers. The ear is a qualitative wave analyzer. The use of Eq. (3.11) may be time consuming. We should do at least one problem in which the component frequencies can be recognized at a glance and the relative amplitudes computed. Since two waves of the same frequency combine to give a resultant wave of that frequency,

$$A_k \sin k\omega t + B_k \cos k\omega t = C_k \sin (k\omega t + \alpha_k),$$

where C_k is the amplitude of the resultant wave and α_k is the phase at time $t = 0$. Substituting in Eq. (3.11) we have

$$y = C_0 + C_1 \sin (\omega t + \alpha_1) + C_2 \sin (2\omega t + \alpha_2)$$
$$+ C_3 \sin (3\omega t + \alpha_3). \qquad (3.12)$$

The subscripts in Eq. (3.12) are the harmonics.

As a simple illustration of the use of Eq. (3.12), suppose that we have recognized that the compound wave of Fig. 42(b) is made up of a first and third harmonic, the displacements of each being zero at time zero. We wish to calculate the amplitudes of the two components. By substituting two known values of y at two particular times in the first half cycles, we may write two simultaneous equations with two unknowns C_1 and C_3.

$$\begin{cases} y' = C_1 \sin \omega t' + C_3 \sin 3\omega t' \\ y'' = C_1 \sin \omega t'' + C_3 \sin 3\omega t''. \end{cases} \qquad (3.13)$$

Care must be taken to choose times which yield the greatest precision. Times should not be chosen too close together. If there are six unknowns the measured displacements may be taken at six equally spaced instants over the cycle. This method is satisfactory only if the compound wave has no discontinuities in slope. If the equation of the compound wave is known, then the coefficients in Eq. (3.11) may be expressed in terms of integrals of the wave function taken over the cycle.[5]

3.8 Composition of Spectral Lines

When a spectrometer of sufficient resolving power is used, a spectral line is found to have a finite width. The distribution of intensity in the spectral line is expressed approximately by the Gaussian equation

$$\frac{I}{I_0} = \epsilon^{-(\lambda_0 - \lambda)^2/\alpha^2}, \qquad (3.14)$$

where I is the intensity of radiation, I_0 is the maximum intensity of radiation and associated with wavelength λ_0, and α is a constant.

[5] L. P. Smith, *Mathematical Methods for Scientists and Engineers:* Englewood Cliffs, N.J., Prentice-Hall (1953) Secs. 159–163.

Since the Gaussian curve approaches the wavelength axis asymptotically, it is convenient to express the width of the line at some fraction of maximum intensity. The width at half maximum is generally employed, but the algebra of this discussion will be simpler if we treat the width at $I = I_0/\epsilon$, where ϵ is the Napierian base and $\Delta\lambda$ is the width. The sharpness of the line may be expressed as $\lambda_0/\Delta\lambda$. For a radio frequency tube oscillator $\lambda_0/\Delta\lambda$ is of the order of 10^4, but extends as high as 10^6 for crystal-controlled oscillators. It is noteworthy that carefully measured natural widths of spectral lines in the visible spectrum yield also $\lambda_0/\Delta\lambda$ about 10^6.

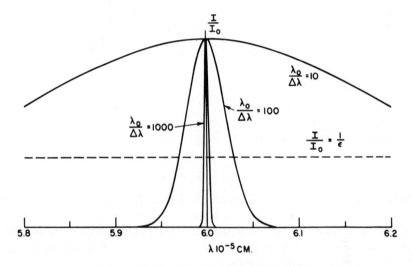

Figure 43. Gaussian distribution of intensity.

Since the natural widths of spectral lines are much too small to measure on student spectrometers, it is not surprising that a course in physical optics often deals with monochromatic waves even though no wave is strictly mono-chromatic.

In Fig. 43 are shown three Gaussian plots of intensity of radiation versus wavelength calculated from Eq. (3.14), where λ_0 was chosen in the visible range at 6.0×10^{-5} cm, and α is a constant which we can evaluate most easily for the case $I = I_0/\epsilon$. In that case $\alpha = \lambda_0 - \lambda = \Delta\lambda/2$. Plots are made for $\lambda_0/\Delta\lambda$ equal to 10, 100, and 1000.

The Gaussian curve is generally associated with a statistically large number of small random disturbances. Spectral lines broaden with increase of temperature of the gas source. This is a Doppler effect resulting from random motion of the molecules. Broadening of lines also occurs with increased pressure in the gas source and the accompanying greater number of collisions which effect the vibrations of the emitting atoms. At low temperatures and pressures a third type of broadening persists due to the natural damping of the individual atomic oscillators. The wave form of the damped oscillation can be calculated as a function of the intensity distribution in the spectral line. Thus the measurement of natural widths of spectral lines is a means of studying the behavior of atoms. We shall only indicate the nature of the mathematical process, giving our primary attention to the calculated graphical wave forms.

Much as we may analyze a complex sound wave as a Fourier series of frequencies, we may relate the form of a light wave to the intensity distribution of its spectral line on a frequency scale or the reciprocal of the wavelength scale.

For brevity we shall define $\kappa = 2\pi/\lambda$ and $\kappa_0 = 2\pi/\lambda_0$. If the wave form is given by the function $y = F(x)$, the energy distribution $f(\kappa)$ may be found from the integral equation

$$f(\kappa) = \frac{1}{\sqrt{2\pi}} \int_{-\infty}^{\infty} F(x)\epsilon^{j\kappa x}\, dx. \tag{3.15}$$

On the other hand, if the energy distribution in the spectrum is given, the wave form may be found from the integral equation

$$F(x) = \frac{1}{\sqrt{2\pi}} \int_{-\infty}^{\infty} f(x)\epsilon^{-j\kappa x}\, d\kappa. \tag{3.16}$$

Note the symmetry of the two equations. Except for the negative sign in the exponent, κ and x could be interchanged in one equation to make the equations identical. These symmetrical equations known as *Fourier transforms* are treated in mathematics under the topic *orthonormal functions*, a topic beyond the scope of this textbook.[6]

For light $F(x)$ can not be measured directly, but $f(\lambda)$ has been measured for many spectral lines and represented by Eq. (3.14). We wish to replace $f(\lambda)$ by a function in κ.

$$\kappa - \kappa_0 = 2\pi\left(\frac{1}{\lambda} - \frac{1}{\lambda_0}\right) = 2\pi\frac{\lambda_0 - \lambda}{\lambda\lambda_0}.$$

If $|\lambda_0 - \lambda| \ll \lambda_0$, then approximately

$$\kappa - \kappa_0 = \frac{2\pi}{\lambda_0^2}(\lambda_0 - \lambda) \tag{3.17}$$

so that

$$\frac{I}{I_0} = f(\kappa) = \epsilon^{-(\kappa - \kappa_0)^2/a^2}, \tag{3.18}$$

where a is a constant which is most easily evaluated from the case $I = I_0/\epsilon$.

$$a = \kappa - \kappa_0 = \frac{\Delta\kappa}{2}.$$

[6] L. P. Smith, *Mathematical Methods for Scientists and Engineers*, Englewood Cliffs, N.J., Prentice-Hall (1953) Chap. 13.

From Eq. (3.17),

$$\Delta\kappa = \frac{2\pi}{\lambda_0}\frac{\Delta\lambda}{\lambda_0}$$

so that
$$a = \frac{\pi}{\lambda_0}\frac{\Delta\lambda}{\lambda_0}.$$

If we substitute the intensity distribution $f(\kappa)$ from Eq. (3.18) in integral (3.16),

$$F(x) = \frac{1}{\sqrt{2\pi}}\int_{-\infty}^{\infty}\epsilon^{-(\kappa-\kappa_0)^2/a^2}\epsilon^{-j\kappa x}\,d\kappa. \tag{3.19}$$

We may integrate this expression by the method of residues.[7]

$$F(x) = C\epsilon^{-a^2x^2/4}\epsilon^{-j\kappa_0 x}.$$

Substituting for a and κ_0,

$$F(x) = C\epsilon^{-(\pi/2)^2(\Delta\lambda/\lambda_0)^2(x/\lambda_0)^2}\epsilon^{-j2\pi x/\lambda_0}. \tag{3.20}$$

We are not concerned with the constant C but only with the shape of the wave. The first exponential factor is the amplitude which is a variable depending on x/λ_0. The second exponential expresses the phase, and $-2\pi x/\lambda_0$ is the phase angle.

In Fig. 44 is plotted the wave form for the case $\lambda_0/\Delta\lambda = 10$ and 100. The broken line, the envelope of the wave, is a plot of the variable amplitude expressed by the first exponential in Eq. (3.20). For the spectral lines of sharpness $\lambda_0/\Delta\lambda$ equal to 10, 100, and 1000, the corresponding wave forms damp to $1/\epsilon$ of maximum amplitude in 6.4, 64, and 640 wavelengths, respectively. For a sharp spectral line with $\lambda_0/\Delta\lambda = 10^6$ the amplitude damps to $1/\epsilon$ of maximum value in 640,000 wavelengths.

These calculated wave forms have had recent confirmation in the wave mechanics of matter. Dirac[8] has shown that a radiating atom is a damped oscillator and that the amplitude of the emitted light wave damps to $1/\epsilon$ times maximum amplitude in 10^7 wavelengths or more.

Note the reciprocal relation between the width of the spectral line and the length of the wave bundle. If $\lambda_0/\Delta\lambda$ were reduced to unity the spectral line would be spread over the whole visible spectrum. The wave calculated for the whole width of the white light spectrum would be but a single pulse. This might seem contrary to Newton's conclusion that white light is made up of all the colors. Actually there is no contradiction. Consider a large number of continuous waves distributed uniformly throughout the spectrum. If they are traveling out from a common source and are all in phase at one point, they superpose to form a pulse about that point, but away from the point the

[7] R. V. Churchill, *Introduction to Complex Variables and Applications:* New York, McGraw-Hill (1948) Chap. VII.

[8] A. Rubinowicz, *Repts. Progr. in Phys.*, **XII**, 233 (1949).

component waves fall gradually out of phase and are never all in phase again. The pulse and the infinite group of continuous waves are equivalent ways of describing white light. In the following section we shall consider the group waves in a dispersive medium, that is, a medium in which waves of different frequencies travel with different velocities.

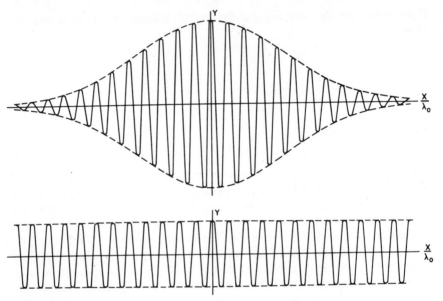

Figure 44. Wave forms which yield Gaussian distribution of intensity in a spectral line.

3.9 Group Velocity

If a group of two or more waves of slightly different frequency is traveling in a medium, the resultant wave form will lie within an envelope. If there are but two component waves, the envelope will be sinusoidal and of a lower frequency, the beat frequency. In general, the velocity of the envelope of the group is not the same as the velocity of the wave.

We may use two audio oscillators and a cathode ray oscilloscope as in Fig. 41 to demonstrate group velocity. If one oscillator is set at 400 cycles/sec and the internal sweep circuit of the oscilloscope is set at 25 cycles/sec, 16 wavelengths will be observed on the oscilloscope. The synchronization knob may be set at zero and the frequency of the oscillator increased slightly until the wave form on the oscilloscope moves to the right at about 5 waves/sec. This is an artificial means of producing a slow, low-frequency wave that the eye can follow easily. Similarly the other oscillator may be set at 450 cycles/sec with the same amplitude. If the longer wavelength has the higher velocity, the wave will be seen to move to the right through the group and to slip through the neck between groups. For convenience in observation the group may be made to stand still relative to the observer so that only the motion of the wave through the group is seen. If the longer wavelength has the higher velocity, the group will travel more slowly than the wave.

The velocity of the group is the velocity of the energy. The velocity of light measured between two points as described in Chapter IV is always group velocity. The wave velocity is often called the *phase velocity*. The phase fronts formed by Huygen's wavelets have the wave velocity. The wave

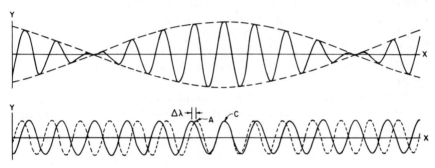

Figure 45. Component waves of slightly different wavelengths and velocities and the resulting group wave.

velocity determines the bending of wave fronts when they move from one medium to another.

In Fig. 45 are shown two component waves of slightly different wavelengths at a particular instant. Above them is shown the resultant wave. The broken line is the envelope or beat wave. The two component waves are traveling to the right. As is true for waves of the visible spectrum in a transparent medium, the wave of longer wavelength is given the higher velocity.

Let C be a point where crests of the two waves coincide. This is the position of maximum displacement of the group. We may take our position at point A on the next crest of the shorter wave to the left of C. In a short time Δt a crest of the longer wave will have moved a short distance $\Delta\lambda$ to point A. The velocity of the long wave relative to the short wave is

$$\Delta v = \frac{\Delta\lambda}{\Delta t}. \tag{3.21}$$

In the same time Δt the crest of the group will have moved backward from C to A. The velocity of the group relative to the wave is $-\lambda/\Delta t$. Substituting for Δt from Eq. (3.21), we may express the velocity of the group relative to the wave as $-\lambda \, \Delta v/\Delta\lambda$. If v, the velocity of the wave, varies continuously with wavelength λ, the velocity of the group relative to the wave is $-\lambda \, dv/d\lambda$.

We may now take a position of reference in the medium. If U designates the velocity of the group,

$$U = v - \lambda \frac{dv}{d\lambda}. \tag{3.22}$$

If v decreases with increasing wavelength, the group velocity exceeds the wave velocity. In a vacuum there is no dispersion. Thus in vacuum the group velocity and phase velocity are equal. For transparent media and portions of the spectrum sufficiently far from absorption lines, the group velocity never exceeds the velocity of light in vacuum. The phase velocity v in a medium has no such limitations. The phase velocity of x-rays in most media exceeds the velocity in a vacuum. Artificial dielectrics may be built for microwaves for which the phase velocity is either greater or less than in a vacuum. In Chapter XV we shall consider dispersion throughout the electromagnetic spectrum.

We may derive the equation of the resultant wave from the equations of the two components. The general equation of a wave traveling in the positive x direction is

$$\mathbf{u} = u\left[\cos \frac{2\pi}{\lambda} (vt - x) + j \sin \frac{2\pi}{\lambda} (vt - x)\right],$$

where $\mathbf{u}$ is the complex amplitude, and u is the magnitude of the complex amplitude and may be a constant or may be a variable dependent on v, t, and x.

The two component waves shown in Fig. 45 have complex amplitudes $\mathbf{u}_1$ and $\mathbf{u}_2$. Let the magnitudes of the two amplitudes be the same and expressed by u_1. Let λ be the average of the wavelengths and v the average of the velocities of the two components. Here $\lambda + (d\lambda/2)$ and $v + (dv/2)$ are the wavelength and velocity of one component wave; $\lambda - (d\lambda/2)$ and $v - (dv/2)$ are the wavelength and velocity of the other wave. The equations of the component waves are

$$
\begin{cases}
\mathbf{u}_1 = u_1\left\{\cos \frac{2\pi}{\lambda + \dfrac{d\lambda}{2}}\left[\left(v + \frac{dv}{2}\right)t - x\right] \right. \\
\qquad\qquad \left. + j \sin \frac{2\pi}{\lambda + \dfrac{d\lambda}{2}}\left[\left(v + \frac{dv}{2}\right)t - x\right]\right\} \quad (3.23) \\[4ex]
\mathbf{u}_2 = u_1\left\{\cos \frac{2\pi}{\lambda - \dfrac{d\lambda}{2}}\left[\left(v - \frac{dv}{2}\right)t - x\right] \right. \\
\qquad\qquad \left. + j \sin \frac{2\pi}{\lambda - \dfrac{d\lambda}{2}}\left[\left(v - \frac{dv}{2}\right)t - x\right]\right\}. \quad (3.24)
\end{cases}
$$

We may abbreviate by letting the phase angles of the fast and slow waves be, respectively, ϕ_1 and ϕ_2. Then Eqs. (3.23) and (3.24) become

$$\left\{ \begin{array}{ll} \mathbf{u}_1 = u_1(\cos \phi_1 + j \sin \phi_1) & (3.25) \\ \mathbf{u}_2 = u_1(\cos \phi_2 + j \sin \phi_2). & (3.26) \end{array} \right.$$

Let $\mathbf{u}$ be the complex amplitude of the resultant wave. Thus

$$\mathbf{u} = \mathbf{u}_1 + \mathbf{u}_2. \tag{3.27}$$

The equation of the resultant wave may be written

$$\mathbf{u} = u(\cos \phi + j \sin \phi), \tag{3.28}$$

where u and ϕ represent the amplitude and phase of the resultant wave. They are unknown functions of v, t, and x. Equation (3.27) implies that

$$\left\{ \begin{array}{l} u \cos \phi = u_1(\cos \phi_1 + \cos \phi_2) \\ u \sin \phi = u_1(\sin \phi_1 + \sin \phi_2). \end{array} \right.$$

From these two simultaneous equations we may solve for the unknown amplitude and phase. The procedure as in problems of superposition is to divide the equations to solve for the phase angle and to square and add the equations to solve for the amplitude.

$$\left\{ \begin{array}{l} \tan \phi = \dfrac{\sin \phi_1 + \sin \phi_2}{\cos \phi_1 + \cos \phi_2} = \tan \tfrac{1}{2}(\phi_1 + \phi_2) \\[2mm] u^2 = 2u_1^2(1 + \cos \phi_1 \cos \phi_2 + \sin \phi_1 \sin \phi_2) \\[1mm] \quad = 2u_1^2[1 + \cos (\phi_1 - \phi_2)]. \end{array} \right.$$

The phase and amplitude of the resultant wave are

$$\left\{ \begin{array}{ll} \phi = \tfrac{1}{2}(\phi_1 + \phi_2) & (3.29) \\[2mm] u = \pm 2u_1 \cos \left(\dfrac{\phi_1 - \phi_2}{2} \right). & (3.30) \end{array} \right.$$

These two expressions could also be obtained simply from the geometry of rotating vectors shown in Fig. 38 for a particular time and position. Substituting for ϕ_1 and ϕ_2 from Eqs. (3.23) and (3.24), and neglecting the square of small differences $d\lambda$ and dv as compared to λ and v, we have

$$\left\{ \begin{array}{l} \phi_1 + \phi_2 = \dfrac{4\pi}{\lambda} (vt - x) \\[3mm] \phi_1 - \phi_2 = \dfrac{2\pi \, d\lambda}{\lambda^2} \left[\left(\lambda \dfrac{dv}{d\lambda} - v \right) t + x \right]. \end{array} \right.$$

Substituting in Eqs. (3.29) and (3.30), we obtain the phase and amplitude.

$$\phi = \frac{2\pi}{\lambda}(vt - x) \tag{3.31}$$

$$u = \pm 2u_1 \cos \frac{\pi \, d\lambda}{\lambda^2}\left[\left(v - \lambda \frac{dv}{d\lambda}\right)t - x\right]. \tag{3.32}$$

It is seen that the equation for the amplitude is itself two equations of two waves. They are the equations of the group wave represented by either of the two broken lines that form the envelope. The amplitude of the group wave is twice the amplitude of a component wave. If λ_g is the wavelength of the group and U the group velocity, we may write the equation for the group wave

$$u = \pm 2u_1 \cos \frac{2\pi}{\lambda_g}[Ut - x]. \tag{3.33}$$

Thus the group wavelength is

$$\lambda_g = \frac{2\lambda^2}{d\lambda}$$

and the group velocity is

$$U = v - \lambda \frac{dv}{d\lambda}.$$

The complex equation for the resultant wave is

$$\mathbf{u} = \left\{\pm 2u_1 \cos \frac{\pi \, d\lambda}{\lambda^2}\left[\left(v - \lambda \frac{dv}{d\lambda}\right)t - x\right]\right\}$$

$$\times \left[\cos \frac{2\pi}{\lambda}(vt - x) + j \sin \frac{2\pi}{\lambda}(vt - x)\right]. \tag{3.34}$$

In the following chapter we shall consider the methods of measuring the *group velocity*, the velocity with which wave energy moves through a medium. The proof that the group velocity equals the velocity of energy transfer in a transparent medium is too difficult to be made here. An interesting treatment is given in Sommerfeld's textbook on Optics.[9]

PROBLEMS FOR CHAPTER III

3.3.1. Making use of trigonometric identities, express in simplest form the amplitude and phase of the resultant of two simple harmonic motions of the same frequency for the special case in which the amplitudes u_1 and u_2 of the component waves are equal.

[9] Arnold Sommerfeld, Trans. by O. Laporte and P. A. Moldauer, *Optics:* New York, Academic Press (1954) Sec. 22.

3.6.2. Prove that, if two superposed simple harmonic motions of the same frequency are at right angles to each other, in phase, and of the same amplitude, the resultant motion is simple harmonic.

3.6.3. Prove that, if two superposed simple harmonic motions of the same frequency are at right angles to each other, of the same amplitude, and 90° out of phase, the resultant motion is circular.

3.6.4. Show by construction the resulting motion when two simple harmonic motions at right angles to each other, of the same amplitude, and 180° out of phase are combined.

3.6.5. In Fig. 40(d) the resultant motion is in a counterclockwise circle. What must be the phase of the horizontal motion relative to the vertical motion if the resultant motion is to be a clockwise circle?

3.7.6. Assume that you have recognized the compound wave of Fig. 42(a) to be made up of two waves, a first and second harmonic, which are in phase at time zero. By Fourier methods find the amplitudes of the two component waves. Use the two components indicated in the diagram only as a check.

3.8.7. Plot the spiral of Eq. (3.20) between $x/\lambda_0 = 0$ and 1 for the case $\Delta\lambda/\lambda_0 = 10$. Let $C = 1$. Tables of values of ϵ to a negative exponent are given under the heading *exponential functions* in mathematical tables such as those of *Handbook of Chemistry and Physics*, Chemical Rubber Publishing Co.

3.8.8. Plot $F(x)$ of Eq. (3.20) versus x/λ_0. Note that this may be done mechanically by projecting the spiraling point of the previous problem on a line parallel to the real axis and moving along the imaginary axis.

chapter IV

The Velocity of Light

4.1 The Next Decimal Place

The measurement of the velocity of light is a "romance of the next decimal place."[1] Galileo attempted to measure the velocity of light between two men with lamps and shutters on hills a mile apart. The velocity was too great to be detected.

Without knowing so, Galileo made a contribution to the determination of the velocity of light when he pointed his telescope at the planets and discovered the satellites of Jupiter. In 1676 the Danish astronomer Olaf Römer made more precise determinations of the periods of Jupiter's satellites. Since the period of the inner satellite was less than two days, he could make as many as 200 determinations per year. He discovered that the measured period was dependent on the velocity of the earth toward and from Jupiter. He could account quantitatively for this effect by assuming that light had finite velocity. Fifty years later the English astronomer James Bradley explained the effect of the component of the velocity of the earth perpendicular to the direction of observation upon the angular setting of the telescope on a star by assuming that light had a finite velocity. Bradley's work was of the next-decimal-place variety. The reversal of the velocity of the earth in a six month period required a change in the angular setting of the telescope of only 40″.

---

[1] A phrase from a popular lecture by F. K. Richtmyer.

76

In 1849 Hippolyte Fizeau made the first terrestrial measurements in air and Jean Foucault in water in 1850. High-speed toothed wheels and rotating mirrors replaced Galileo's hand operated shutter. A mirror on the other mountain replaced the second observer. Foucault's measurement of the velocity of light in water was an independent proof of the wave nature of light which convinced the last die-hards. The bending of a beam of light toward the normal as it moved from air into water had been explained by both wave and corpuscular theory. Huygen's principle had shown that, if the wave had a lower velocity in water than in air, the beam would bend toward the normal. By the corpuscular theory the corpuscle obliquely incident would, as it approached the water, have its speed increased by attractive forces and its path bent toward the normal and thus have higher velocity in water. Foucault found the velocity to be less in water and confirmed the wave theory.

When Maxwell showed by theory that the equivalence of the velocity of light and the ratio of the size of the electromagnetic unit charge to the electrostatic unit charge was no coincidence, he stimulated measurement of the two constants to another significant figure. Measurements of the velocity of light in 1882 by Michelson and of the electrical constant in 1907 by Rosa and Dorsey agreed to 1 part in 3000.

Michelson and Morley's failure to find any effect of the motion of the earth and the accompanying ether drag on the velocity of light was the experimental basis for the first theory of relativity. In turn, Einstein's theory of relativity showed that the velocity of light in vacuum could not be exceeded by the velocities of matter or energy.

4.2 Römer's Method

The astronomical methods of determining the velocity of light have consisted in finding the ratio of the velocity of light to the velocity of some astronomical body relative to the earth. Römer's method was essentially the Doppler effect except that the frequency observed was not a frequency of a light wave but a much lower-frequency signal sent from the planet Jupiter.

Three satellites of Jupiter have orbits in nearly the same plane as Jupiter's orbit. Thus, unlike our moon, they pass through the shadow of the parent planet every revolution. Römer observed the times of emergence from the shadow. The period of the near satellite is 1.75 days. Thus Römer observed 208 emergences per year. Römer knew that his measurements of the time of emergence were reliable within 1 sec but the measured period was 30 sec greater when the earth's velocity was radially away from Jupiter than when it was toward Jupiter as indicated in Fig. 46. The deviations from the mean value of the period varied approximately sinusoidally with time.

From Fig. 24, Sec. 1.9, one observes that this is the same as the Doppler problem.

$$v = v_0\left(1 - \frac{v \cos \theta}{c}\right),$$ (4.1)

where v is the observed frequency of emergence and v_0 is the average frequency of emergence taken over a complete cycle of deviations. A complete cycle of deviations requires a little more than a year since Jupiter will have moved about 30° in its orbit during an earth year. Here v is the velocity of the earth relative to Jupiter, the source. Since the signal is by light, we need not

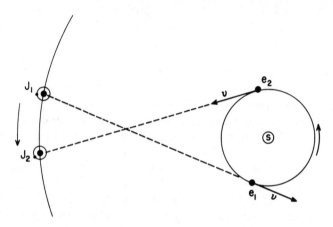

Figure 46. Römer's determination of the velocity of light by observation of Jupiter's moons.

consider motion relative to a medium of propagation but only the velocity of the observer relative to the source. Here θ is the angle between a radial line from Jupiter to the earth and the direction of the earth's velocity, and $v \cos \theta$ is the component of the earth's velocity radially away from Jupiter.

If v_1 is the frequency of emergence when the earth is moving toward Jupiter and v_2 the frequency when the earth is moving radially away as indicated in Fig. 46, then

$$v_1 = v_0\left(1 - \frac{v}{c}\right)$$ (4.2)

$$v_2 = v_0\left(1 + \frac{v}{c}\right).$$ (4.3)

Subtracting Eq. (4.2) from Eq. (4.3), we have

$$v_2 - v_1 = 2v_0\frac{v}{c}.$$

If Δv is the greatest deviation from the mean value v_0,

$$\Delta v = v_0 \frac{v}{c}. \tag{4.4}$$

Since Δv is small compared to v_0, we may also express Eq. (4.4) in terms of the periods between emergence by

$$\Delta T = T_0 \frac{v}{c}. \tag{4.5}$$

Actually Römer did not use the Doppler principle directly. Doppler's discovery came a century and a half later. Römer's data were taken in sets when the earth was receding from Jupiter and when the earth was approaching Jupiter. He took nine sets and computed the time for light to cross the earth's orbit.[2] The low-frequency Doppler treatment is modern.

4.3 Bradley's Method

Römer's conclusion that light has a finite velocity was not generally accepted. Fifty years later the English astronomer Bradley observed another discrepancy in astronomical measurements which he explained by considering light to have a velocity approximately that found by Römer.

Bradley was measuring the angular positions of the "fixed" stars with estimated errors less than 1". For convenience we may think of a transparent celestial sphere large enough so that the solar system may be considered a point at the center. By geometrical measurements with a telescope we can determine only the angular positions of the stars. If we draw a line from a star to the center of the sphere, it will intersect the sphere at a point. Some of the very near stars are at distances from the solar system of only about 100,000 times the diameter of the earth's orbit. As the position of the earth changes during the year, these near stars will appear to move across the background of more distant fixed stars. This is the common phenomenon of parallax.

Bradley observed something different from parallax. When he measured angular positions of fixed stars in directions approximately at right angles to the earth's orbit, he observed that the star moved in a small circle during the year. The diameter of this circle always subtended an angle of 40" at the earth. This effect, which he called *aberration*, is a simple problem in relative motion. We may use a theorem from elementary physics of motion. The vector sum of the velocity of body number 1 relative to body 2 plus the velocity of 2 relative to 3 is equal to the velocity of body number 1 relative to 3. For instance,

[2] Bernard Cohen, *Römer and the First Determination of the Velocity of Light:* New York, Burndy Library (1942).

relative to an observer on a train of Fig. 47, raindrops have a velocity which slants toward the rear. Relative to an observer on the ground, the same drops are falling vertically. The vector sum of the velocity of the drop relative to the earth plus the velocity of the earth relative to the train equals the resultant velocity of the drop relative to the train.

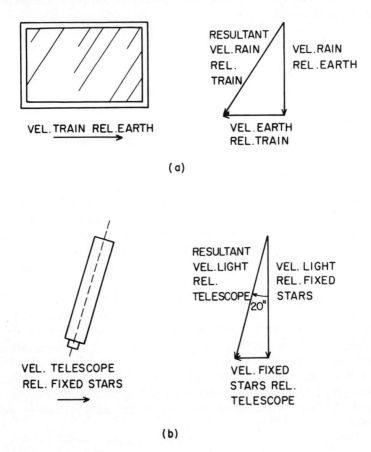

Figure 47. Determination of velocity of raindrop with respect to train, and velocity of beam of light with respect to telescope.

Likewise, the vector sum of the velocity of a beam of light relative to the fixed stars plus the velocity of the fixed stars relative to the telescope equals the velocity of the light relative to the telescope. The axis of the telescope must be set parallel to the direction of velocity of the light relative to the telescope. The velocity of the ray of light relative to the telescope makes an angle of 20″ with the velocity of the same ray of light relative to the celestial sphere. Six months later the angle will be in the opposite direction. The stars will appear to move in a circle on the celestial sphere. From Fig. 47 we obtain

$$\tan \theta = \frac{v}{c}. \tag{4.6}$$

Bradley's classical argument yields a velocity of light relative to the telescope larger than c. A relativity treatment gives $\sin \theta$ instead of $\tan \theta$ in Eq. (4.6). However, at an angle of 20″ we can not distinguish experimentally between $\tan \theta$ and $\sin \theta$. Here v is the magnitude of the velocity of the earth in its orbit. Since θ is small,

$$\theta = \frac{c}{v}. \tag{4.7}$$

Note that in Bradley's method v is at right angles to the direction of observation. In Eq. (4.4) for Römer's method, v is the velocity of the earth along the line of observation, a radial line from Jupiter. At present Eq. (4.7) is used to determine the velocity of the earth in its orbit from the known velocity of light and the measured angle of aberration.

The velocity of the solar system through our galaxy is greater than the earth's orbital velocity, and the velocity of our galaxy relative to other galaxies is still greater, but, if these velocities do not change in magnitude or direction during the history of man's observations, they can not be detected by the aberration methods.

4.4 Terrestrial Methods of Fizeau and Foucault

Over 100 years elapsed after Bradley had established the finite velocity of light before the first terrestrial measurements were made. Arago, we recall, had salvaged Fresnel's first paper on diffraction. Noting that the measurement of the velocity of light in a dielectric would be another crucial test of whether light were wave or corpuscle, Arago made plans for measuring the velocity of light. He proposed a high-speed toothed wheel as a shutter to replace the shutter of Galileo's lantern. Charles Wheatstone, who had used a rotating mirror to study the duration of a spark discharge, suggested to Arago that a rotating mirror might be used instead of a shutter. Arago was an old man with poor eyesight. He could not make the measurements himself. Two younger men developed the final equipment and made the measurements. Fizeau used the toothed wheel and Foucault the rotating mirror.

Figure 48 is a diagram of Fizeau's apparatus. Light from a vertical slit source S is partially reflected by a plate of plane glass P and brought to focus in the plane of the toothed wheel W. If the wheel is at rest and the light passes through a space between teeth, the diverging ray is rendered parallel by a lens, travels several miles, and is focused by another lens on mirror M, which reflects the beam by the same path to plate P where some of the light passes through to the observer. The wheel has 720 teeth. Each space and each tooth are 15' wide, the same as the finest division on the protractor of a student spectrometer. If the speed of the wheel is increased from rest, a speed will be reached for which the returning light is intercepted by the adjacent tooth.

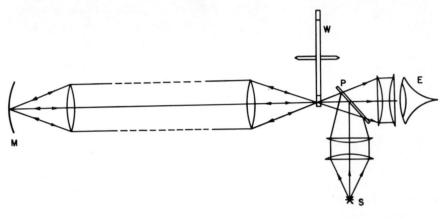

Figure 48. Fizeau's toothed-wheel method for determination of velocity of light.

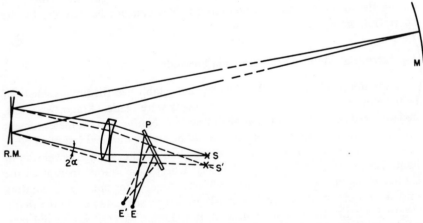

Figure 49. Foucault's rotating-mirror method for determination of velocity of light.

If that speed is doubled, the light will return in time to pass through the next opening. Fizeau measured a velocity of 3.15×10^{10} cm/sec. Others improved his method.[3] This method is now of historical interest only.

Figure 49 is a diagram of Foucault's apparatus. Light from the vertical slit is reflected from the rotating mirror, brought to focus on the spherical

[3] F. Cajori, *A History of Physics:* New York, Macmillan (1929) p. 159.

mirror 10 m away, and reflected back along the same path to the rotating mirror. If, during the time the light travels the 20 m out and back, the mirror rotates through angle α, then the reflected ray will make an angle 2α with the incident ray, and the image will appear at S'. Here S' was only 0.7 mm from S, and the observer could not be that near the source. Thus the plane glass P was introduced and the distance EE' measured, where E is the image when the mirror is at rest and E' when the mirror is rotating. Foucault measured a velocity of 2.98×10^{10} cm/sec. Foucault's method could be used to detect the velocity of light over shorter distances than Fizeau's. Thus Foucault's method was adapted to measuring the velocity of light in water. Foucault found the velocity in water to be less than in air, as had been predicted by Huygens from wave theory.

4.5 Michelson's Method

The next chapter in "the romance of the next decimal place" centered around the life work of Albert Michelson, began with measurements under the direction of Newcomb, and was completed 50 years later, just after Michelson's death, by his colleagues Pease and Pearson.

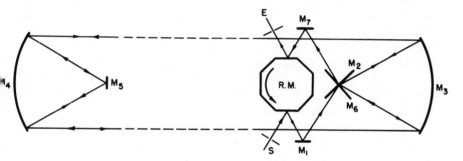

Figure 50. Michelson's method for determination of velocity of light.

Figure 50 is a diagram of the apparatus used by Michelson[4] between Mount Wilson and Mount San Antonio in 1927. A cone of light from vertical slit S fell upon a face of the rotating octagonal sided mirror RM, thence to fixed mirrors M_1 and M_2, to concave mirror M_3 which rendered the beam parallel. The beam traveled 22 miles to a like mirror M_4, to plane mirror M_5, and back to M_4, M_3, M_6, M_7, RM, and through a slit to observer E. Parts S, M_1, RM, M_2, M_6, M_7, and E were above the parallel beam. The mirror was driven by an air stream at such velocity that it rotated $\frac{1}{8}$ revolution while the light traveled 22 miles and back. Since E was in the same position whether the mirror was rotating or at rest, the method is more like Fizeau's than

[4] A. A. Michelson, *Astrophys. J.*, **65**, 1 (1927).

Foucault's. In practice the speed of the mirror was not adjusted to send the light exactly through the fixed slit. Micrometer adjustments of the slit positions were made involving small corrections. The small correction due to deviation was essentially Foucault's method.

Michelson's work was an engineering feat for pure science. The distance between mirrors M_2 and M_4 was measured by the U. S. Coast and Geodetic Survey to within 1 part in 6 million, the most precise measurement of its kind. The stroboscope fork for measuring the frequency of rotation of the mirror was checked with a standard pendulum of the U. S. Coast and Geodetic Survey. Mirrors M_3 and M_4 had the unusually long focal lengths of 30 ft with 2 ft apertures.

Several sets of rotating mirrors were used of 8, 12, and 16 sides. Some were made of solid nickel steel and some of glass. The values of the velocity obtained with each agreed within 1 part in 300,000.

Michelson also made measurements between mountains 82 miles apart, but he did not consider the results reliable because of bad atmospheric conditions. Indeed, the measurements between the 22 mile points could be made only for a short time before sunrise and after sunset when atmospheric conditions were most dependable. A possible source of error in the fifth significant figure was the unreliable values for the index of refraction of air under varying conditions. To eliminate this error, Michelson, Pease, and Pearson[5] measured the velocity of light in a mile-long pipe 3 ft in diameter, evacuated to pressures of about 1 mm mercury. By multiple reflections the beam traveled 10 miles before returning to the rotating mirror of 32 sides.

Parallel to the work of Michelson was that of Rosa and Dorsey in measuring the number of electrostatic units of charge in an electromagnetic unit of charge. They collected a charge upon a capacitor made up of two precisely measured concentric spheres and measured the potential difference to determine the charge in *electrostatic units*. The same charge was measured ballistically in *electromagnetic units* by discharging the capacitor through a tangent galvanometer. Rosa and Dorsey obtained $299,781 \pm 10$ km/sec. Michelson, Pease, and Pearson obtained $299,774 \pm 2$ km/sec. The two measurements agree within the limits of experimental error.

4.6 Electro-optical Shutter Method

The Kerr cell electro-optical shutter, used by Karolus and Mittelstaedt[6] to measure the velocity of light, can interrupt a beam of light at tens of megacycles per second, a frequency 1000 times higher than that of any mechanical shutter such as a rotating toothed wheel or mirror. With the

---

[5] Michelson, Pease, and Pearson, *Astrophys. J.*, **82**, 26 (1936).
[6] O. Karolus and O. Mittelstaedt, *Physik. Z.*, **29**, 698 (1928).

higher-frequency shutter, measurements may be made in shorter distances inside a building where atmospheric conditions are uniform.

An electro-optical shutter consists of two Nicol prisms or Polaroids with a Kerr cell between. The Kerr cell consists of two parallel condenser plates one or two millimeters apart, sealed in a glass cell filled with nitrobenzene. An electric field in the nitrobenzene renders it doubly refracting. If the electric field makes an angle of 45° with the direction of polarization of the wave from the polarizer, the wave will be broken into two components vibrating at right angles to each other. The relative retardation of the two components is proportional to the square of the electric field strength. If the field strength is made large enough so that the two components emerge from the cell 180°

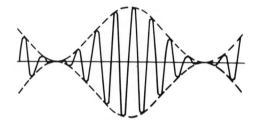

Figure 51. Modulated wave.

out of phase as in problem 3.6.4, then the light coming from the cell will be polarized at right angles to that entering. If the analyzer is set with its principal plane either parallel or crossed with that of the polarizer, and an alternating potential difference applied whose maximum value will cause 180° of relative retardation, the intensity of the light will vary approximately sinusoidally with time.

The Kerr cell will be treated more fully under the topic of *interference of polarized waves*. It is sufficient here to note that the Kerr cell serves as a shutter to modulate the amplitude of the light wave either sinusoidally or by any other desired form such as a square wave or short pulse.

In radio parlance the light wave of frequency 10^{14} cycles/sec is the *carrier wave*. The velocity is the group velocity of light. The radio-frequency wave of 10^7 cycles/sec is the *modulating wave*. Figure 51 shows a modulated wave. Note the difference between the modulated wave of Fig. 51 and the group wave of Fig. 45.

Figure 52 is a diagram of apparatus used by Anderson[7] to measure the velocity of light with about the same precision as did Michelson. Source S is a 1000 w projection lamp; P_1 and P_2 are Polaroid disks; K is the Kerr cell which modulates the light wave at 19.2 megacycles/sec. The oscillator which

[7] W. C. Anderson, *J. Opt. Soc. Amer.*, **31**, 187 (1941).

drives the Kerr cell is controlled by a 50 kilocycles/sec crystal oscillator and multipliers.

The frequency of the crystal oscillator was checked against the standard frequencies broadcast by the U. S. Bureau of Standards from Arlington. The error in the frequency of oscillation was less than one part per million.

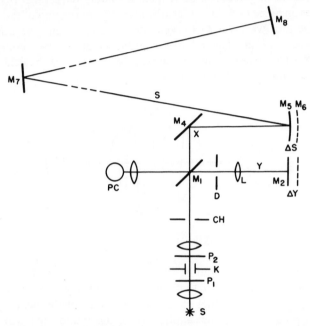

Figure 52. Anderson's method for determination of velocity of light.

The group velocity of the light may be expressed by

$$U = \frac{\lambda}{T},$$ (4.8)

where λ and T are the wavelength and period of the modulating high-frequency radio wave. Since T is known to one part per million, the greatest source of error is in measuring the length. Anderson devised an ingenious method whereby it was not necessary to make corrections for optical paths through lenses and the Kerr cell, nor to take into account the end effects due to fringe fields in the Kerr cell.

In Fig. 52, CH is a cross hair in a circular aperture. M_1 is a silvered half-reflecting mirror. Of the wave that splits at M_1, part goes to mirror M_2 and back to photocell PC, and part goes by the longer path out to mirror M_8, back to M_1, and thence to the photocell. The two beams form two images of the cross hair CH of equal size just in front of the photocell. By adjusting the angle of mirror M_1 one may make the two images coincide. The resulting image is focused on the photocell by the short focal length lens.

If the amplitudes of the two modulating radio waves are the same and the path difference of the two waves is an odd number of half wavelengths, then the radio-frequency component of the photoelectric current will be zero. Diaphragm D is used to reduce the intensity of the beam that travels the shorter distance until the intensities of the two beams are equal. Mirror M_2 is moved by a micrometer screw along a lathe bed. Mirrors M_5 and M_6 are mounted so as to be easily interchanged, and M_6 reflects the beam from M_1 back along itself.

Let distance M_1, M_2 be represented by Y; M_1, M_4, M_5 by X; M_5, M_7, M_8 by S; M_5, M_6 by ΔS. When mirror M_5 is in place, the position of M_2 is adjusted until the path difference is an odd number of half waves as indicated by a minimum in the radio-frequency component of the photoelectric current. That is,

$$2S + 2X - 2Y = \frac{(2n - 1)\lambda}{2}, \tag{4.9}$$

where n is an integer and λ the wavelength of the modulating wave. When M_5 is replaced by M_6 the path difference is approximately $\frac{1}{2}$ wavelength. Mirror M_2 is then moved by a micrometer screw to the position for which the radio-frequency component of the photoelectric current is a minimum. Then

$$2X + 2\,\Delta S - 2Y - 2\,\Delta Y = \frac{\lambda}{2}, \tag{4.10}$$

where ΔY is the small displacement of mirror M_2. If Eq. (4.9) is subtracted from Eq. (4.8),

$$2S - 2\,\Delta S + 2\,\Delta Y = n\lambda, \tag{4.11}$$

where ΔS and ΔY were measured with a micrometer screw. The approximate value of λ can be determined from the approximate value U to three significant figures and the period T of the radio wave in Eq. (4.8). From the approximate value of λ the approximate value of n can be found from Eq. (4.11). The value found will differ by much less than unity from the correct integer n. The exact integer is then substituted in Eq. (4.11) and the value of λ computed with the same percentage error as S. The group velocity of light is determined from Eq. (4.8). Since the period T is known to closer than one part per million, the percentage error in U is determined by the precision of measuring S and of adjusting the path differences to integer wavelengths.

Anderson's results, 299,776 $\pm$ 6 km/sec, were of about the same precision as Michelson's. Higher-frequency oscillators are continually being produced. It appears that electrical shutters will replace mechanical shutters in future measurements of the velocity of light.

4.7 Bergstrand's Method

The greatest source of error in the electro-optical shutter method of Anderson was in the use of the photocell. If the two beams were not exactly superposed, the transit times of the electrons from the emitting surface to the plate were different for the two beams. The two beams were detected when the electrons reached the plate of the photoelectric cell. Bergstrand[8] devised a method which employed but one beam of light. As indicated in Fig. 53, a

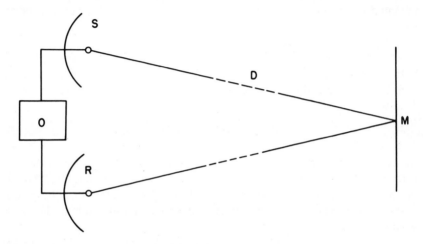

Figure 53. Bergstrand's method for determination of velocity of light.

crystal-controlled oscillator O of frequency 8 megacycles/sec, constant, and known to 1 part in 10 million, served to modulate light source S and simultaneously provide the potential difference across the photocell. A spherical mirror directed the light from the source in a beam upon mirror M, 9 km distant. A similar mirror received the reflected beam and focused it upon the photocell.

Mirror M was moved along a line perpendicular to its surface. For certain distances D the wave that modulated the light beam arrived at the receiver R in phase with the applied potential difference across the photocell. For such distances the photocell was most sensitive when the light beam was brightest.

By reversing the phase of modulation of the light source relative to that of the detector at a frequency low compared to the modulation frequency, Bergstrand made the current curve exactly symmetrical with respect to the zero line. Thus he obtained sharply marked positions of the mirror for which the current was zero.

[8] I. E. Bergstrand, *Nature*, **163**, 338 (1949); **165**, 405 (1950).

The result for which Bergstrand made a most complete evaluation of systematic errors was 299,793 ± 2 km/sec. This was 17 km/sec higher than Anderson's determination, a difference greater than the estimated errors of the observations.

Using a piezoquartz crystal subjected to a high frequency potential difference as an intermittent diffraction grating and thus an electro-optical shutter, R. A. Houston[9] has obtained results in agreement with those of Anderson.

4.8 The Velocity of Microwaves

The measurement of the velocity of electromagnetic waves described in the previous sections were all made with light. Maxwell's equations reveal that all the waves of the spectrum have the same velocity in vacuum.

Microwaves have a unique place in the spectrum for the measurement of velocity of the waves. The frequencies of microwave sources can be kept constant and measured directly to 1 part in 10 million. The United States Bureau of Standards maintains crystal-controlled oscillators whose oscillations may be counted directly. By means of frequency multipliers higher-frequency standards are produced. The Bureau of Standards transmitter WWV transmits a series of frequencies in the range from 5 to 100 megacycles/sec against which other oscillators may be compared.

The wavelengths of microwaves in resonant cavities are the distances that can be measured with light interferometers to 1 part in 10 million. Thus the velocity of microwaves can be determined from the product of frequency and wavelength by the same standing-wave methods that are used to measure the velocity of sound in elementary laboratories.

The first measurement of the velocity of electromagnetic waves by standing-wave methods was made by Mercier.[10] Two parallel wires from the source served to guide waves of electric and magnetic field to the end of the line, where they were reflected back to interfere with the incident wave and form standing waves. From the measured wavelength and frequency, Mercier found a velocity which agreed with that of light within the limits of experimental error.

A need for more precise measurement of the velocity of electromagnetic waves was found by the United States Air Force. They were using microwave beam methods to measure distances of a few hundred miles with high precision. The method was to send out a microwave beam which triggered the transmitter of a distant beacon, which returned a pulsed signal to the original source. Radar methods were used to measure the time for the pulse to go to the second station and the triggered pulse to return.

[9] R. A. Houston, *Nature*, **164**, 1004 (1949).

[10] J. Mercier, *J. phys. radium*, **5**, 168 (1924).

The first measurements were made of six distances between four triangulation stations of the Coast and Geodetic Survey. By using the accepted value of the velocity of light in vacuum c as 299,776 km/sec, they obtained distances less than the known measurements. After measuring 40 other known distances by the same microwave methods, Aslakson,[11] who directed the work, published a value for the velocity of microwaves in vacuum of 299,792 ± 2.4 km/sec.

Measurements of the velocity of microwaves by standing-wave methods have been made in evacuated, variable length, cylindrical, resonant cavities by Essen[12] and in fixed cavities by Hansen and Bol.[13]

Standing-wave methods yield phase velocity. The phase velocity in free space can be calculated from electromagnetic theory if the frequency, length, diameter, and Q of the cavity are known. Here Q defines the sharpness of resonance of the cavity by the equation

$$Q = \frac{\nu}{\nu_1 - \nu_2},$$

where ν is the resonant frequency, and ν_1 and ν_2 are the frequencies below and above the resonant frequency at which the power output of the resonator is half the output at the resonance frequency.

Essen obtained a velocity of microwaves of 299,792.5 ± 3.0 km/sec. Hansen and Bol obtained 299,789.3 ± 0.8. This is 15 km/sec higher than the values obtained by Pearson and Pease and by Anderson, a difference greater than the estimated error of any of these observers.

4.9 Re-evaluation

The velocity of light in vacuum is a constant which appears throughout quantum theory of radiation and wave mechanics of matter. It is a factor in the calculations of many of the constants of nuclear and atomic physics. By 1946 many atomic constants had been measured with such precision that the value of the velocity of light c was the limiting factor.

At the request of the National Science Foundation, DuMond and Cohen[14] determined the values of the atomic constants which included as first step the re-evaluation of the determinations of the velocity of light. In an effort to assess their own determination of the ratio of Planck's constant to the charge on the electron, Bearden and Watts[15] also re-evaluated the measurements of

[11] C. I. Aslakson, *Nature*, **164**, 711 (1949); *Trans. Am. Geophys. Union*, **30**, 475 (1949).

[12] L. Essen, *Proc. Roy. Soc.* (*London*), **A204**, 260 (1950).

[13] K. Bol, *Phys. Rev.*, **80**, 298 (1950).

[14] J. W. DuMond and E. R. Cohen, *Revs. Modern Phys.*, **20**, 82 (1948); *Phys. Rev.*, **82**, 555 (1951).

[15] J. A. Bearden and H. M. Watts, *Phys. Rev.*, **81**, 73 (1951).

J. F. Mulligan, *Am. J. Phys.*, **20**, 165 (1952).

the velocity of light. Both these evaluations gave the greatest weight to the determination by Hansen and Bol. Hansen and Bol had used numerous independent methods of determining systematic errors the greatest of which was due to the effect of silver oxide and sulfides on the surface resistance of their cavities.

Bearden and Watts noted that in a period of ten years the techniques had improved so greatly as to render the measurements of Michelson, Pease, and Pearson of historic value only.

Because of the need for more precise determinations of the velocity of light in atomic physics, astronomy, and navigation, we may expect new chapters in the "romance of the next decimal place." With the availability of microwave sources having directly determined frequencies, the determination of the velocity of electromagnetic waves will probably become a standard laboratory experiment similar to the determination of the velocity of sound.[16]

The treatment of the velocity of light in moving media and the measurements that were the experimental basis of the special theory of relativity will be treated in a later chapter following the study of interferometers.

PROBLEMS FOR CHAPTER IV

4.2.1. Römer found the mean period of Jupiter's inner moon to be 1.75 days. When the velocity of the earth was toward Jupiter the period was shortened by 15 sec. Find the velocity of light from these data and the more recent determination of the radius of the earth's orbit of 93,000,000 miles. Express in miles per second.

4.2.2. A microwave oscillator is placed on Jupiter and given pulses of oscillation having duration of 1 microsecond each. The pulses occur at the frequency of 1000.0/sec. What pulse frequency will be observed on the earth when the velocity of the earth is radially away from Jupiter?

4.3.3. Recent measurements of the angle of aberration 2θ yield 40.96 sec. Find the orbital velocity of the earth.

4.5.4. Michelson and his predecessors assumed that they were measuring phase velocity when in fact they were measuring the group velocity of light in air. Michelson proceeded to compute the velocity in vacuum from $n_p = c/v$, where n_p is the phase index of refraction. From the relation between the group velocity and phase velocity of Chapter III, determine in which significant figure Michelson made an error by assuming that he had measured phase velocity. The indices of refraction for blue and red light, respectively, are 1.000279 and 1.000276. Take the wavelengths of blue and red light as 4×10^{-7} m and 7×10^{-7} m.

---

[16] C. H. Palmer, Jr. and G. S. Spratt, *Am. J. Phys.*, **22**, 481 (1954).

chapter V

Standing Waves

5.1 The Measurement of Wavelengths

It is impossible to measure the wavelengths of moving sound waves or moving electromagnetic waves by running along beside them with a meter stick. The only way that we have succeeded in measuring wavelengths is by producing a stationary interference pattern between waves from two or more secondary sources. Much of physical optics is concerned with the spectrometers and interferometers used in measuring wavelengths.

The simplest case of interference is the standing wave. A *standing wave* is the resultant of two waves of the same frequency and amplitude moving in opposite directions along the same path. A standing wave is most commonly produced by letting a plane wave be incident normally upon a reflector and reflected back along the same path. At certain points the two waves will be 180° out of phase. These points of no vibration are called *nodes*. The nodes are one-half wavelength apart. Midway between them the waves are in phase yielding points of maximum amplitude or *antinodes*. Standing waves in strings, standing sound waves, and standing electromagnetic waves of convenient length can be measured directly on a meter stick.

5.2 Equation of a Standing Wave

We wish to derive the equation of a standing wave as the resultant of two waves of the same amplitude and frequency traveling in opposite directions.

We may let a wave be incident normally along the x axis in the direction of decreasing x upon a mirror at $x = 0$ and reflected back along the axis in the direction of increasing x. The incident wave is represented by

$$y_1 = Y \sin \left[2\pi \left(\frac{x}{\lambda} + \frac{t}{T} \right) + \delta_1 \right] \qquad (5.1)$$

and the reflected wave by

$$y_2 = Y \sin \left[2\pi \left(\frac{x}{\lambda} - \frac{t}{T} \right) + \delta_2 \right], \qquad (5.2)$$

where y_1 and y_2 are displacements of the incident and reflected waves, Y is the amplitude, and δ_1 and δ_2 are phase constants. The displacement of the resultant standing wave is

$$y = y_1 + y_2. \qquad (5.3)$$

We may make the constant $\delta_1 = 0$ merely by starting our clock at a time when $y_1 = Y \sin 2\pi x/\lambda$. The constant δ_2 may be evaluated at the origin where the reflector lies. If the reflector is a rigid wall for a wave in a string, a rigid surface for a sound wave, or an electric conductor reflecting the electromagnetic wave, the incident and reflected waves are 180° out of phase at $x = 0$. Thus $y_1 + y_2 = 0$ and $\delta_2 = 0$.

The reflectors above provide illustrations of *boundary conditions* which the simultaneous wave equations must satisfy. The boundary condition of rigidity where the string is fastened to the wall requires that the resultant displacement of the incident and reflected waves at that point be zero. The boundary condition of rigidity also requires that the resultant longitudinal displacement of the two sound waves at the boundary be zero. The perfect conductor requires zero resultant electric field parallel to the boundary.

Expanding the sine of the sum and difference of two angles in Eqs. (5.1) and (5.2) and substituting in Eq. (5.3), we obtain

$$y = 2Y \sin \frac{2\pi x}{\lambda} \cos \frac{2\pi t}{T}. \qquad (5.4)$$

This is the equation of a standing wave when the traveling wave undergoes a change of phase of 180° at the reflector placed at $x = 0$. The reader may evaluate δ_2 and solve for the equation of the standing wave for the case in which the reflected wave undergoes no phase change.

We shall give close attention to the interpretation of Eq. (5.4) both analytically and graphically. Standing waves and the standing-wave equation have features in common to all interference patterns and their equations.

We may compare the standing wave with a traveling wave. The amplitude

$2Y$ of the standing wave is twice that of the traveling component waves. The displacements of both the traveling and standing waves are functions of two independent variables, position x and time t. However, the displacement of the traveling wave is a function of the sum or difference of x/λ and t/T, while the displacement of the standing wave is a product of trigonometric functions of x/λ and t/T. The latter is a common feature of interference patterns.

The displacement in the standing wave of Eq. (5.4) is zero at points $x/\lambda = n\pi$ no matter what time it is. These are the nodal points. Likewise the displacement is zero at times $t/T = (2n + 1)\pi/2$ no matter what the position x may be.

Since y is a function of two independent variables, y may be plotted against x and t in a three dimensional graph. However, less time is consumed in making a series of plots of y against x for fixed values of t. Figure 54 is a

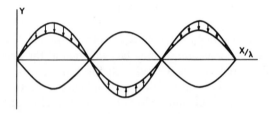

Figure 54. Graph of displacement against z/λ for $t/T = n/8$, where n is given integer values from zero to 3.

series of plots of y against x/λ for $t/T = n/8$, where n is given integer values from 0 to 3. The arrows indicate displacements during the first $\frac{1}{8}$ period. Note that all the displacements between consecutive nodes are in phase with each other, while the points in two loops separated by a node are 180° out of phase.

If we fix the value of x at x_1 some arbitrary value and let t vary, Eq. (5.3) is the equation of simple harmonic motion of the point at x_1. The amplitude is $2Y \cos 2\pi x_1/\lambda$. The amplitudes of the particles in the loop vary as $2Y \cos 2\pi x/\lambda$.

5.3 Demonstration of Standing Waves on an Oscilloscope

The addition of two waves of like frequency and amplitude traveling in opposite directions to produce a standing wave may be demonstrated effectively on a cathode ray oscilloscope with the arrangement of audio oscillators and oscilloscope shown in Fig. 41. The internal sweep circuit of the oscilloscope is set at about 200 cycles/sec and the synchronization at zero. Oscillator I is given a frequency of 100 cycles/sec. Two wavelengths will appear on the oscilloscope. The frequency of oscillator I is then increased slightly until the wave on the oscilloscope moves to the right with a frequency of about five waves per second. This is an artificial means of producing a low-frequency wave that can be followed with the eye.

With the amplitude and frequency controls left fixed, oscillator I is switched off and oscillator II given the same frequency and amplitude. The frequency of oscillator II is then reduced slightly, producing a wave on the oscilloscope moving to the left at a frequency of five waves per second.

By switching on I alone, II alone, and both together, we may show a wave to the right, a wave to the left, and the resultant standing wave, each of which is slow enough to be followed with the eye.

5.4 Standing Microwaves in Free Space

Because of their convenient wavelength, standing microwaves may be demonstrated side by side with standing waves in strings and standing sound

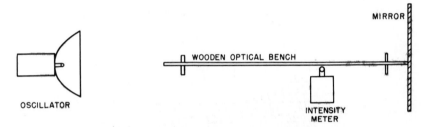

Figure 55. Arrangement for studying standing microwaves.

waves. Figure 55 indicates an arrangement for studying standing microwaves. The metal mirror should be at least five wavelengths wide. The oscillator is that of Fig. 11 and the intensity meter of Fig. 19. For quantitative measurements the intensity meter may be replaced by a probe which produces a minimum disturbance on the waves which are being measured. Figure 56 shows a silicon crystal detector in a glass capsule.[1] The wire leads of the detector serve as a dipole antenna. A twisted lead has been soldered to the antenna at each end of the glass capsule and extended in a direction at right angles to the electric field to a galvanometer, oscilloscope, or audio amplifier. Figure 57 is a plot of two experimental observations of standing waves of 4.0 cm wavelength made by driving the probe along the line of propagation and recording the intensity of radiation with a recording galvanometer. Because of the finite diameter of the probe, the center of the probe could not reach the mirror surface at the right to indicate the node there. At a few wavelengths from the mirror the nodes are no longer of zero intensity. This is because the beam is divergent both at incidence and reflection. At a large distance from the mirror the incident wave has larger amplitude than the reflected wave.

[1] IN82A hermetically sealed diode, Sylvania Electric Products, Woburn, Mass.

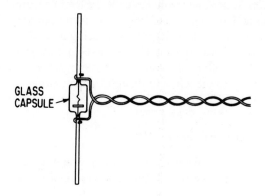

GLASS
CAPSULE

Figure 56. Microwave probe.

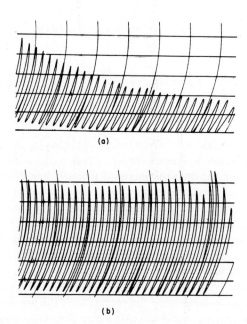

(a)

(b)

Figure 57. Experimental records of intensity of radiation of standing microwaves
of wavelength 4.0 cm.

Thus the intensity measured is that of a standing wave superposed on a traveling wave. Figure 57(a) was plotted when the source was only 6 ft away and the beam more divergent. Figure 57(b) was plotted when the source was 20 ft from the mirror.

5.5 Oblique Incidence upon a Mirror

If microwaves are incident upon a plane metal mirror with the electric field polarized perpendicularly to the plane of incidence, and the electric dipole probe moved along the normal to the mirror, planes of destructive interference will be observed parallel to the mirror and separated by distances greater than one-half wavelength. As the angle of incidence is increased from zero, the distance between nodes inceases from $\lambda/2$. In Fig. 58 is the distance from the mirror to the first antinode. Two rays are indicated which meet at point C on the first antinode, while AC is a phase front of the incident beam. The phase difference between the waves arriving at C is zero. Since the wave of electric field undergoes 180° phase change upon reflection at the mirror, path ABC must equal one-half wavelength. We wish to express this distance in terms of distance d from the mirror to the antinode and the angle of incidence ϕ.

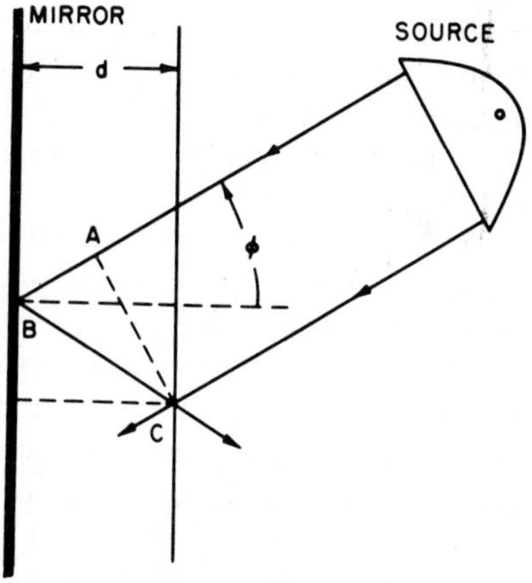

Figure 58. Interference pattern produced by oblique incidence upon a mirror.

$$BC = \frac{d}{\cos \phi},$$

$$AB = BC \cos 2\phi = \frac{d \cos 2\phi}{\cos \phi},$$

$$AB + BC = \frac{d(1 + \cos 2\phi)}{\cos \phi} = \frac{\lambda}{2}.$$

From the trigonometric expression for the cosine of twice an angle we obtain

$$d \cos \phi = \frac{\lambda}{4}. \tag{5.5}$$

The distance between successive nodes is $2d$. By using a mirror 4 ft wide as measured in the plane of incidence, one may measure the distance between nodes and check Eq. (5.5) for 12 cm wavelength and angles of incidence up to

60°. For larger angles of incidence, the necessary width of mirror and width of beam increase rapidly with angle of incidence.

The case of polarization in the plane of incidence will be treated under the topic of *elliptical polarization*.

5.6 Wave Guides

Since the reflected wave in a wave guide must follow the reverse path of the incident wave, standing waves occur frequently in wave guides. All electromagnetic waves ranging from light at 10^{14} cycles/sec to electric power at 60 cycles/sec can be transmitted by wave guides from the source to the place of use. Bent rods of transparent glass, quartz, plastics, and even streams of water serve to guide light by total internal reflection provided the radius of curvature is sufficiently large compared to the diameter of the cross section of the guide.

The space between the electrically conducting ionosphere and the earth serves as a wave guide for radio waves. The energy is confined to a thin shell around the earth, making world-wide communication possible.

The electric power industry is able to transmit a large per cent of its electric energy output directly to the consumer by transmission-line wave guide. In this course we shall not be concerned with power transmission at low frequencies. However, the power engineer has solved transmission-line problems that are useful at high frequencies. Knowledge of transmission lines on the one hand and physical optics on the other served in the solution of the problems of microwave frequencies lying between.

One might question whether the electric energy that comes to our homes and is measured by watthour meters comes in the electromagnetic waves that surround the wires or in the electric fluid inside the wires. This used to be a matter for heated arguments but now we know that we can measure the energy from either point of view. A similar argument was once carried on concerning gravitational energy. When a book was lifted, was the potential energy stored in the earth and book that were pushed apart, or in the gravitational field between? The total energy may be determined by either method. We now think of the energy in either position, whichever is more convenient.

The sizes of wave guides for light waves and for 60 cycles/sec waves is not determined by the wavelengths but solely by the size of man that builds and handles the wave guide. Plastic wave guides for light are thousands of wavelengths in diameter. The wave guided to a lamp by the transmission line of lamp cord has a wavelength billions of times greater than the distance between the wires.

Figure 59(a) is a diagram of a two-wire transmission line guiding a traveling electromagnetic wave to the right from an oscillator or a-c dynamo. The lines with arrows indicate lines of force in a sinusoidally distributed intensity of electric field. The crosses indicate magnetic field into, and dots magnetic field out of the plane of the diagram. Figure 59(b) indicates the electric and magnetic fields in a plane perpendicular to the transmission line. The intensity of field diminishes rapidly with distance from the transmission line as does the field around an electric or magnetic dipole. The transmission line in Fig. 59 may be considered either as having a perfect absorber of waves

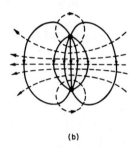

(b)

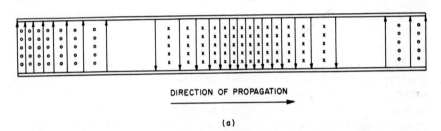

DIRECTION OF PROPAGATION

(a)

Figure 59. Traveling electromagnetic waves along a transmission line. (a) Wave in plane of transmission line. Crosses indicate magnetic field in, and circles magnetic field out of the plane. (b) Cross section perpendicular to transmission line viewed along line of propagation.

at the other end or an antenna that radiates all the energy into space so that there are no waves reflected back. In practice, the power of the wave diminishes along the line for two reasons, (1) heating of the wire and (2) radiation of some of the wave into space.

The transmission line shown in Fig. 59 is defined as a *long line*. It is long compared to a wavelength. Transmission lines for 60 cycles/sec are *short lines*. The long transmission line with an oscillator at one end and load at the other is not a simple series circuit. At high frequency a short section of the transmission line has sufficient capacitance between wires to present a low-capacitance reactance to the high-frequency current. At high frequency a short piece of wire may have high-inductive reactance. The transmission line may be considered as a repeating network of resistances and inductive reactances along a wire, and capacitive reactances between the wires.

The current varies sinusoidally along the wires just as does its accompanying magnetic field. The potential difference between the lines varies sinusoidally as does its accompanying electric field.

One may speak of current waves and potential difference waves just as one does of electric and magnetic waves. We are concerned only with the electric and magnetic waves. Fuller treatment of the currents and potential differences in transmission lines are found in textbooks of electricity.[2,3]

5.7 Standing Waves along a Transmission Line

If standing waves are to be produced in a transmission line, it must be terminated by a reflector. Two nearly perfect reflectors are a short-circuited end and an open end.

At the short-circuited end the intensity of electric field between the lines is zero. The reflected wave of electric field undergoes 180° phase change. The current at the short-circuited end is a maximum as is also the accompanying magnetic field. The magnetic field has undergone no phase change upon reflection but reinforces the incident wave at that point to give an antinode of magnetic field. Note that the short circuit in the transmission line produces the same effect on the electric and magnetic waves as the mirror of Sec. 5.4.

At the open end of the transmission line where the current and accompanying magnetic field are zero, the magnetic field of the traveling wave has undergone 180° phase change to yield a node in the standing magnetic wave at that point. The electric field of the reflected traveling wave undergoes no phase change so that there is an antinode of electric field at the open end.

If a transmission line is open at both ends or short-circuited at both ends and is an integer number of half waves long, it is *resonant* to the corresponding frequency like the string that is fixed at both ends. If a transmission line is open at one end and closed at the other and is an odd number of quarter wavelengths long, it is resonant to the corresponding frequency.

We may recall the nature of resonance by reference to the quarter-wave line of Fig. 60. The maximum downward electric field of a traveling wave is now entering the open end. One-half period later it will have traveled one-quarter wavelength, undergone a 180° phase change on reflection, and traveled back another one-half wave. At the open end it is reflected again but without phase change. It is in phase with and superposed upon the entering maximum of upward electric field. Thus the standing wave is continuously reinforced. In practice the internal reflection is not 100% efficient. A small percentage of the power is reradiated. The amplitude of the standing wave in

[2] R. P. Winch, *Electricity and Magnetism:* Englewood Cliffs, N.J., Prentice-Hall (1955) pp. 529–530.

[3] L. P. Page and N. I. Adams, *Principles of Electricity*, 2nd ed.: New York, Van Nostrand (1948) Sec. 130.

the resonant line ceases to increase when the reradiated power equals that entering the transmission line.

The transmission line of Fig. 60 might be considered as a resonant antenna for radio waves. The upper line is the antenna and the lower line the ground.

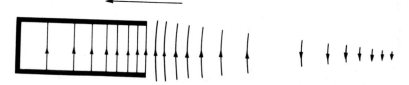

Figure 60. Traveling wave entering a quarter-wave transmission line.

Generally the two waves traveling in opposite direction in a transmission line are not of equal amplitude. Thus a standing wave is superposed on a traveling wave. In the experimental plot of intensity of radiation E^2 in Fig. 57(a) the nodes on the left-hand side are not of zero intensity, thus indicating a traveling wave superposed on the standing wave. The standing-wave ratio is defined as

$$\frac{E_{max} - E_{min}}{E_{max} + E_{min}},$$

where E_{max} and E_{min} are intensities of fields at two consecutive maxima and minima. It is to be remembered that the intensity of electric field is proportional to the square root of the intensity of radiation.

For a pure standing wave the standing-wave ratio is unity. For a pure traveling wave the intensity of radiation is everywhere the same and the standing-wave ratio is zero. Zero standing-wave ratio is the ideal for which the communications engineer strives in the transmission line between his transmitter and antenna. Every bend in the wire, every insulator, and the antenna itself reflect part of the wave.

If a transmission line a foot long extends from the 2400 megacycle/sec oscillator of Fig. 11 to an antenna as shown in Fig. 61, it will be observed that a supporting copper wire frame one-quarter wavelength long does not alter the transmission appreciably. It acts as an insulating support for a transmission line. An electric field which travels down the quarter-wave line and changes phase upon reflection returns by the quarter-wavelength path to be in phase with the wave traveling out the line. The open end of the quarter-wave section has a node of electric field and an antinode of magnetic field. In the parlance of a-c circuits, the impedance of the quarter-wave section looked at from the open end is the ratio of the root-mean-square potential difference to the root-mean-square current, and likewise the ratio of

102

the intensity of electric field to intensity of magnetic field at that end. Thus the ideal impedance of the quarter-wave section is infinite at the open end.

If such quarter-wave sections are attached closely together above and below the transmission line, they form a rectangular wave guide. This picture forms a simplified, qualitative introduction to rectangular wave guides.

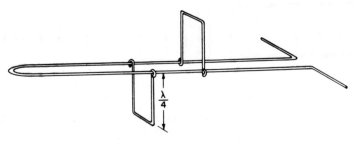

Figure 61. Quarter-wave supports for a transmission line.

Figures 62(a) and (b) indicate the electric fields in the cross sections of circular and rectangular wave guides. The width in the direction at right angles to the field must be at least one-half wave if it is to transmit the wave. The other dimension is not so critical but is usually about half the width. If

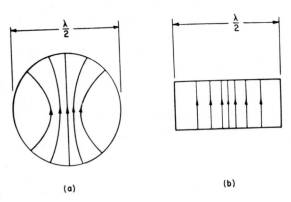

(a)

(b)

Figure 62. The electric field in the cross section of a circular and rectangular wave guide.

the transverse dimensions are increased by more than 50% beyond one-half wavelength the guide begins to transmit complex modes. For use with 12 cm waves of the educational band, the transverse section of the rectangular metal wave guide may be 3 in. by 1.5 in. A 3 in. stovepipe serves as a demonstration wave guide. A rectangular wave guide maintains the direction of polarization.

Figure 63 indicates a test to show that the rectangular wave guide is opaque to the 12 cm waves when the electric field is parallel to the long edge of the 3 in. by 1.5 in. wave guide. The wave guide transmits when the electric field is perpendicular to the long edge.

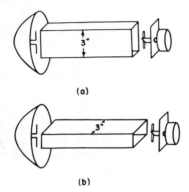

(a)

(b)

Figure 63. Demonstration that the rectangular wave guide is (a) opaque to 12 cm waves when the electric field is parallel to the long edge, (b) transparent when the electric field is parallel to the short edge.

5.8 Standing Waves in a Coaxial Line

Since the microwave oscillators that we employ are made up of coaxial resonant cavities, we shall treat coaxial wave guides. The two conductors of a coaxial transmission line are a hollow cylinder and a smaller coaxial rod. In long lines the center conductor is supported by insulating beads. The radial electric field between the two cylinders lies entirely inside the guide. At any transverse cross section the currents are equal and opposite in the two cylinders at any instant. The magnetic field of a long current-bearing wire varies inversely as the radial distance from the center. Thus the magnetic fields of the two cylinders cancel outside the outer shell. The electromagnetic wave is confined inside the coaxial line.

The resonant cavity of a microwave oscillator looks more like a whistle or organ pipe than like a conventional radio oscillator. Indeed, a graphical description of a standing wave in an organ pipe makes a good analogue for studying transverse electromagnetic waves in a resonant cavity.

Figure 64 shows diagrammatically and graphically the standing waves in cylindrical cavities. Figure 64(a) is a quarter-wave sound resonator open at one end, shown when the displacement to the left is a maximum. Figure 64(b) is the same tube one-half period later when displacements are a maximum to the right. Below the resonator is a graphical plot of the pressure above atmospheric against position along the length of the tube at the two times. Pressures below atmospheric are negative. Displacement is the other aspect of sound waves. Displacement of particles to the right is also plotted against

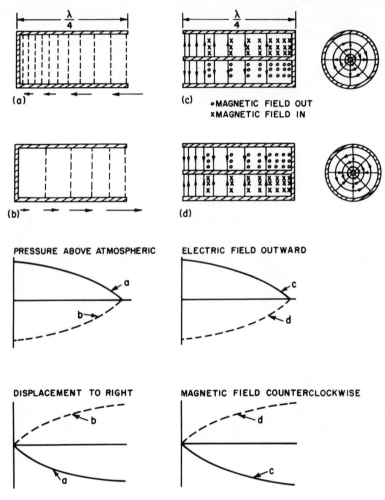

Figure 64. Analogy between resonant cavity for sound and coaxial resonant cavity for microwaves.

neutral position of the particles along the tube. Displacements to the left are negative.

The second column Fig. 64(c) shows a quarter-wave resonant coaxial cavity open at one end and closed at the other at an instant when the radially outward field is a maximum. Figure 64(d) shows the same cavity one-quarter period later when the radially inward electric field is a maximum. Crosses represent magnetic field into the paper and small circles magnetic field out. The cross sections on the right showing the radial electric fields and the circular magnetic fields are observed by looking to the left from the closed end of the tube.

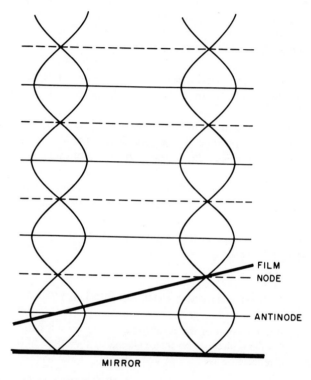

Figure 65. Wiener's apparatus for photographing standing light waves.

The closed end of the resonant coaxial cavity for electromagnetic waves is analogous to the open end of the sound cavity. In the sound cavity there is a node of pressure and antinode of displacement at the open end. At the closed end is an antinode of pressure and a node of displacement. At the short-circuited end of the resonant cavity for electromagnetic waves is a node of electric field and an antinode of magnetic field. At the open end is an antinode of electric field and a node of magnetic field.

Analogies prove nothing but they are an aid to thinking in a new field. Those who perform the cut-and-try processes of designing new types of microwave "plumbing" attest to the values of analogies taken from the fields of sound, light, and transmission lines.

5.9 Standing Light Waves

The discovery by Hertz in 1888 that waves were emitted from a spark discharge was the first observation and measurement of standing electromagnetic waves.

Two years later Wiener[4] succeeded in observing standing light waves. Monochromatic light was incident normally and reflected from a polished mirror in front of which was placed a photographic film only $\frac{1}{20}$ wavelength thick mounted on a glass plate and set at an angle of only 4' with the plane of the mirror as shown in Fig. 65. The developed film showed the dark and light bands of the interference pattern. Because of the small angle between the film and the nodal planes, the distance between nodal planes was greatly amplified on the film.

A node was observed at the mirror. Hertz had previously observed a node of electric field and an antinode of magnetic field at the mirror, so that Wiener could conclude that it was the electric field which was effective in the photographic process.

Wiener's experiment is too difficult to perform in the student laboratory. It is not a precise means of measuring the wavelength of light. However, standing waves are the simplest case of interference. Wiener's experiment was a beautiful conclusion to a series of demonstrations that light and Hertzian waves are identical except for wavelength.

PROBLEMS FOR CHAPTER V

5.1.1. Find the equation of the resulting standing wave for the case in which the reflected wave undergoes no phase change at the origin of the x axis. The incident and reflected waves are given by Eqs. (5.1) and (5.2).

5.2.2. Plot graphs of displacement y of a standing wave against t/T for cases $x/\lambda = n/8$. Let n have integer values from 0 to 6.

5.5.3. Derive Eq. (5.5) for the distance from the mirror to the first antinode more simply. Show a mirror image C' of C in Fig. 58 and make use of triangle $AC'C$. Note that the interference pattern might be treated as a resultant of waves from the image source and the real source. The image source is 180° out of phase with the real source.

5.7.4. Prove that the standing-wave ratio is equal to the ratio of the smaller amplitude to the larger amplitude of the two component traveling waves.

5.7.5. Find the ratio of maximum to minimum intensity in waves having standing-wave ratios of 0.9 and 0.5.

[4] O. Wiener, *Ann. Physik*, **40**, 203 (1890).

5.7.6. What is the standing-wave ratio near the left-hand end of the wave in Fig. 57(a)?

5.8.7. Indicate diagrammatically the densities of gas in an organ pipe open at both ends and sounding its fundamental when the displacements are a maximum. Indicate by arrows below the pipe the distribution of displacements. Figure 64 serves as an example. Make a similar diagram of the pipe one-half period later. On the same coordinates plot graphs of *displacements to the right* against neutral position along the tube. Displacements to the left will be negative. Label the curves to correspond to the diagrams. Plot graphs of *pressure above atmospheric*, pressure below atmospheric being negative, against *neutral position* along the pipe.

5.8.8. Make a diagrammatic sketch of the fundamental electromagnetic standing wave in a metal coaxial cavity closed at both ends when the radially outward electric field is a maximum. Make a similar sketch of the cavity one-half period later. On the same coordinates plot graphs of the *radially outward electric field* against *position* along the length of the tube corresponding to the two diagrams. On another set of coordinates plot the *counter-clockwise magnetic field* against *position* along the tube for each of the cases in the diagrams. Clockwise magnetic fields will be plotted negatively. Compare the graphs with those of problem 5.8.7.

chapter VI

Interference of Waves from Two Secondary Sources

6.1 Interference between Two Spherical Waves

In this chapter we shall be concerned with the interference patterns of spherical waves from two point sources and cylindrical waves from two parallel line sources. By a *point source* we shall mean, for the present, a source small compared to a wavelength. Later, when we treat the special case of distant interference patterns, a point source will be a source whose linear dimensions subtend small angles at the point of observation. Secondary light sources are not generally small compared to a wavelength. Radio antennas and microwave dipoles are often small compared to a wavelength.

In Sec. 5.6 the interference between two plane waves was treated. Geometrically, the next simplest case is that of interference between two spherical waves. This is the historic experiment of Thomas Young. In Fig. 22, by construction of instantaneous wave crests and troughs in a plane including the two sources, the locus of all points at which the two spherical waves are in phase has been found as a family of hyperbolas drawn through the crosses. The circles indicate points of destructive interference through which another family of hyperbolas may be drawn.

In regions much closer to one of the sources than to the other, the points of minimum intensity do not quite coincide with the points where the waves are exactly out of phase. However, at distances greater than twice the distance between the sources, the difference between the lines of minimum intensity and lines of phase opposition can scarcely be detected. In the near region the resulting amplitude and phase must be found from the superposition of the two waves, or more simply by the addition of the two rotating vectors which represent those waves as they pass a point.

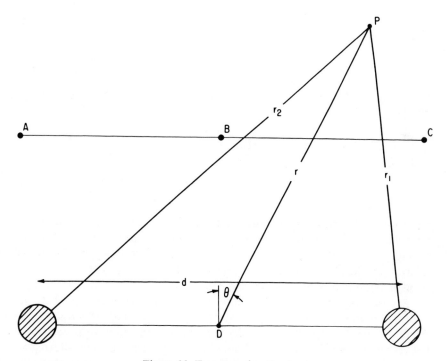

Figure 66. Two secondary sources.

The amplitude and phase at any point are given by

$$\mathbf{u} = \mathbf{u}_0 \left\{ \frac{1}{r_1/\lambda} e^{j[(2\pi r_1/\lambda) + \pi/2]} + \frac{1}{r_2/\lambda} e^{j[(2\pi r_2/\lambda) + \pi/2]} \right\}, \qquad (6.1)$$

where r_1 and r_2 are the distances from the secondary sources to the point of observation indicated in Fig. 66. The ratios r/λ express distance in wavelengths. We note that the amplitudes of the spherical waves are inversely proportional to their radii. This follows from conservation of energy. Since the areas of the spherical wave fronts are proportional to the squares of their radii and the intensity is power per area of spherical surface, the intensity is inversely proportional to the square of their radii. Thus the amplitudes of the spherical waves are inversely proportional to the first power of the radii.

Here $\pi/2$ expresses a phase advance near the source, the experimental discovery of which will be discussed in the following section. The sources are in phase with each other. Here **u** is the complex amplitude and $\mathbf{u}_0$ is the complex amplitude taken as reference, called the *reference vector*. Since our purpose is to compare the resultant amplitudes and phases in the interference pattern, the value of $\mathbf{u}_0$ may be picked arbitrarily. For instance, we might wish to let the resultant wave midway between the two sources be the reference wave and assign it an amplitude of unity and phase zero. At that point Eq. (6.1) becomes

$$1 = \mathbf{u}_0 \frac{2}{d/2\lambda} e^{j[(2\pi d/2\lambda)+(\pi/2)]}$$

where d is the distance between the centers of the sources. Solving for $\mathbf{u}_0$ we obtain

$$\mathbf{u}_0 = \frac{d}{4\lambda} e^{-j[(\pi d/\lambda)+(\pi/2)]},$$

and Eq. (6.1) becomes

$$\mathbf{u} = \frac{d}{4r_1} e^{j2\pi(r_1 - d/2)/\lambda} + \frac{d}{4r_2} e^{j2\pi(r_2 - d/2)/\lambda}. \tag{6.2}$$

If we are determining the amplitudes and phases along the line ABC, we may choose $\mathbf{u}_0$ so as to make the amplitude unity and phase zero at B. As an example we may determine the amplitudes and phases along line BC which is two wavelengths from the line between the sources. Let the distance between sources be four wavelengths.

The calculated complex amplitudes at points between B and C are indicated in Fig. 67. The amplitude and phase at point B have been chosen as reference and are represented by the vector from the origin to point 1.0 on the real axis. The distances x/λ from B along the line BC are indicated by numbers along the spiral. The amplitudes and phases at those points in space are represented by vectors from the origin to the corresponding points on the complex spiral.

Actually the choice of the resultant phase at B as reference phase turns out to be awkward and time consuming. Even the spiral of Fig. 67 is of awkward shape, and the points which indicate position on line BC are not uniformly distributed.

A more convenient choice is to let the amplitude be unity at B, but to choose as reference phase the phase of the wavelet from one of the two sources arriving at each point P at which the amplitude and phase are to be determined. Figure 68 shows the spiral computed by letting the phase of the wave from the left-hand source be reference for the amplitudes and phases along line BC. The positions on the line BC are indicated again by cross lines on the spiral. The amplitudes represented by distances from the origin to the cross lines are identical on the spirals of Figs. 67 and 68. The two cases have been given to show the importance of the art of picking the reference phase.

If we require only two significant figures for the amplitude, we may save still more time by adding the two vectors with ruler and protractor. Figure 68 was plotted by this quick method.

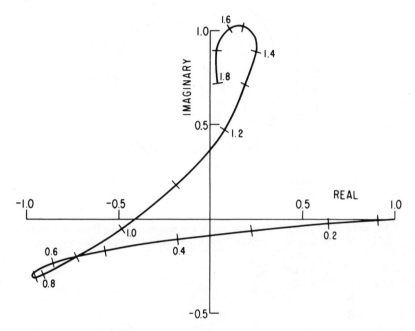

Figure 67. Calculated complex amplitudes at points between B and C of Fig. 66. Amplitude and phase at B are taken as reference.

Figure 69 shows graphs of the amplitude and intensity of radiation relative to that at point B plotted against distance in wavelengths from point B along the line BC. The vertical broken lines indicate the points where the two waves are in phase opposition.

This condition for phase opposition in the interference pattern is

$$r_2 - r_1 = \frac{(2n + 1)\lambda}{2}, \tag{6.3}$$

n being any positive integer or zero. This is an equation of a family of hyperboloids of two sheets each with common foci at the two sources. In a cross section through the sources it is an equation for a family of hyperbolas. From Fig. 66 we see that r_1 and r_2 may be expressed in terms of the polar coordinates r and θ, where r is the distance from the midpoint between

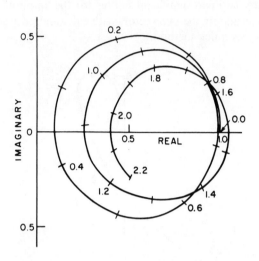

Figure 68. Complex spiral of amplitudes and phases at points between B and C of Fig. 66. Phase of wave arriving from left-hand source is taken as reference.

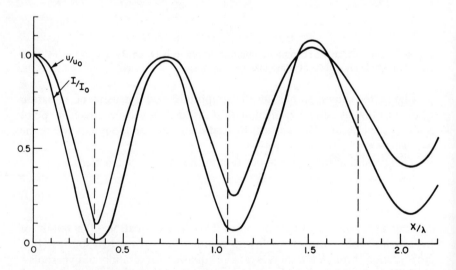

Figure 69. Amplitude and intensity of radiation plotted against distance from B along the line BC.

sources to the point of observation P, and θ is the angle between r and the normal to the line between the sources at its midpoint. Employing the cosine law for triangles, we obtain

$$\left[\begin{array}{l} r_2^2 = r^2 + \left(\frac{d}{2}\right)^2 + rd\cos\left(\frac{\pi}{2} - \theta\right) \\[3mm] r_1^2 = r^2 + \left(\frac{d}{2}\right)^2 + rd\cos\left(\frac{\pi}{2} + \theta\right). \end{array} \right.$$

Substituting these values for r_1 and r_2 in Eq. (6.3), we obtain

$$2\left[r^2 + \left(\frac{d}{2}\right)^2\right] - 2\sqrt{\left[r^2 + \left(\frac{d}{2}\right)^2\right]^2 - r^2 d^2 \sin^2 \theta} = \frac{(2n+1)^2 \lambda^2}{4}.$$

Solving for $r^2 d^2 \sin^2 \theta$, we obtain

$$r^2 d^2 \sin^2 \theta = \left[\left(\frac{d}{2}\right)^2 + r^2\right](2n+1)^2 \frac{\lambda^2}{4} - (2n+1)^4 \frac{\lambda^4}{64}. \qquad (6.4)$$

In the distant interference pattern of Young's experiment for light, $r \gg d \gg \lambda$, and

$$d \sin \theta = \frac{(2n+1)\lambda}{2} \qquad (6.5)$$

for minimum intensity.

We may note the physical significance of the eccentricities of the conics which appear in this chapter. If d is the distance between the sources of Fig. 66 and a is the distance between the two intercepts of a hyperboloid of two sheets with the axis through the two sources at the focal points, the eccentricity $e = d/a$ the locus of all points where the two waves are in phase is expressed by $a = r_2 - r_1 = n\lambda$. If the distance between sources is expressed in wavelengths by $d = N\lambda$, the eccentricity is $e = N/n$.

6.2 Interference between a Plane Wave and a Spherical Wave

The superposition of a plane wave and a spherical wave at any point P may be expressed by

$$\mathbf{u} = u_1 e^{j 2\pi x/\lambda} + u_2 \frac{\lambda}{r} e^{j[(2\pi r/\lambda) + \delta]}, \qquad (6.6)$$

where u_1 is the amplitude of the plane wave, x is the distance of the point P from a plane wave front through "point" source S in Fig. 70, u_2 is the amplitude of the spherical wave at one wavelength from the point source, and r the distance from the source to P; δ is the phase angle of the spherical wave leaving the source relative to that of the plane wave at the source. For point sources it will be shown experimentally that δ is a variable depending on distance for distances less than a wavelength or two from the point source. At larger distances δ is essentially constant. The condition for phase coincidence of the two waves arriving at point P is expressed by

$$2\pi\left(\frac{r}{\lambda} - \frac{x}{\lambda}\right) + \delta = 2\pi n,$$

where n is any integer or zero. If θ is the angle between the directions of the motions of the spherical wave and the plane wave reaching P,

$$r(1 - \cos\theta) = \lambda\left(n - \frac{\delta}{2\pi}\right). \tag{6.7}$$

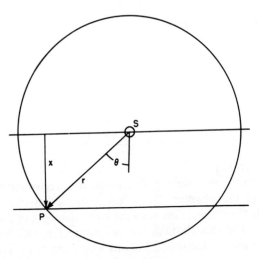

Figure 70. Interference between a plane wave and a spherical wave.

Since the right-hand side of Eq. (6.7) is constant for each value of n, the equation is that of a family of parabolas with the principal focus at source S, as is shown by the construction in Fig. 21.

In 1890 Gouy[1] made a study of interference between a plane wave and a spherical wave. Light from illuminated pinhole S fell on plane mirror M and spherical mirror M_c, cut from a spectacle lens, as shown in Fig. 71. The mirrors were 1.5 m from the source. With an eye-piece he studied the interference pattern near the focal point F where the cone of light from M_c overlapped the beam from M. On the converging side where the cone approached F he observed a white center surrounded by circular fringes of

[1] G. Gouy, *Ann. de chim. et phys.*, **24**, 145 (1891).

color. Gouy was surprised to find that on the diverging side of F the center of the pattern was black indicating that the spherical wave had undergone 180° phase change on passing through the focal point.

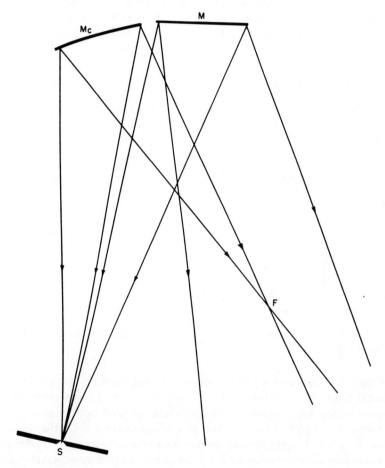

Figure 71. Gouy's apparatus, with which he discovered the phase advance at the focal point.

A repetition of Gouy's experiment with microwaves[2] reveals that half the 180° phase change takes place before the wave reaches the focal point and half after it has passed the focal point. Most of the phase advance takes place within one wavelength on either side of the focal point. The two interfering waves may be a plane wave incident along the axis of a parabolic reflector and the spherical reflected wave. The experimental arrangement is that of Fig. 56

[2] C. R. Carpenter, *Am. J. Phys.*, **27**, 98 (1959).

for standing waves except that the plane mirror is replaced by a parabolic mirror with a focal length of four or more wavelengths, as indicated in Fig. 72.

In Gouy's experiment the plane and spherical waves were traveling in nearly the same direction. In the microwave demonstration the waves are moving in opposite directions. The resulting standing wave pattern reveals more precisely where the phase advance takes place.

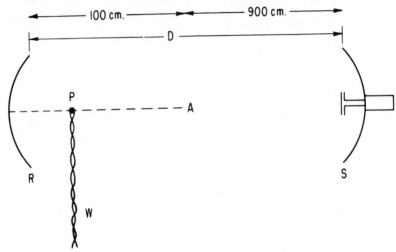

Figure 72. Arrangement for studying the phase advance of microwaves near a focal point.

Figure 73 is a recording of the intensity of the standing microwaves near the focal point. The numbers N of the nodes are indicated below the recording of the standing-wave intensity. Most of the half-wavelength gain is seen in the range $N = 4$ to 6. Figure 74 is a plot of the distance from the reference minimum in wavelengths against the number of the minimum. A similar plot for a standing wave obtained with a plane mirror and the same wavelength is also shown with label SW. The asymptotes to the standing-wave curve through the focal point are parallel to the standing-wave curve for the plane mirror. The difference between the two intercepts of these asymptotes with the vertical axis reveals nearly a half-wave gain and the corresponding 180° phase advance as the wave passes the focal point.

The δ of Eqs. (6.6) and (6.7) is a variable at distances of less than one-half wavelength from the focal point, but is approximately constant at greater distances. The result of Gouy's experiment will be used to explain observations of diffraction. The secondary Huygens' wavelets which Fresnel has postulated as continuous wavelets originating at a wave front behave as the

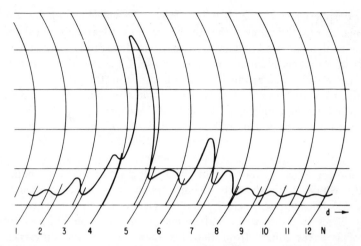

Figure 73. Recording of the intensity of radiation of standing microwaves near a focal point.

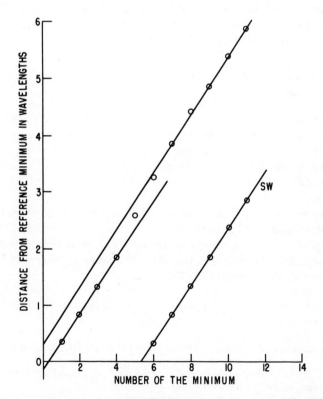

Figure 74. A plot for the determination of the phase advance near a focal point.

focused spherical wave studied by Gouy. The wavelet undergoes a phase advance of $\pi/2$, the same as that of the wave as it leaves the focal point.

To explain how secondary spherical wavelets produced resultant wave fronts of the experimentally observed phase, Fresnel had assumed that the spherical wavelet was advanced $\pi/2$ in phase from the primary wave. Gouy explained Fresnel's observation by noting that any spherical wave proceeding from a point source undergoes a phase advance of $\pi/2$, and that this advance does not take place at a point but over distance of one wavelength from the source.

In advanced treatments of wave theory,[3] solutions of the differential equation for spherical waves yield phase velocities and corresponding wavelengths which diminish with distance from the source approaching the constant values of phase velocity and wavelength for a plane wave. Thus the Gouy effect is an experimental confirmation that the phase velocity of spherical waves differs from that for plane waves, the difference being measurable in the region where the radius of curvature is of the order of one wavelength.

Understanding the Gouy phase advance will be important when we are studying the whole interference pattern near sources, scatterers, and diffracting objects. Examples are treated in the problems.

6.3 Interference between a Plane Wave and Reradiation from a Resonant Metal Rod

If a plane electromagnetic wave is incident upon a metal rod whose length is one-half wavelength with the electric field parallel to the rod, the reradiated wave observed in a plane perpendicular to the rod through its center is effectively a spherical wave at distances of greater than two wavelengths. In practice, the half-wave resonant metal rods are 0.01 to 0.1 wavelength in diameter.

It has been shown from electromagnetic theory[4] and experiment[5] that the constants u_2 and δ of Eq. (6.6) become, respectively, $u_1/4$ and $\pi/2$ for a half-wave dipole. Indeed, the equation is exact for short as well as long distances if the distance from the end of the rod to the point of observation in Fig. 75 is substituted for r in Eq. (6.6). That is,

$$\frac{\mathbf{u}}{\mathbf{u_0}} = e^{j2\pi x/\lambda} + \frac{\lambda}{4\rho} e^{j2\pi(\rho/\lambda + 1/4)}. \tag{6.8}$$

As shown in Sec. 2.6 and 2.7, the relative intensity I/I_0 is equal to the square

[3] J. A. Stratton, *Electromagnetic Theory:* New York, McGraw-Hill, (1941) pp. 392–422.
[4] Stratton, *op. cit.* pp. 454–457.
[5] C. L. Andrews, *J. Appl. Phys.*, **22**, 465 (1951).

of the absolute value of the complex amplitude, which in turn is equal to the product of the complex amplitude and its conjugate.

$$\frac{I}{I_0} = 1 + \left(\frac{\lambda}{4\rho}\right)^2 + 2\left(\frac{\lambda}{4\rho}\right) \sin 2\pi\left[\frac{x}{\lambda} - \frac{\rho}{\lambda}\right]. \tag{6.9}$$

From Fig. 75(b) we see that $x = r \cos \theta$ and from Fig. 75(a) that

$$\frac{r}{\lambda} = \left[\left(\frac{\rho}{\lambda}\right)^2 - \left(\frac{1}{4}\right)^2\right]^{1/2}.$$

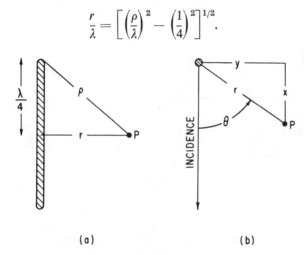

(a)   (b)

Figure 75. Reradiating half-wave dipole.

Thus the relative intensity may be expressed in terms of ρ and θ,

$$\frac{I}{I_0} = 1 + \left(\frac{\lambda}{4\rho}\right)^2 + 2\left(\frac{\lambda}{4\rho}\right) \sin 2\pi\left\{\left[\left(\frac{\rho}{\lambda}\right)^2 - \left(\frac{1}{4}\right)^2\right]^{1/2} \cos \theta - \frac{\rho}{\lambda}\right\}. \tag{6.10}$$

We shall express Eq. (6.10) graphically for three special cases.

(1) When $\theta = 0°$ the bracket diminishes rapidly with increase in ρ/λ as the terms of opposite sign approach equality and the intensity approaches rapidly toward that of the incident beam as shown for positive values of x/λ in Fig. 76.

(2) When $\theta = 180°$ the terms in the bracket are of the same sign and the third term of the expression becomes a standing-wave term. The diminishing standing wave is shown for negative values of x/λ in Fig. 76.

(3) When $\theta = 90°$ we are treating the interference pattern along the y axis of Fig. 75(b). This is the plane of the incident wave front through the rod. In Fig. 77 the intensity of the interference pattern relative to that of the unperturbed beam is plotted along the y axis. The scale of ρ/λ is indicated along the top.

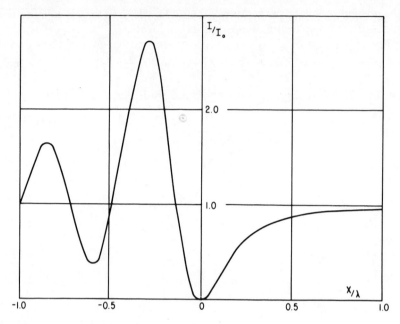

Figure 76. Plot of intensity of radiation along a path in the direction of propagation of the incident beam through the center of the half-wave dipole.

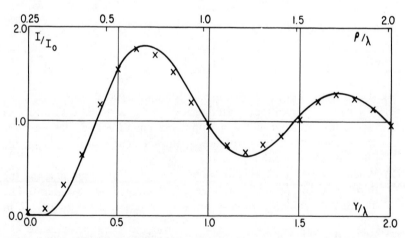

Figure 77. Plot of intensity of radiation along the y axis measured from the center of the half-wave dipole.

6.4 Interference between a Plane Wave and a Cylindrical Wave

The superposition at any point P of a plane wave and a cylindrical wave, each polarized in the same direction, may be expressed by

$$\mathbf{u} = u_1 e^{j2\pi x/\lambda} + \left(\frac{u_2}{\sqrt{\frac{r}{\lambda}}}\right) e^{j[(2\pi r/\lambda)+\delta]}. \tag{6.11}$$

Equation (6.11) differs from Eq. (6.6) only in that the amplitude of the cylindrical wave varies inversely as the square root of the distance from the

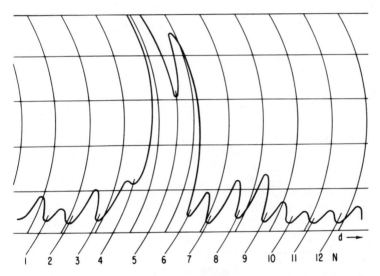

Figure 78. Recorded plot of intensity of radiation of the standing waves taken through the focal line of a parabolic cylinder.

source instead of inversely as the first power. Since the areas of the cylindrical wave fronts are proportional to the radii, the intensities are inversely proportional to the radii and the amplitudes inversely proportional to the square roots of the radii.

By the same method that he studied a converging spherical wave as it passed through a focal point, Gouy[6] also studied a cylindrical wave as it passed through a focal line and found that the wave velocity was increased near the focal line. The total phase advance as the wave passed this region near the focal line was $\pi/2$.

[6] Gouy, *loc. cit.*

The precise region where the phase advance takes place may be obtained by studying the interference pattern between a plane microwave beam incident on a parabolic cylinder and the reflected converging cylindrical wave. Figure 78 shows a recorded plot of the intensity of radiation of the standing waves taken through the focal line of the parabolic cylinder with the numbers N of

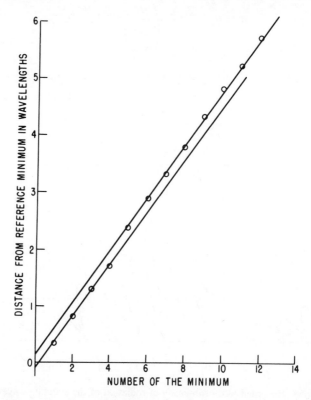

Figure 79. A plot of the distance of each node from the reference minimum against the number of the minimum. The intercepts of the asymptotes with the ordinate indicates a phase advance of $\pi/2$.

the nodes indicated below. Figure 79 is a corresponding plot of the distance of each node from the reference minimum against the number of the minimum. The intercepts of the asymptotes indicate an advance of one-quarter wavelength and a corresponding phase advance of $\pi/2$.

In treating secondary cylindrical wavelets, Fresnel had found it necessary to assume that the wavelets were advanced $\pi/4$. Gouy verified Fresnel's assumption by observing experimentally that all cylindrical waves from a line source are advanced in phase by $\pi/4$, and that the advance takes place over a region rather than at a point.

We may note that the treatment of the phase advance as converging waves pass focal lines or points is part of the subject of diffraction to be treated later. The patterns in the neighborhood of a focal point are diffraction patterns of a circular aperture. Those near a focal line are diffraction patterns of a slit. There are no geometrical focal points or focal lines. These matters will be treated under the topics of *diffraction* and *formation of images.*

In the meantime the treatment of phase advance near foci and of the phase advance of waves proceeding from point and line sources is essential to the application of the concept of Fresnel's secondary wavelets. In summary, a secondary spherical wavelet proceeding from a point on the primary wave front undergoes a phase advance $\pi/2$, most of which takes place in the first wavelength. A secondary cylindrical wave undergoes a similar phase advance of $\pi/4$. The treatment of secondary radiations applied by Huygens to pulses and by Young and Fresnel to continuous wavelets is a convenient mathematical device used in the solution of problems in physical optics.

6.5 Young's Experiment

Young's historic experiment with light was a special case of interference between two coherent spherical waves which we have treated in Sec. 6.1. When $r \gg d \gg \lambda$, Eq. (6.4), which expressed the condition for phase opposition of the two waves, reduced to

$$d \sin \theta = \frac{(2n + 1)\lambda}{2}.$$

As this standard experiment is now performed in laboratories of physical optics, Young's two secondary hole sources have been replaced by slits S_1 and S_2 of Fig. 80. Secondary slits about one-half millimeter apart can be made by drawing a razor blade across a photographic emulsion. Precision double slits may be purchased from scientific supply companies. The primary slit S is illuminated by a carbon arc or a coiled tungsten filament wound with a straight axis placed within one centimeter of the primary slit. A red filter provides a narrow wavelength range. A sodium arc lamp is also sufficiently bright.

If the distance D from the plane of the slit to the plane of observation is of the order of 1 m, the pattern can be seen with a low power eyepiece. When a long black tube 1 in. in diameter is placed between the eyepiece and the double slit to exclude extraneous light, the room need not be darkened. If D is of the order of 10 m the interference pattern may be measured with a centimeter scale on a ground-glass screen.

Since the wavelength is about 0.00005 cm and the distance between slits 0.5 cm, we note that r is 1000 times larger than d and d 1000 times larger than λ, satisfying the condition $r \gg d \gg \lambda$. The angle θ is a few minutes.

Two simplifications arise in this special case of interference treated by Young.

(1) The intensity maxima are equal.

(2) The distances between consecutive dark bands in the interference pattern are equal.

The equality of the intensity maxima arises from the fact that the distances of point P from the two sources are approximately equal so that the amplitudes of the interfering waves are equal. However, the path differences are the order of a few wavelengths, thus yielding differences in phases of the waves

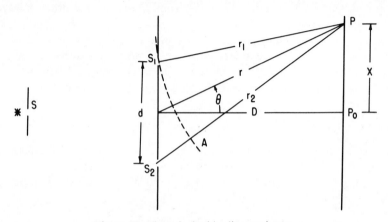

Figure 80. Young's double-slit experiment.

reaching P. If we construct an arc with P as center through S_1 cutting S_2P at A, the path difference of the two waves is S_2A. To a good approximation arc S_1A equals cord S_1A. Angle S_2S_1A equals θ. The path difference of the two waves is the product $d \sin \theta$ and the phase difference which we shall call ϕ may be expressed

$$\phi = \frac{2\pi d \sin \theta}{\lambda}. \tag{6.12}$$

As shorthand for adding the two waves we may add the two rotating vectors that sweep out the waves as indicated in Fig. 81, where $\mathbf{u}_1$ and $\mathbf{u}_2$ are vectors of equal magnitude corresponding to the waves that have traveled distances r_1 and r_2, respectively,

$$\mathbf{u} = \mathbf{u}_1 + \mathbf{u}_2.$$

If the wave of complex amplitude $\mathbf{u}_1$ is taken as reference with phase zero at a particular time, and the two waves have equal amplitude u_0, then the resultant wave may be expressed

$$\mathbf{u} = u_0 + u_0 e^{-j\phi}. \tag{6.13}$$

The intensity of radiation is proportional to the square of the absolute value of the complex amplitude.

$$\frac{I}{I_0} = \left|\frac{\mathbf{u}}{u_0}\right|^2 = (1 + e^{j\phi}) + (1 + e^{-j\phi}) = 2(1 + \cos\phi). \qquad (6.14)$$

By a familiar trigonometric identity,

$$\frac{I}{I_0} = 4\cos^2\frac{\phi}{2}. \qquad (6.15)$$

We see that the intensity maxima are equal to each other and four times the intensity I_0 of either component wave reaching the plane of observation.

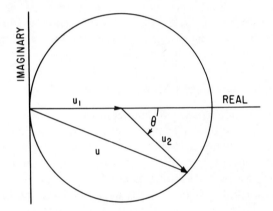

Figure 81. Addition of the two rotating vectors.

The intensity is a maximum when $\phi = 2n\pi$ and zero when $\phi = (2n + 1)\pi$. However, we can measure only the positions where the intensity is maximum and minimum, so we shall wish to express the phase angle in terms of the distance x from the central maximum. We note that

$$\phi = \frac{2\pi d \sin\theta}{\lambda} = \frac{2\pi x d}{\lambda D}$$

and

$$x = \frac{\lambda D \phi}{2\pi d}.$$

Thus the intensity is maximum when

$$x = \frac{nD\lambda}{d}, \qquad (6.16)$$

and minimum when

$$x = \left(n + \frac{1}{2}\right)\frac{\lambda D}{d}.$$ (6.17)

Since D, λ, and d are constants, the distances to the orders are proportional to the integers n so that the lines are equally spaced.

Visually, the distance between centers of dark lines may be determined more precisely than between centers of maximum intensity. If Δx is the mean distance between lines,

$$\lambda = \frac{d\,\Delta x}{D},$$ (6.18)

where d and x may be measured with a micrometer microscope or on a scale of 0.1 mm scale divisions etched on a glass and observed through a magnifying eyepiece. To obtain the sharpest interference pattern, one should adjust the primary source slit S. Under the subject of *diffraction* we shall discuss the optimum width of the primary slit. At present the best width may be found by cut-and-try adjustment.

6.6 Fresnel's Biprism, Fresnel's Mirrors, and Lloyd's Mirror

Objectors to Young's theory of interference of light waves proposed that light corpuscles corresponding to the various colors were differently attracted by the edge of the slit to produce bands of color. Fresnel and Lloyd later devised means of effectively producing the two sources without the edges thus eliminating the possibility of attraction at edges.

Fresnel's biprism, Fig. 82(a), consists of two prisms P_1 and P_2 with angles of the order of 1°. Each of the prisms deviates, the incident cones of light, causing the two cones to overlap. To an observer on the right, the two cones appear to originate at the virtual sources S_1 and S_2. The interference pattern is observed in the shaded region where the two cones overlap.

Fresnel's mirrors, Fig. 82(b), consist of two plane glass surfaces which reflect the incident cones of light so that they overlap and interfere. The cones appear to come from virtual sources S_1 and S_2.

Lloyd's mirror, Fig. 82(c), consists of one plane mirror of metal or dielectric. The interfering cones are the direct beam and that reflected from the mirror. Source S is real and S_1 virtual. Each of the three experiments may be set up on an optical bench. In each of the three cases the interference pattern will be observed to sharpen as the refracting or reflecting surfaces are set parallel to the primary slit. In the cases of the biprism and double mirrors, this is accomplished when the lines of intersection of the refracting and reflecting planes are parallel to the primary slit. As in Young's experiment, the width of the primary slit may be adjusted to give the best visibility of the interference pattern.

Equation (6.18) for the determination of wavelength by Young's experiment applies to each of the cases illustrated in Fig. 82.

$$\lambda = \frac{d \, \Delta x}{D},$$

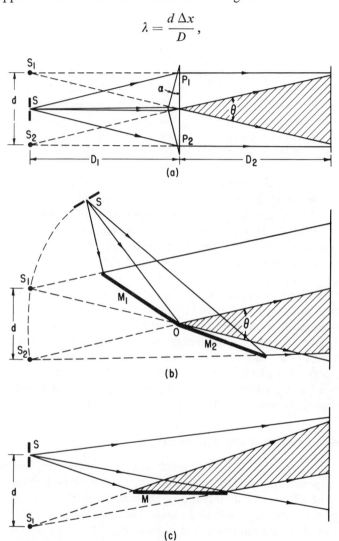

Figure 82. (a) Fresnel's biprism, (b) Fresnel's mirrors, (c) Lloyd's mirror.

where $D = D_1 + D_2$, D_1 is the distance from the slit to the biprism and D_2 from the biprism to the screen, and $d = D_1\theta$. The angle by which the interfering cones overlap may be measured on a spectrometer. The parallel beam from the collimator will be split into two beams with the angle θ between them in the same way that the central ray in Fig. 82(a) is divided into two parts. Thus the wavelength may be found from four measurable quantities:

$$\lambda = \frac{\theta D_1}{D_1 + D_2} \, \Delta x.$$

The same equation may be used to find the wavelength with Fresnel's mirrors. Here D_1 is the distance from the source to the line of intersection of the mirrors and D_2 the distance from the line of intersection to the screen. From geometrical optics one may prove that the primary source and two secondary sources lie on a common circle with point O at the intersection of the two mirrors as center. The angle of overlap of the interfering cones is twice the angle between the mirror surfaces.

The Lloyd's mirror experiment is historically famous as the first to reveal that a wave incident at glancing angle on a surface between two dielectrics undergoes a 180° phase change upon reflection. We shall treat this subject for all angles of incidence under the topic of *polarization by reflection*. If the observing screen or plane of observation on the right of Fig. 82(c) is moved up to the mirror, we observe a black band at the surface of the mirror. Since the surface of the mirror is equidistant from the two sources we might expect constructive interference in that plane as in Young's experiment. Lloyd concluded that the reflected wave had undergone 180° phase change.

Of all the experiments in interference the Lloyd's mirror pattern has been observed over the widest wavelength range. Lloyd's mirror patterns are obtained with x-rays of 8 A wavelength. In radioastronomy the surface of a lake serves as a Lloyd's mirror. The ionosphere 100 miles above the earth's surface is a Lloyd's mirror for broadcast radio waves. Thus Lloyd's mirror patterns have been observed with wavelengths ranging from 10^{-8} cm to 10^6 cm.

6.7 Young's Experiment with Microwaves

If Young's experiment is performed with microwaves, the interference pattern is spread over the laboratory table and can be measured on a meter stick. Figure 83 shows a double dipole adaptor which gives two secondary sources of the same amplitude and phase. The single loop is coupled to the plate cavity of the transmitter as indicated in Fig. 84. This coupling loop is soldered to two television twin-leads terminated by two folded dipoles of spring brass which may be attached to a meter stick as indicated. The transmission lines are of equal length to give two secondary sources of the same phase. The lengths are also adjusted for maximum output. The sources are placed at least two feet above the table top since at glancing angle even dry wood is a good reflector and serves as a Lloyd's mirror. The meter stick is supported by a wooden clamp and wooden tripod.

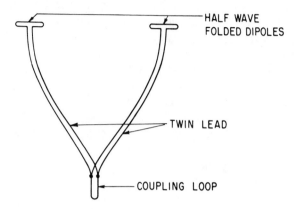

Figure 83. Double dipole adaptor for performing Young's experiment with microwaves.

Figure 84. Double dipole adaptor attached by single loop to a microwave oscillator.

A spacing of about four wavelengths between the secondary sources is recommended for the first measurements. The family of hyperbolas in the interference pattern may be traced with the intensity meter. To avoid reflections from the observer, a probe antenna may be mounted on the end of a long wooden dowel or meter stick. The crystal detector capsule itself serves as antenna. A twisted lead of fine wire may be used to bring the signal to a microammeter, oscilloscope, or audio amplifier. The wire lead will not alter the pattern if it is kept perpendicular to the electric field.

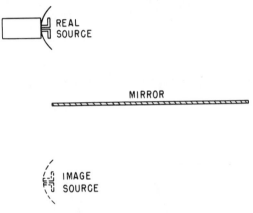

Figure 85. Lloyd's mirror for microwaves.

The positions of minimum intensity may be plotted on the laboratory table or marked off on the school lawn with a tennis court marker as a family of hyperbolas. Calculated patterns like that of Fig. 69 may be checked experimentally.

If one of the antennas is inverted, the two sources will be 180° out of phase and the paths of constructive and destructive interference interchanged. Half this same pattern may be obtained with a single source and Lloyd's mirror as indicated in Fig. 85. This pattern shows that the image source is 180° out of phase with the real source or that the reflected wave has undergone 180° phase shift upon reflection.

Young's experiment with microwaves may also be performed using secondary slot sources in a screen just as in Young's experiment with light. Such an arrangement is indicated in Fig. 86.

Microwaves afford simplicity. The secondary sources may be less than one wavelength wide so that the individual slots will not have complex diffraction patterns. If the slot is one-half wavelength wide, the radiation from each slot will spread through 180°. A recommended arrangement is with slots two wavelengths apart and the transmitter about one wavelength behind the screen. It is interesting to note that the minima of intenstiy may be observed when the antennas of the transmitter and intensity meter lie on a line of sight through one of the slots, while the maxima may occur when the intensity meter is not in sight of the transmitter.

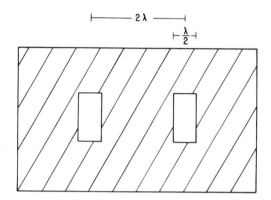

Figure 86. Secondary slot sources for Young's experiment with microwaves.

6.8 Radio Fading

In the days before automatic volume control on radios, it was observed that the signal often faded and rose at a regular rate, the effect being most pronounced just after sunset or before sunrise. The effect is an interference of two waves. One goes from the transmitter to receiver along the ground and the other is reflected by the ionospheres, ionized layers in the upper atmosphere produced when it absorbs certain frequencies of ultra-violet and soft x-rays from the sun.

The ionosphere over any given region of the earth moves upward at sunset as the angle of incidence of the sun's rays increases. Radio waves provide a means of studying the upper atmosphere and measuring the heights of the ionized layers. By measuring the repetition rate of fading and rising of the signal, the rate of rise and fall of the ionosphere can be determined.

This experiment can be simulated in the laboratory with microwaves. Set the transmitter and receiver as indicated in Fig. 87. The mirror may be a 2 ft square sheet of metal or a window screen. As the mirror is slowly raised and lowered the signal will be observed to rise and fall. If the parabolic reflectors are pointed slightly upward, there will be certain positions of the mirror for which the destructive interference is complete.

If the antennas lie in the plane of incidence as indicated in Fig. 87, a maximum of intensity will be observed when the plane of the mirror is through the centers of the two antennas. If the antennas are perpendicular to the plane of incidence, a minimum of intensity will be observed when the plane of the mirror is lowered until it includes the line between the antennas. This subject will be treated in detail under the subject of polarization by reflection from metals and dielectrics.

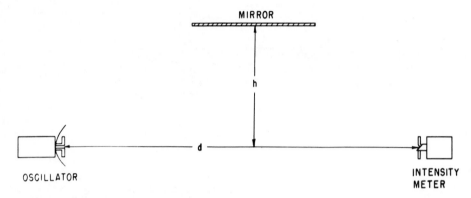

Figure 87. Radio fading demonstration. Electric field in the plane of incidence.

6.9 Direction Finder

Young's experiment with microwaves may be reversed to produce a direction finder. By the law of reversibility of waves, any antenna or system of antennas has the same field pattern when used as a transmitter or receiver.

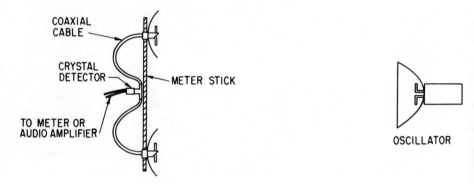

Figure 88. Microwave direction finder.

The two antennas on the meter stick become the secondary receivers and the television twin leads carry the received waves back to the common detector crystal as shown in Fig. 88. If the two antennas are parallel and the common ends point in the same direction, and if the differences in distance from the transmitter to each of the antennas is an integral number of wavelengths, a maximum signal will be received. However, the detector will not indicate in which of the hyperbolic paths of the two-antenna pattern the source lies. To determine the direction to the source approximately, the receiving antennas may be brought in along the meter stick until they are one wavelength apart. Then the set of hyperboloids becomes just one plane, a perpendicular bisector of the line between the two antennas. The meter stick is then turned about an axis through the middle of the stick and perpendicular to the plane of the figure until a maximum intensity is received.

If the receiver antennas are now moved 1 m apart while the meter stick is held in place, the meter stick may then be turned through very small angles to maximize the intensity and the direction determined with greater precision. If one of the antennas is inverted, a null method may be used.

PROBLEMS FOR CHAPTER VI

6.1.1. If the wave at point B in Fig. 66 is arbitrarily given an amplitude of unity and phase zero, show that the arbitrary constant $\mathbf{u}_0$ in Eq. (6.1) becomes $\sqrt{2}\, e^{-j\pi(4\sqrt{2}+1/2)}$. The sources are four wavelengths apart.

6.1.2. As a check upon the complex spiral of Fig. 67, find the amplitude and phase of the wave along the line BC at points of distance $X/\lambda = 0.5$ and 1.0 from B.

6.1.3. Find the intensity of radiation at points of distance $X/\lambda = 0.5$ and 1.0 from B on the line BC of Fig. 66.

6.1.4. Plot the complex spiral to indicate the amplitudes and phases at points along the line DB of Fig. 66. So choose the arbitrary constant $\mathbf{u}_0$ that the amplitude is unity and the phase zero at point D. The sources are four wavelengths apart.

6.1.5. Plot the intensity of radiation along the line DB of Fig. 66.

6.1.6. Derive Eq. (6.4) for the positions of phase opposition of the waves from the two point sources in Fig. 66 in terms of the polar coordinates r and θ.

6.1.7. Find the points of phase opposition along the line between the centers of sources in Fig. 66. The sources are four wavelengths apart.

6.1.8. Find the points of phase opposition along line AC in Fig. 66. The sources are four wavelengths apart and the line AC is two wavelengths distant from the line between sources.

6.1.9. If the sources of Fig. 66 are four wavelengths apart, find the eccentricities of each of the hyperbolas which are loci of points where the two waves are in phase.

6.2.10. A plane-polarized wave is incident upon a short metal rod whose axis is parallel to the direction of polarization. Express an equation in polar coordinates in the plane perpendicular to the reradiating rod through its center for the locus of all points where the plane wave and reradiated spherical wave are in opposite phase.

6.2.11. Show that the condition for phase coincidence between the incident wave and the reradiated wave of problem 6.2.10 is expressed by $y^2 = 2xc + c^2$. If the origin is at the common principal focus of the family of parabolas, $c = \lambda(n - \delta/2\pi)$.

6.2.12. If the origin is taken at the principal focus, the equation for a parabola in terms of its focal length f is $y^2 = 4fx + 4f^2$. Make use of the results of problem 6.2.11 to show that the focal lengths of the family of parabolas is $f = \lambda/2(n - \delta/2\pi)$.

6.2.13. A plane-polarized wave is incident upon a half-wave resonant metal rod whose axis is parallel to the direction of polarization. On polar graph paper plot the loci of points at which the incident wave and the reradiated wave are in phase for the cases $n = 2$ and 3. If $\delta = \pi/2$, let $\lambda = 2$ cm, and plot the pattern to scale. How far is the peak of intensity in Fig. 77 from a point where the two waves are in phase?

6.3.14. A plane-polarized wave is incident upon a half-wave resonant metal rod whose axis is parallel to the direction of polarization. Construct a graph of the imaginary against the real components of the complex amplitude of the resultant wave along the y axis (Fig. 75) by plotting points corresponding to $\rho/\lambda = \frac{1}{4}$ to $\frac{3}{2}$ by increments of $\frac{1}{8}$.

6.3.15. From the spiral of problem 6.3.14, find the first maximum and first minimum of amplitude and intensity and check with Fig. 77.

6.5.16. Plot a graph of the intensity of radiation in Young's interference pattern making use of Eq. (6.14). What is the average intensity of the pattern? How does the average intensity compare with that which would result if the two waves were incoherent and did not interfere?

6.6.17. Prove that the source S and the virtual images S_1 and S_2 formed with Fresnel's mirrors of Fig. 81(b) lie on a circle with center at O, where O is the common edge of the two mirrors.

6.6.18. Prove that the angle θ between the two rays reflected from the common edge O of Fresnel's mirrors is twice the angle between the surfaces of the mirrors.

6.7.19. How many wavelengths apart must the two dipole antennas for Young's experiment with microwaves be placed in order to produce four hyperboloids of minimum intensity in the interference pattern?

6.8.20. Show from the geometry of Fig. 87 that a minimum of radio signal will be received when

$$h = \sqrt{\left(\frac{dn\lambda}{2} + \frac{n^2\lambda^2}{4}\right)}.$$

chapter **VII**

Michelson's Interferometer

7.1 Michelson's Interferometer in Optics

Albert A. Michelson, who received the Nobel prize in 1907 for his work in optics, displayed unusual physical insight and engineering skill in developing an interferometer in which the mirrors producing the secondary coherent sources could be effectively superposed or moved past each other to give path differences of the interfering beams which differed by as much as one-half meter, limited only by the finite frequency width of the spectral line.

Figure 89 is a photograph of a Michelson interferometer for student use, with which can be illustrated the most common measurements of interferometry. (1) Wavelengths can be measured with reference to the displacement of a mirror along a scale or, by reverse methods, distances may be measured in terms of wavelengths. (2) The wavelength difference of two neighboring spectral lines can be measured. For instance, the difference in wavelengths of the lines of the sodium doublet which can just be separated on a student spectrometer can be measured to four significant figures with the Michelson interferometer. (3) The thickness of thin films placed in one of the arms can be measured. (4) Indices of refraction can be determined for thin films and thick blocks. (5) Michelson adapted his interferometer to calibrate the standard meter against the wavelength of a chosen spectral line. (6) Using another adaptation of his interferometer, Michelson searched for the ether drift. His negative results were explained two decades later by Albert Einstein's *special theory of relativity*.

Figure 89. Michelson interferometer. (Equipment by Gaertner Scientific Corporation.)

7.2 Structure of Michelson's Interferometer

Figure 90 is a diagrammatic sketch of the Michelson interferometer, where S is a source of narrow-wavelength range such as a sodium lamp or a mercury lamp with a filter to transmit the green line and S' is a ground-glass screen to give an extended plane source. If the primary source is a sodium lamp with extended surface 1 inch square, S' is not necessary. Here M is a plate of glass with parallel plane surfaces. It reflects part and transmits the remainder of the incident light. Sometimes the second surface of M is partially silvered to make the amplitudes of the reflected and transmitted waves equal. This is not usually done on student interferometers. Plate C is a compensating plate cut from the same plate of glass as M; M_1 is a fixed mirror and M_2 a movable mirror driven by a screw over a precision track which can be seen in Fig. 89. Those rays from a point on source S' are divided into two parts. One part is reflected from the second surface of M up to M_2 and back through M to L; the other is transmitted through M and C, reflected at M_1 back through C, and reflected at the surface of M to lens L. The two superposed rays from one point on S' will be focused by lens L on the retina of the eye. The eye may be reinforced with a low-power telescope, or the retina of the eye may be replaced by the film of a camera or the slit of a scanning photocell. Each of the two rays has passed through one of the equal-thickness glass plates three times.

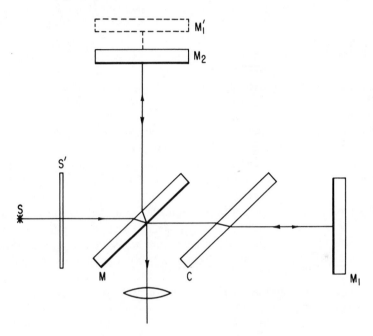

Figure 90. Diagram of Michelson interferometer.

With the use of the compensating plate C the optical path lengths of the two rays can be made equal even when white light is employed. The *optical path length* in a dielectric is the product of the actual length and the index of refraction. To be sure, if the light is monochromatic the optical path lengths could be made identical by moving mirror M_2; but since the index of refraction is different for different wavelengths, the white light interference pattern can be observed only if the path lengths in the given dielectrics are equal. Later we shall treat some uses of white light interference fringes.

7.3 Adjustment of Michelson's Interferometer

For convenience we shall take the plane of reference M'_1, the image of the fixed mirror M_1 observed by reflection from M. Before making measurements with Michelson's interferometer, the student should acquire skill in setting M_2 perpendicular to M_1 and making the path lengths of the superposed rays identical, that is, superposing surfaces M_2 and M_1. The first two steps are crude, employing only geometrical optics. The next two are more precise, employing the interference fringes themselves. (1) Using a steel ruler we may set the distances of M_1 and M_2 equal within one-half millimeter from the middle of the reflecting surface M. (2) Using a bright pinhole source to replace S', we may set M_1 perpendicular to M_2 by rotating it about a vertical and horizontal axis until the two images of the pinhole are superposed. In the student interferometer of Fig. 89 two screws on the back of M_1 may be used to rotate that mirror about the two axes. If we focus the eye on the plane of M_2, the interference bands may be seen. (3) The screws on the backs of the mirrors should be adjusted so that the bands become wider and have a smaller radius of curvature. Finally, a circular interference pattern will appear. When the center of the circular pattern is in the middle of the field, the two mirror surfaces are perpendicular to each other. (4) With the micrometer screw and its calibrated head seen in the foreground of Fig. 89, M_2 may be driven along the track in such direction that the circles move to the center and disappear one by one. This may be a slow tedious process of watching 1000 circles collapse to the center. The process is quicker if the screw is turned rapidly until the circles have all collapsed to the center and start to spread out again. The mirror M_2 will have passed M_1'. If we reverse the direction of turning, the circular bands will again collapse at center and appear wider as they come into the field until only three or four circles are seen. Then we turn slowly until the whole field is uniform and dark. Now M_2 and M_1 are equidistant from M and perpendicular. Surfaces M_2 and M_1' are superposed. If M is not silvered, the field will appear dark, indicating that any two rays from the same point on S' arrive out of phase. This is because one of the two rays reflected at M was incident from the more dense toward the less dense side upon reflection and underwent no phase change, while the other was incident from less dense toward more dense and underwent π phase change upon reflection.

If the micrometer screw is turned again until three or four circles appear and the sodium light is replaced by white light, we observe the spectral colors separated in the first order but superposed in the higher orders, finally tapering off to a gray in the fifth order.

We are now prepared to explain our observations as the interferometer was adjusted. As we look into mirror M of Fig. 90 we observe secondary sources S_1 and S_2 reflected by virtual mirror M_1' and mirror M_2. Primary source S' is effectively behind the head of the observer. In Fig. 91 mirrors M_1' and M_2 and sources S', S_1, and S_2 are all perpendicular to the center line CL, and E is the eye of the observer. We might stop to ponder at Michelson's ingenuity. With the aid of mirrors he has built an interferometer in which the head of the observer is effectively transparent and mirror M_2 moves through M_1' as though it were not there.

The distance between mirrors is d and that between the secondary source planes is $2d$. Two parallel rays arriving at the eye from a common point on S' will meet at a common point on the retina provided the eye is focused at infinity. The path differences, either from a common point on S' or the two virtual-image points on S_2 and S_1, are $2d \cos \theta$, where θ is the angle which

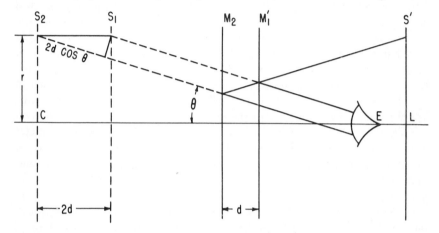

Figure 91. Diagram of Michelson interferometer simplified by use of image planes.

the rays make with the normal to the mirrors. The rays interfere destructively if the path difference

$$2d \cos \theta = m\lambda, \tag{7.1}$$

where m is any integer including zero. We recall that one of the rays underwent π phase change upon reflection. Otherwise Eq. (7.1) would be a condition for constructive interference. In practice the centers of black bands can be located visually with greater precision than centers of bright bands. If we rotate Fig. 91 about the center line CL, we note that for a given value of m Eq. (7.1) applies to rays reaching the eye from a circle on source S'. Contrary to the first quick guess of the uninitiated, the path difference from corresponding points S_1 and S_2 decreases with increasing θ, as expressed by Eq. (7.1).

The Michelson interferometer circular interference pattern is like that of the Newton ring pattern and parallel plate patterns which we shall treat in the following chapter. We may show next that the radii of the rings in this pattern are as the square roots of the integers. The letter m is the number of the rings counted from the outermost inward. The largest value of m we shall call m_0. It corresponds to θ equal to zero; $m_0 = 2d/\lambda$. If N represents the integer number of rings counted from the center spot outward, $N = m_0 - m$. Substituting from Eq. (7.1), we obtain $N = 2d(1 - \cos \theta)/\lambda$. In practice θ is small so that $\cos \theta$ may be expressed by the first two terms in Maclaurin's series, $\cos \theta = 1 + \theta^2/2$ and $N = d\theta^2/\lambda$. If r is the radius of the ring indicated in Fig. 91, $\theta = r/CE$. Since d, λ, and CE are constants, $N = \text{const.} \times r^2$. *The radii of the circles are as the square roots of the integers.*

We may calibrate the micrometer screw head of the Michelson interferometer against the mean wavelengths of the two sodium D lines. With each successive appearance or collapse of a circular ring at the center, the mirror moves one-half wavelength. Using the sodium doublet, we may count 1000 half wavelengths if we move M_2 a distance of 500 half wavelengths up to coincidence with M_1' and beyond by 500 more half waves. Scale readings may be plotted graphically against integer number of half waves. If mirrors M_2 and M_1' are not parallel, nearly straight-line fringes will be observed. If they are too fine to be counted with the naked eye, a low-power telescope with cross hair may be used. If the calibration is made with the sodium doublet, only about 1000 lines may be counted from the position of coincidence before the maxima in the interference pattern of one wavelength fall on the minima in the interference pattern of the other wavelength. The intensities of the two interference patterns add to give uniform intensity so that no lines can be seen. Thus we can use the mean sodium doublet wavelength to calibrate only one revolution of the screw. In the next section we shall use this overlapping of interference patterns to measure wavelength differences.

7.4 Measurement of Wavelength Difference

Using the fact that the two Newton's ring interference patterns for two slightly different wavelengths go in and out of step, Fizeau and Foucault had determined the wavelength difference. Michelson, employing his interferometer, refined the method to produce separation of spectral lines which could be seen only as one line with a grating spectrometer. By plotting visibility curves[1] and performing a Fourier analysis with a harmonic analyzer which he invented, he determined the relative intensity and wavelength differences of the several component lines. Michelson's was the first of a series of interferometers developed by himself and others to measure fine structure of spectral lines.

The student will find it instructive to measure the wavelength difference between the two sodium D lines of nearly equal intensity. If we count interference fringes from the coincidence of M_1 and M_2,

$$2d_1 = m_1\lambda = (m_1 - \tfrac{1}{2})\lambda',$$

where λ is the shorter of the two wavelengths, and m_1 is the number of

---

[1] R. W. Wood, *Physical Optics*, 3rd ed.: New York, Macmillan (1934) p. 303.

interference fringes out to the middle of the first region where the intensities of the two interference patterns add to give uniform intensity. We should emphasize that the two wavelengths do not interfere. If it were possible to distinguish the colors of the two yellow lines of sodium visually, we would see alternating color where the two patterns combine to give constant intensity. If we solve for λ and λ' and subtract, the difference

$$\Delta\lambda = \frac{d_1}{m_1(m_1 - \frac{1}{2})}.$$

Since we can not count fringes conveniently in the fadeout region, we may express m and $m - \frac{1}{2}$ in terms of λ and λ'. Thus $\Delta\lambda = \lambda\lambda'/4d_1$. If λ and λ' are identical to as many significant figures as we can measure d_1, we may replace λ' by λ and $\Delta\lambda = \lambda^2/4d_1$. Similarly, if m_n is the number of interference fringes for wavelength λ out to fadeout number n,

$$2d_n = m_n\lambda = \left(m_n + \frac{2n - 1}{2}\right)\lambda'$$

and

$$\Delta\lambda = \frac{\lambda\lambda'(2n - 1)}{4d_n}. \tag{7.2}$$

If m_k is the number of interference fringes out to the fadeout k,

$$2d_k = m_k\lambda = \left(m_k + \frac{2k - 1}{2}\right)\lambda'$$

and

$$\Delta\lambda = \frac{\lambda\lambda'(2k - 1)}{4d_k}. \tag{7.3}$$

If we do not wish to measure from coincidence of mirrors M_2 and M_1 but only between fadeouts n and k, we may combine Eqs. (7.2) and (7.3) to obtain

$$\Delta\lambda 2(d_k - d_n) = \lambda\lambda'(k - n).$$

If we replace λ' with λ, let $d_k - d_n = D$ and $k - n = N$,

$$\Delta\lambda = \frac{\lambda^2 N}{2D}. \tag{7.4}$$

With the student interferometer of Fig. 89 we can count over 100 fadeouts. Since the wavelength difference of the lines in the sodium doublet is about 0.001 as great as the wavelength, there are about 1000 interference bands between consecutive fadeouts. When measuring wavelength difference we can turn the screw much more rapidly than when measuring wavelengths, recording the positions of the mirror for every tenth fadeout. If one of the wavelengths has been given to six significant figures, the other may be determined also to six figures merely by measuring the wavelength difference to three figures.

7.5 Comparison of Wavelengths with the Standard Meter

Having developed a means of determining wavelength differences of neighboring spectral lines, Michelson next developed a means of measuring wavelengths directly on the standard meter. Michelson and Benoit measured the wavelengths of three prominent red, green, and blue lines of cadmium to eight significant figures. After observing that the greatest source of error was in locating the centers of the two scratches on the standard meter with a microscope, Michelson proposed that the wavelength of the red cadmium line be used instead as standard of length.

The requirements of primary standards of length, time, and mass are invariance, indestructibility, and availability to all laboratories. Spectral lines of the elements satisfy these conditions for a length standard. The best lines to yield good visibility in the interference pattern when the path difference of the component waves is large are singlets with the smallest value of $\Delta\lambda/\lambda$, where $\Delta\lambda$ is the width at half maximum.

To have counted three million dark lines as mirror M_2 of Fig. 90 was moved 1 m would have been time consuming even if the visibility of the patterns were good for that great path difference. Michelson built an intermediate standard of length known by the French word *etalon*, with distance d about ten centimeters between the optically flat reflecting surfaces indicated in Fig. 92. Another etalon was built approximately half as long as the first, a third etalon approximately half as long as the second, and so on to the ninth etalon which was $(10/2^8)$ cm $= 0.0391$ cm long.

Michelson measured the lengths of his etalons in wavelengths with the interferometer indicated in Fig. 93. If he were looking toward mirror M_2, he would also see the images of the front mirrors of the two etalons side by side in the lower half of the field of M_2. In the upper half he would see the images of the back mirrors of the two etalons. The two mirrors on each of the etalons could be adjusted for parallelism with mirror M_2 by two screws, just as was the mirror of the interferometer of Fig. 89. The front mirrors of the two shortest etalons E_1 and E_2 and mirror M_2 were each set at the same distance from the source by use of white light fringes. Monochromatic light was next used and M_2 driven outward, the dark bands being counted as they passed the cross hair, until it was at the same distance from the source as the second mirror of etalon E_1 as again determined by white light fringes. Michelson estimated distances to $\frac{1}{50}$ the distance between bands. Thus he estimated the distance d_1 between the mirrors of the first etalon to within 0.01 wavelength.

Next E_1 was driven outward until its first mirror was at the previous position of its second mirror, as determined by white light fringes in the light reflected from M_2 and the first mirror of E_1. In this case he did not need to count the lines. The purpose of moving E_1 forward by its length was to

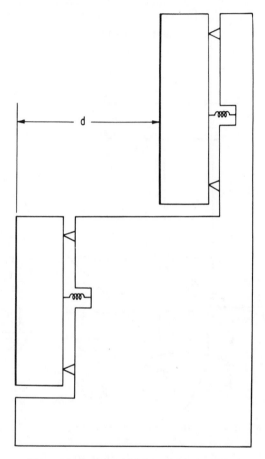

Figure 92. Etalon with plane-parallel mirrors.

permit the determination of the integer number of the interference line he was observing without actual counting. Mirror M_2 was then moved and a comparatively few lines counted until M_2 was at the same distance from the source as the second surface of E_2. Thus the length of E_2 was measured to 0.01 wavelength. The precision of measuring E_2 was not dependent on the precision of measuring E_1, since E_1 merely aided in determining the exact integer number of a black band that passed the cross hair without counting them all. The precision in determining the length d_2 between the mirrors of etalon E_2 was determined by the precision of estimating the final position of the cross hair between black bands, where E_1 had merely served to indicate the integer number of a black band.

Likewise, E_2 and E_3 were mounted in the interferometer and the length of E_3 measured in wavelengths, and so on until the length of the ninth etalon, the 10 cm etalon, had been estimated within 0.01 wavelength.

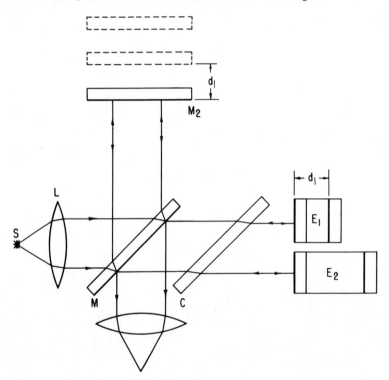

Figure 93. Michelson interferometer for measuring etalons in wavelengths.

The 10 cm E_9 etalon and the standard meter were mounted on the interferometer and the front surface of E_9 set with the zero ruling on the meter bar. Mirror M_2 was moved out to the image of the second mirror of E_9, and E_9 moved forward by its length as checked with white light fringes. This process of laying E_9 by steps along the standard meter was repeated ten times. In this last process any error in the length of E_9 was cumulative. However, this error was estimated to be less than the error in locating the centers of the two scratches on the standard meter. The difficulty in estimating the centers of the scratches on the standard meter was a reason for Michelson's suggesting that the length of the red cadmium line be taken as the primary standard of length. At the time that the standard meter was made the lines could be ruled more precisely than the ends of the meter stick could be ground. With the development of interferometry, standard gage blocks for use in machine shops are all end gages with optically flat surfaces.

The Swedish engineer Johansson[2] developed slip gages or gage blocks by interferometry which were used in laboratories for standards at the beginning of the twentieth century. By these gages interferometry found its way from

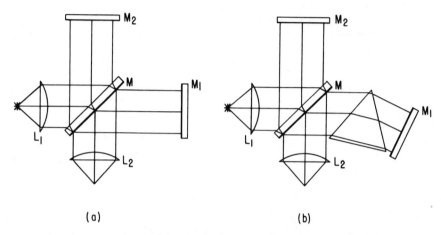

(a)   (b)

Figure 94. Twyman and Green interferometer. (a) Arranged for testing optical elements. (b) Prism inserted for testing.

the academic laboratory to the machine shop. Inspection gages used in mass-production machine shops producing interchangeable parts are specified by the Bureau of Standards to have errors in flatness and parallelism to less than a few millionths of an inch, that is, less than one-half wavelength of visible light.

7.6 Twyman and Green Interferometer

In 1916 Twyman and Green patented an adaptation of Michelson's interferometer, with which a worker in an optical shop can learn in a few hours to detect and correct for imperfections in the surface and local variations in the index of refraction of elements of optical systems such as lenses, prisms, and diffraction gratings.[3] The system for testing and correcting optical elements is indicated in Fig. 94(a); Fig. 94(b) shows it used on a prism. Since monochromatic light is employed, no compensating plate is

[2] C. Candler, *Modern Interferometers:* Glasgow, Scotland, Hilger and Watts (1951) Chap. VIII.
[3] Candler, *op. cit.*, Chaps. VI and VIII.

needed. An illuminated pinhole source is placed at the principal focus of lens L_1, and lens L_2 focuses the parallel beam to the retina of the eye.

Mirror M_1 is set so that its image observed in M coincides with M_2. The prism is turned to give minimum deviation, and M_1 set perpendicular to the refracted beam so that the rays reverse their paths through the prism. If the prism is perfect, the plane wave front or phase front remains plane, and if the rays reflected from M_1 and M_2 are of equal optical length, a uniform field will be observed. Local differences in optical path in the prism may be

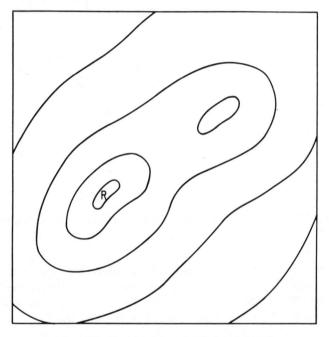

Figure 95. Contours of equioptical path length.

caused by (1) lack of flatness of the surfaces of the prism, or (2) local variations of the index of refraction within the prism. Combinations of these imperfections yield an interference pattern like a contour map, each line being an equioptical path line.

If region R of Fig. 95 is a valley, it will expand when M_2 is moved away. The outline of the contours is painted with rouge and hills polished away until the whole surface is one of equioptical path length within closer than one-quarter wavelength. We shall show under the topic of *diffraction and resolving power* that the lens or prism is essentially perfect if the optical path differences are less than one-quarter wavelength. Smaller imperfections are hidden by the diffraction effects of finite wavelengths.

Previous to the general use of this adaptation of Michelson's interfero-meter, precision lenses had areas with path differences of several wavelengths, and prisms whose surfaces were optical flats still had poor resolving power because of internal variations of index of refraction. Then the best prism for resolving neighboring spectral lines was found by sorting a large number of prisms. Now all prisms are effectively perfect, having the ideal resolving power determined by the size of the prism and the wavelength, which we shall treat in Chapter IX on diffraction by a single slit.

7.7 Michelson-Morley Experiment

Michelson first designed his interferometer in Potsdam, Germany in 1881 for the purpose of studying the motion of the earth through the ether. After receiving an encouraging letter from Lord Rayleigh six years later, Michelson and Morley[4] performed their famous experiment at Case School of Applied Science. Michelson's measurement of fine structure of spectral lines and calibration of the standard meter with this same general design of inter-ferometer which we discussed in the preceding section came ten years later.

Figure 96 is a diagram of the Michelson interferometer seen by an ethereal ghost fixed in the ether and watching the earth go by with velocity v to the right. The solid drawing indicates the position of the interferometer when a phase front reaches the middle of the reflecting surface of M. Broken lines indicate the positions of M_2 and M_1 when rays from M reach them. The compensating mirror has been omitted in this diagram. Mirror M is indicated by a broken line at the instant the ray returns to M.

Assuming that, as is true of sound waves, the velocity of the wave relative to the medium is a constant, dependent solely on the physical properties of the medium, we shall represent the velocity of the wave relative to the ether by c. The velocity of the wave relative to the interferometer as the wave moves from mirror M to mirror M_2 is the vector sum of the velocity of the wave relative to the ether plus the velocity of the ether relative to the interferometer indicated in Fig. 97. Note of course that, since the velocity v of the inter-ferometer relative to the ether is to the right as indicated in Fig. 96, the velocity of the ether relative to the interferometer is to the left.

The time t_2 for the wave to go from M to M_2 and back is

$$t_2 = \frac{2d}{\sqrt{c^2 - v^2}}. \tag{7.5}$$

The time for the wave to go from M to M_1 and back is

$$t_1 = \frac{d}{c - v} + \frac{d}{c + v}, \tag{7.6}$$

[4] A. A. Michelson and E. W. Morley, *Phil. Mag.*, **24**, 449 (1887).

where d is the distance from M to M_2 and the equal distance from M to M_1, and the distances are set equal with the use of straight white light fringes.

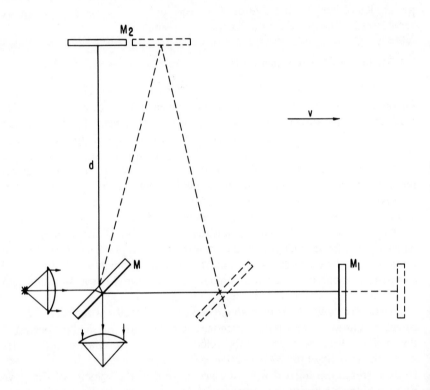

Figure 96. Michelson interferometer used in search for ether drift.

If we expand Eqs. (7.5) and (7.6) by the binomial theorem, and keep only terms through v^2/c^2,

$$t_2 = \frac{2d}{c}\left(1 + \frac{1}{2}\frac{v^2}{c^2}\right)$$

and

$$t_1 = \frac{2d}{c}\left(1 + \frac{v^2}{c^2}\right).$$

The wave reflected from M_1 returns to M later than that reflected from M_2 by

$t_1 - t_2 = dv^2/c^3$. The wave from M_1 lags behind that from M_2 by the distance $c(t_1 - t_2)$ and the phase difference is

$$\frac{2\pi dv^2}{\lambda c^2} \; .$$

We may expect the fringe pattern to be shifted by $\dfrac{d}{\lambda} \dfrac{v^2}{c^2}$ lines because of the velocity v of the earth relative to the ether. If the interferometer were rotated 90° about an axis perpendicular to the plane of

the diagram, $\dfrac{2d}{\lambda} \dfrac{v^2}{c^2}$ lines of destructive interfer-

ence should pass the cross hair of the telescope. The path d was increased by reflection of each of the beams back and forth between eight mirrors as indicated in Fig. 98.

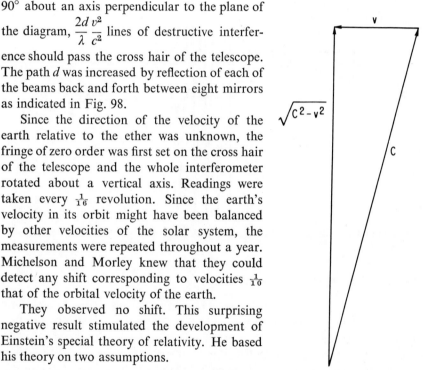

Since the direction of the velocity of the earth relative to the ether was unknown, the fringe of zero order was first set on the cross hair of the telescope and the whole interferometer rotated about a vertical axis. Readings were taken every $\frac{1}{16}$ revolution. Since the earth's velocity in its orbit might have been balanced by other velocities of the solar system, the measurements were repeated throughout a year. Michelson and Morley knew that they could detect any shift corresponding to velocities $\frac{1}{10}$ that of the orbital velocity of the earth.

They observed no shift. This surprising negative result stimulated the development of Einstein's special theory of relativity. He based his theory on two assumptions.

I. *Uniform motion of translation of a system can not be detected by an observer on that system from observations confined to the system.*

Figure 97. Vector sum of velocity of wave relative to the ether plus the velocity of the ether relative to earth.

Thus no motion of the earth through an ether can be detected by use of light originating on the earth.

II. *The velocity of light in space is constant and independent of the relative velocity of the source and observer.*

The broad implications and experimental checks of the special theory of relativity, as well as the general theory of relativity which includes accelerated systems, is treated in books of modern physics.[5,6,7]

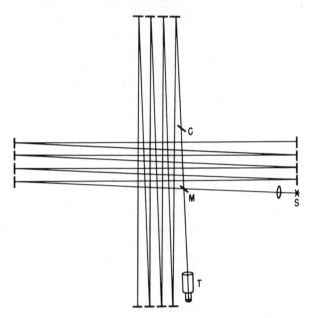

Figure 98. Arrangement for extended path lengths in the Michelson-Morley experiment.

7.8 Measurement of Index of Refraction

If a block of transparent dielectric is inserted in one of the branches of Michelson's interferometer, the straight-line fringes will be displaced. The optical path through the block is nt, t being the thickness of the block. The optical path through an equal thickness of air is t. Since the light passes through the block twice, the optical path difference is $2(n-1)t$. The number of lines displaced past the cross hair is $N = 2(n-1)t/\lambda$. If the dielectric is a thin sheet of mica inserted part way into the beam, the interference pattern with and without the sheet of mica may be compared. If the displacement is but a few fringes, white light may be used to identify the corresponding fringes.

If the index of refraction of a thicker parallel face block is to be determined,

[5] P. G. Bergmann, *Introduction to Relativity:* Englewood Cliffs, N.J., Prentice-Hall (1946).

[6] F. K. Richtmyer, E. H. Kennard, and T. Lauritsen, *Introduction to Modern Physics:* New York, McGraw-Hill (1955) pp. 56–76.

[7] D. H. Menzel, editor, *Mathematical Physics:* Englewood Cliffs, N.J., Prentice-Hall (1953) Part V.

a block with parallel, optically flat surfaces may be cut in two parts to be inserted in the arms. If one of the blocks is rotated slowly about an axis perpendicular to the ray, the fringes passing the cross hair, because of increase in path length, can be counted. The optical path length is determined by the thickness t, the index of refraction n, and the angle of incidence ϕ. As seen from Fig. 99, the path difference in one passage through the two blocks is

$$nAE + EF - nAB + BC.$$

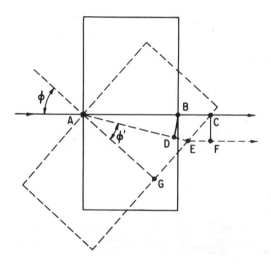

Figure 99. Determination of index of refraction with Michelson interferometer.

If an arc with center at A is struck through B to cut AE at D, the algebra is simplified somewhat. The path difference is now $nDE + EF - BC$. Since the rays pass through the blocks twice,

$$2(nDE + EF - BC) = N\lambda. \tag{7.7}$$

From the geometry

$$2[n(AE - t) + (\sin \phi)(GC - GE) - (AC - t)] = N\lambda$$

and

$$nAE + (\sin \phi)(GC - GE) - AC = \frac{N\lambda}{2} + t(n - 1),$$

where AE, GC, GE, and AC may be expressed in terms of t and trigonometric functions of ϕ and ϕ'.

$$\frac{n - \sin \phi \sin \phi'}{\cos \phi'} + \frac{\sin^2 \phi - 1}{\cos \phi} = \frac{N\lambda}{2t} + n - 1.$$

From Snell's law,

$$n \sin \phi' = \sin \phi,$$

where ϕ' may be expressed in terms of ϕ and n. Thus

$$\sqrt{n^2 - \sin^2 \phi} = \frac{N\lambda}{2t} - 1 + n + \cos \phi$$

and

$$n = \frac{(2t - N\lambda)(1 - \cos \phi) + (N^2\lambda^2/4t)}{2t(1 - \cos \phi) - N\lambda}.$$

For the cases treated experimentally, $N^2\lambda^2/4t$ is small compared to the other terms and may be neglected.

7.9 Measurement of Index of Refraction of Gas

Figure 100 is a diagram of a Jamin interferometer for determining the index of refraction of gas. It is simpler than the Michelson interferometer used in measuring indices of refraction of solids in that optical path lengths

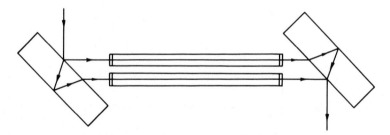

Figure 100. Jamin interferometer.

are changed by merely changing the pressure of the gas in one of the paths. Also, there is no reversal of rays over the same paths. The mirrors M_1 and M_2 are cut from the same parallel-sided optical flat. Two tubes with optically flat glass ends provide equal optical paths for the two beams. If the tubes are evacuated and one slowly filled with gas, the number of lines passing the cross hair is found to be proportional to the measured density ρ.

$$N\lambda = (n - 1)t = \text{const.} \times \rho.$$

Commercial interferometers of the Jamin type[8] have been developed to measure small differences in indices of refraction of liquids as a means of analysis in chemistry and biology.

Figure 101 is a diagram of a type of Jamin interferometer designed by

[8] Candler, *op. cit.*, Chap. XXI.

Mach and Zehnder in 1891. Because of the difficulty of adjusting four plates it is not used as a student interferometer. With the development of aircraft moving at supersonic speeds, the Mach-Zehnder interferometer has been employed to measure the two dimensional distribution of air pressure flowing past airfoils and projectiles. The optically flat glass windows of the wind tunnel are in one beam and an equivalent thickness of glass in the other beam. Figure 102 is a photograph of the interference pattern formed by the air flowing past a cone in the wind tunnel. If all the mirrors are parallel, the interference pattern will appear to the observer to be at infinity. An advantage[9] of the Mach-Zehnder interferometer for this purpose is that the fringes may be localized precisely and easily in the plane of the airfoil by rotating the beam-splitting mirror M_1.

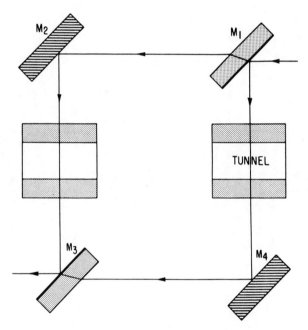

Figure 101. Mach-Zehnder interferometer.

7.10 Michelson's Interferometer with Microwaves

Although some of the interferometers which we have described have been among the most expensive research instruments of their time, Michelson's interferometer for microwaves may be constructed very simply. Mirrors A and B of Fig. 103 are of sheet metal or window screen. They should be at least three wavelengths square. The half-reflecting screen may be chicken

[9] S. Tolansky, *An Introduction to Interferometry:* New York, Longmans (1955) p 115.

Figure 102. Mach-Zehnder interference pattern of air flowing past a cone in a wind tunnel at 2.5 times the velocity of sound. The mirrors are tilted so that the interference lines are uniformly spaced in the undisturbed region on the left. (Courtesy of H. H. Hurzweg, U.S. Naval Ordnance Laboratory.)

wire with mesh about one-fifth wavelength across, or two sheets of polystyrene separated by an air gap of about one-quarter wavelength adjusted to make the screen half reflecting. Mirror B may be moved between two meter sticks as guides over a range of 15 half wavelengths. The output of the transmitter and position of the meter may be adjusted until the motion of mirror B causes the reading of the meter to vary by half scale for every half wavelength that mirror B is moved. More permanent designs[10] of Michelson's interferometer for microwaves have been built.

[10] T. G. Bullen, *Am. J. Phys.*, **24**, 525 (1956).

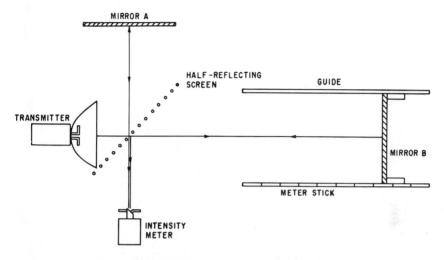

Figure 103. Michelson interferometer for microwaves.

7.11 The Identity of Wheatstone's Bridge and Michelson's Interferometer

Michelson's interferometer and Wheatstone's a-c bridge are two devices employing the balancing of amplitude and phase of electromagnetic waves in their respective parts of the spectrum. With the exploitation of the microwave portion of the spectrum midway between light and alternating current, a wave-guide bridge or interferometer was designed having all the functions of its neighbor instruments but called by the unfortunate name of *magic T,* a name descriptive only of its external appearance. Far from being mystifying, the magic T may serve as an elementary introduction to its spectral neighbors on either side.

Figure 104 indicates the forms that the Wheatstone bridge or Michelson interferometer take across the spectrum, where S and D are corresponding source and detector in each and A, B, C, and E are corresponding branch points. From right to left are Michelson's interferometer, the magic T, Lecher wire system with the detector line attached as in the magic T, and finally the a-c Wheatstone bridge used at audio frequencies. The Lecher wire bridge is convenient for use with wavelengths of the order of 3 m. In the transmission line and wave-guide bridges the distributed capacitances and inductances are not indicated in the drawing. At 60 cycles/sec the lumped impedances are indicated by the boxes.

The transition from one interferometer to the next is understood most readily in terms of fields. An electric line of force from the source reaching AB has no component parallel to CE as indicated in Fig. 105(a). The wave

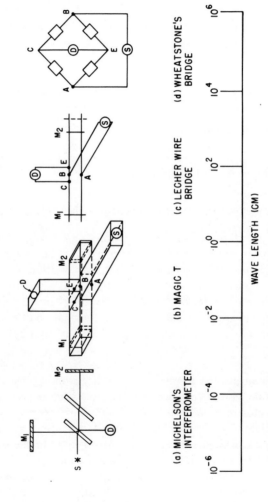

Figure 104. Forms of Michelson interferometer or Wheatstone bridge across the spectrum.

splits and goes down the two paths to be reflected by the short circuits, metal plungers, or mirrors as the case may be. If the reflected waves return to AB in phase, they can excite no field in the detector line but return to the source. If the two electric fields return to AB π out of phase, the resultant electric field has no component parallel to AB but does have a component parallel to CE. None of the wave returns to the source but all goes to the detector. The Michelson interferometer for 12 cm waves may take either the form of the interferometer for light or the magic T. The magic T has the advantage that the wave can not escape from the metal wave guide.

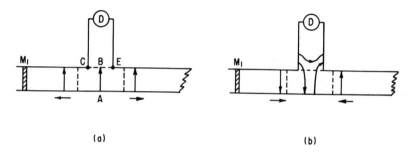

Figure 105. Phase conditions for transmission of wave to the detector. (a) Components return in phase. (b) Components return out of phase.

PROBLEMS FOR CHAPTER VII

7.3.1. Using the red line of cadmium of wavelength 6438 A, Michelson was able to observe interference lines when one of the mirrors was driven 25 cm from the position of coincidence as indicated by white light fringes. How many dark lines passed the cross hair? Express to only three significant figures.

7.3.2. In 1954 Terrian and Haman[11] succeeded in obtaining interference over a path difference of 1 m. They employed an infrared line of wavelength 9856 A from Kr^{86} at a temperature of 60 deg K. How many lines were counted from the position of coincidence? Express to three significant figures.

7.4.3. A mirror of the student interferometer of Fig. 89 can be driven 3.0 cm. How many fadeouts in the combined interference patterns of the sodium D lines of wavelengths 5895.92 A and 5889.95 A will be observed?

7.8.4. A thin sheet of mica with a straight edge is inserted into one arm of the Michelson interferometer to cover the upper half of the field. The pattern is observed first with white light fringes and then with sodium light. The vertical black bands in the interference pattern of yellow light are shifted 2.3 fringes by the mica. If the wavelength of the sodium yellow is 5900 A and the index of refraction of the mica is 1.59, find the thickness of the mica sheet.

7.8.5. If two glass blocks cut from the same optical flat, so as to be of the same 1.20 cm thickness, are inserted into the two arms of a Michelson interferometer and the mirrors set at equal distance by white light fringes, and one of the blocks is slowly rotated through 30.00° about an axis perpendicular to a beam of sodium light, how many black bands will pass the cross hair? The index of refraction of the glass is 1.526 and the mean wavelength of the sodium D line is 5893 A.

7.9.6. At 0.00 deg C and a pressure of 76.0 cm mercury the index of refraction of air is 1.000293. If the air is pumped from one of the arms of a Jamin interferometer the internal length of which is 20.0 cm, how many fringes of sodium light will pass the cross hair?

7.10.7. It is possible to count a million fringes of green light as the mirror is driven along the track of a Michelson interferometer. How far would the mirror of a Michelson interferometer for microwaves be driven to produce the same number of minima? Let the wavelength be 12 cm.

[11] J. Terrian and J. Haman, *C. R. Acad. Sci., Paris,* **239,** 586 (1954).

chapter VIII

Interference in Thin Films

8.1 Films in Optics

The optics of thin films began when Young used Newton's measurements of the thickness of air films between a lens and an optical flat to develop the theory of interference. Interference patterns observed in soap bubbles, films of oil on water, and air films between glass plates provide simple demonstrations of the wave nature of light. Modern interferometers used in spectroscopy employ films both thick and thin. Step gages of fatty acid crystals formed by depositing a series of monomolecular layers on glass provide a simple quantitative means of determining the thickness of thin films by comparing interference colors. A new art of building interference filters by evaporation of layers of dielectric and metal with maximum transmission at any desired wavelength is freeing the spectroscopist from the frequency restrictions of natural absorption filters.

8.2 Interference of Reflected Waves

Interference colors in a soap film obtained by reflection are more brilliantly colored than by transmission. If a single color such as that from a sodium lamp is used, the contrast between dark and light bands is sharper by reflection than by transmission. In the following two sections we shall explain these observations and lay a basis for the study of modern interferometers.

Figure 106 is a diagram of a thin film of dielectric in which the ray from primary source S is reflected and refracted repeatedly at the parallel surfaces to give two bundles of parallel rays focused by lenses to points P and P'. The figure is distorted for clarity. In practice the film is a few wavelengths thick. The lenses are thousands of times thicker than the films and the

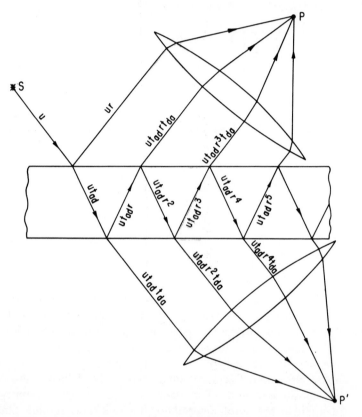

Figure 106. Interference of successively reflected rays in thin film of dielectric.

distance from the film to the lens greater than the diameter of the lens, so that the percentage path difference is too small to affect the relative amplitudes of the reflected rays. Nevertheless, the path differences are of the order of wavelengths and do determine the phase differences. The lens may be that of the eye with points P or P' lying on the retina. In some optical instruments the lenses are telescope objectives. The letters beside the rays indicate amplitudes: u is the amplitude of the incident wave and r is the fraction of amplitude reflected at the particular angle of incidence. One of the results of the law of reversibility given by Eq. (2.12) is that the percentage reflection is the same when the ray is incident from the less dense to more dense medium as when it is incident along the same path from the more dense toward the less dense. A negative sign indicates that there is a phase change π in one of the reflections. Lloyd showed that this phase change occurred for reflection after incidence from the optically less to the more dense medium. We shall restrict our

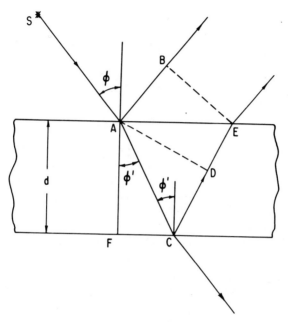

Figure 107. Diagram for finding phase between the first two reflected rays from thin film.

treatment to small angles of incidence until we treat the topic of polarization upon reflection from dielectrics. The symbols t_{ad} and t_{da} express the fractions of amplitude transmitted when the ray is incident from air to dielectric and dielectric to air, respectively.

For dielectrics like water or glass in air the amplitudes diminish rapidly with each reflection. Thus in elementary treatments only the first two reflections are considered. Since we wish to determine the resulting intensities quantitatively, we shall consider many reflections. By using the law of reversibility, we shall find that it is simpler to consider an infinite number of reflections than to treat three or four. This is one of several cases we shall meet in optics in which "the whole is simpler than its parts."

To find the relative phases we shall first treat the two reflections indicated in Fig. 107. The optical distances from B and E to the point where they meet beyond the lens are the same. Thus the optical path difference of these two rays originating at S and meeting again at P is $n(AC + CE) - AB$, where n is the index of refraction of the thin dielectric. Since between the effective wave fronts AD and BE the optical path $AB = nDE$, the optical path difference may also be expressed as $n(AC + CD)$. From geometry, $AC = d/\cos \phi'$, ϕ' being the angle of refraction and d the thickness of the film,

$$CD = AC \cos 2\phi' = d \cos \frac{2\phi'}{\cos \phi'} .$$

Thus the path difference is

$$\Delta = \frac{nd(1 + \cos 2\phi')}{\cos \phi'} . \tag{8.1}$$

From a trigonometric identity, $1 + \cos 2\phi' = 2 \cos^2 \phi'$, and the path difference becomes simply

$$\Delta = 2nd \cos \phi'. \tag{8.2}$$

Since the result is so simple, we might expect a simpler solution. A simpler and geometrically elegant solution is retained for the problems. The factor $\cos \phi'$ may come as a surprise. The path difference decreases as the angle of incidence increases.

The phases of the two rays reaching P differ for two reasons: (1) path difference and (2) the change in phase of π in the first reflected ray which is incident from air toward the more dense dielectric. Thus the total phase difference which we shall call δ is

$$\delta = \frac{2\pi}{\lambda} (2nd \cos \phi') - \pi.$$

When the angle of incidence and the thickness are such that the two rays are opposite in phase,

$$\frac{2\pi(2nd \cos \phi')}{\lambda} - \pi = (2N - 1)\pi,$$

which reduces to $2nd \cos \phi' = N\lambda$, where N is any integer or zero.

The path difference between any two successive rays reaching P is the same as between the first and second ray. However, only the first ray undergoes phase change on reflection so that, if the externally reflected ray is π out of phase with the first internally reflected ray, all the internally reflected rays are in phase at P. Thus the amplitudes of all the rays reaching P may be added algebraically, the first being positive and the remaining negative. The amplitude at P

$$u_p = ur[1 - t_{ad}t_{da}(1 + r^2 + r^4 + \cdots)].$$

Since r is less than unity,

$$1 + r^2 + r^4 + \cdots = \frac{1}{1 - r^2}$$

and

$$u_p = ur\left(1 - \frac{t_{ad}t_{da}}{1 - r^2}\right).$$

By Eq. (2.13) which we derived from the law of reversibility of waves in a nonabsorbing medium, $t_{ad}t_{da} = 1 - r^2$ so that $u_p = 0$ when the first externally reflected ray is out of phase with the internally reflected rays arriving at P. The minimum in the interference pattern by reflection in a thin film is zero. We see why the interference pattern by reflection in a soap bubble showed high contrast.

If the reflected ray undergoes phase reversal at only one of the two surfaces, the minimum in the interference pattern by reflection from a thin film occurs when $2nd \cos \phi' = N\lambda$.

If the first two rays are in phase, any two consecutive rays arrive at P exactly out of phase. For constructive interference between the first two rays,

$$2\pi \frac{2nd \cos \phi'}{\lambda} = 2\pi\left(N + \frac{1}{2}\right).$$

If the reflected ray undergoes phase reversal at only one of the two surfaces, the maximum in the interference pattern occurs when $2nd \cos \phi' = (N + \frac{1}{2})\lambda$.

Thus far we have treated only special cases of interference by reflection, those cases which yield maxima and minima of intensity. For those special cases the component waves were all in phase or π out of phase and, since the rotating vectors were either parallel or opposite, the problems could be treated by elementary algebra.

These pages of special cases will have been justified if we appreciate that by use of complex algebra we can express the general case for all angles of incidence in a fraction of the space required for special cases.

The complex amplitude, that is, amplitude and phase, at point P is

$$\mathbf{u}_R = \mathbf{u}r[1 - t_{ad}t_{da}(e^{-j\delta} + r^2 e^{-2j\delta} + r^4 e^{-3j\delta} + \cdots)]. \qquad (8.3)$$

The first reflected wave ur is taken as reference. The negative sign before all the other terms indicates that they do not share in the π phase change which the first ray undergoes upon reflection. Since the phase lag due to path difference of any ray relative to the preceding one is

$$\delta = \frac{4\pi nd \cos \phi'}{\lambda}, \qquad (8.4)$$

and $t_{ad}t_{da} = 1 - r^2$ from the principle of reversibility, Eq. (8.3) may be expressed

$$\mathbf{u}_R = \mathbf{u}r\{1 - (1 - r^2)e^{-j\delta}[1 + (r^2 e^{-j\delta}) + (r^2 e^{-j\delta})^2 + (r^2 e^{-j\delta})^3 + \cdots]\}.$$

Since the series converges,

$$\frac{\mathbf{u}_R}{\mathbf{u}} = r\left(1 - \frac{(1 - r^2)e^{-j\delta}}{1 - r^2 e^{-j\delta}}\right) = r\left(\frac{1 - e^{-j\delta}}{1 - r^2 e^{-j\delta}}\right).$$

The resultant intensity of the reflected rays at P is

$$\frac{I_R}{I_0} = \left|\frac{\mathbf{u}_R}{\mathbf{u}}\right|^2 = r^2\left(\frac{1 - e^{-j\delta}}{1 - r^2 e^{-j\delta}}\right)\left(\frac{1 - e^{j\delta}}{1 - r^2 e^{j\delta}}\right) = r^2\left(\frac{2 - e^{j\delta} - e^{-j\delta}}{1 - r^2(e^{j\delta} + e^{-j\delta}) + r^4}\right),$$

where I_0 is the intensity of the incident beam.

$$\frac{I_R}{I_0} = \frac{2r^2(1 - \cos\delta)}{1 - 2r^2\cos\delta + r^4}, \tag{8.5}$$

where $I_R/I_0 = 0$ when $\cos\delta = 1$ and I_R/I_0 has a maximum value of $4r^2/(1 + r^2)^2$ when $\cos\delta = -1$. Thus $I_R/I_0 = 0$ when $\delta = 2\pi N$, and I_R/I_0 is a maximum when $\delta = 2\pi(N + \frac{1}{2})\lambda$.

When these values of δ are substituted in Eq. (8.4), we have the previously discovered conditions for a minimum and maximum of intensity at point P in the interference pattern formed by reflection from the thin film. Since by conservation of energy the sums of the intensities at P and P' must equal the intensity of the incident beam, we shall postpone the graphical interpretation of Eq. (8.5) until we have treated interference by transmission in Sec. 8.4.

8.3 Extended Sources

Thus far we have considered the resultant intensity at P of light initially from point S. The parallel rays reaching P from the same point source are coherent. Next we shall consider an extended source such as a ground-glass screen S in front of a sodium lamp L shown in Fig. 108. Two pairs of reflected rays from two primary sources are focused at two points on the retina. With changing values of ϕ' the interference pattern on the retina will be made up of alternating dark and light bands. Using the law of reflection, we note that a point source can not give rise to an interference pattern of a thin film on the retina but only a point image whose brightness depends on the angle of incidence.

If one looks vertically downward upon a horizontal film illuminated by a continuous source from above, the locus of all the points for which the angle of incidence is the same is a circle. Thus one will observe a series of concentric

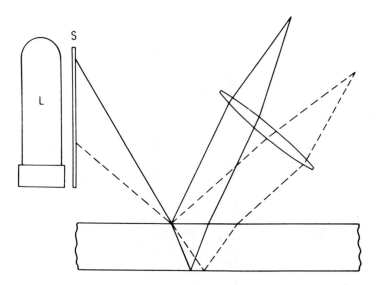

Figure 108. Formation of interference pattern from an extended source.

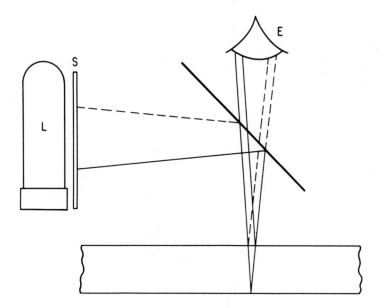

Figure 109. Arrangement for observation of interference at normal incidence.

circular interference bands. Figure 109 indicates a means of effectively putting an extended source behind the "transparent" head of an observer.

If we are to observe interference bands, the distance between two consecutive reflected rays from a common point source must be less than the diameter of the pupil of the eye. To accept rays of greater separation, a telescope with larger objective lens than the pupil of the eye must be used. Since the rays which determine the intensity at a point in a band are parallel as they approach the eye, the eye or telescope must be focused for infinity.

The circles in the interference pattern for the film of parallel surfaces become finer at larger distances from the center. The fineness of the pattern, that is, the smallness of the angular separation of the circles in this infinitely distant pattern, may be expressed in terms of the rate at which Δ the optical path difference between two consecutive interfering rays changes with ϕ'. From Eq. (8.2),

$$\Delta = 2nd \cos \phi'$$

and

$$\frac{d\Delta}{d\phi'} = -2nd \sin \phi'.$$

We see that the interference pattern becomes finer (1) as thickness is increased and (2) as the angle of incidence is increased. Note that those factors which cause a greater separation of consecutive, parallel, interfering rays also cause a finer pattern. With the naked eye we can observe interference patterns in films up to 1000 wavelengths thick. With the aid of telescopes interference patterns have been observed for "thin" films of 100,000 wavelengths, a few centimeters thick. Interference patterns produced with such thick films are known as *Haidinger's fringes*. They are important in modern interferometers for spectroscopy.

8.4 Interference of Transmitted Waves

Since the derivation of the intensity at point P' in the transmitted interference pattern is similar to that for the reflected beam, the reader may prefer to close the book and make the derivation.

The intensity at point P' relative to that of the incident beam is

$$\frac{\mathbf{u}_T}{\mathbf{u}} = t_{ad}t_{da}[1 + (r^2 e^{-j\delta}) + (r^2 e^{-j\delta})^2 + (r^2 e^{-j\delta})^3 + \cdots]. \tag{8.6}$$

Employing the law of reversibility, we obtain

$$\frac{\mathbf{u}_T}{\mathbf{u}} = (1 - r^2)[1 + (r^2 e^{-j\delta}) + (r^2 e^{-j\delta})^2 + (r^2 e^{-j\delta})^3 + \cdots]. \tag{8.7}$$

Since the series converges it may be reduced to the ratio

$$\frac{\mathbf{u}_T}{\mathbf{u}} = \frac{1 - r^2}{1 - r^2 e^{-j\delta}}.$$

The intensity at P' relative to the intensity of the incident ray is the square of the absolute value of the complex amplitude

$$\frac{I_T}{I_0} = \left| \frac{\mathbf{u}_T}{\mathbf{u}} \right|^2 = \frac{(1 - r^2)^2}{1 - 2r^2 \cos \delta + r^4}. \tag{8.8}$$

To our small surprise the sum of the intensities at P and P' given by Eqs. (8.5) and (8.8) is unity. We assumed that the light energy was conserved when we employed the law of reversibility.

May we pause for a paragraph of caution for those who are solving original problems in thin films? The rays that we have been treating are beams of finite width. The width of the beam in the dielectric is less than in air. Even though the rate of passage of light energy by a cross section is the same in air and dielectric, the beam is narrower in dielectric than in air, so that the intensity will be greater in the medium of higher index of refraction. From geometrical optics the reader may show that the ratio of widths of the parallel beam in air and dielectric equals the ratio of cosines of the angles of incidence and refraction.

Note that in Eq. (8.8) the intensity is expressed in terms of a phase angle δ rather than in terms of the thickness of the film and other geometry of the system. In general, simplicity will be gained throughout all studies of interference and diffraction if the intensities are expressed first in terms of phase differences, and the phase differences, in turn, in terms of the geometry of the system.

Interferometers, which are made with thick plates, are often used at nearly normal incidence, in which case the reflectivity r at a single surface may be expressed in terms of the index of refraction of the medium by an equation discovered by Fresnel who treated light as a wave in an elastic solid.

$$r = \frac{n - 1}{n + 1}.$$

This expression will be derived in Chapter XVI from Maxwell's equations for electromagnetic waves and the electrical boundary conditions at the reflecting surface. The fraction of intensity reflected at a single surface is the square of the fraction of amplitude reflected.

For light in glass, microwaves in glass, and microwaves in water the indices of refraction are 1.5, 2.5, and 9.0, respectively. The corresponding values of r^2 are 0.04, 0.18, and 0.64. In Fig. 110 is plotted the transmitted intensity I_T/I_0 against the phase difference δ for r^2 of 0.04, 0.18, 0.64, 0.80. The case of 0.80

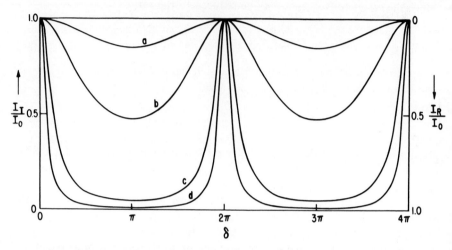

Figure 110. Plots of intensities of interference patterns by transmission and reflection for r^2 of (a) 0.04, (b) 0.18, (c) 0.64, (d) 0.80.

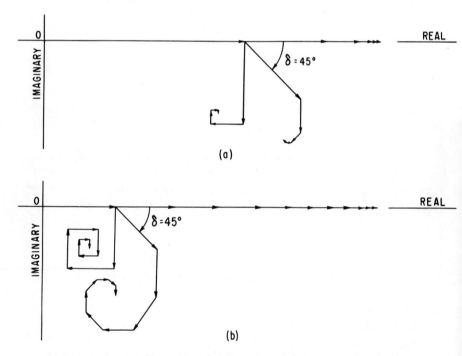

Figure 111. Vector sums of transmitted rays for phase decrements 0°, 45°, and 90°, to indicate sharpening of interference lines with increasing reflectivities at the boundary (a) $r^2 = 0.4$, (b) $r^2 = 0.8$.

intensity reflectivity is obtained by coating the glass with a thin partially reflecting silver film. Since $I_T + I_R = I_0$, I_R/I_0 can also be found from these graphs. The coordinate I_R/I_0 is indicated on the right-hand side of the graph increasing from top to bottom.

If only a small number of the transmitted rays is received by the lens of Fig. 106, Eq. (8.7) must be employed to find the amplitude and phase of the resulting wave. This may be done by representing each term as a vector in complex space as shown in Fig. 111(a) as plotted for the case of intensity reflectivity $r^2 = 0.4$ and 111(b) for $r^2 = 0.8$. In each of the two cases the phase angle δ is given three values: 0°, 45°, and 90°. The reference vector is the complex amplitude of the first ray. In Fig. 111(a) the first six terms of Eq. (8.7) were employed to find the resultant transmitted amplitudes. In Fig. 111(b) the first eleven terms were used. The number of terms in each case was limited by the smallest length of vector that could be constructed conveniently.

The two sets of vector additions (a) and (b) indicate graphically the fact noted in Fig. 110, that as the reflectivity of the surface is increased the lines in the interference pattern become sharper. That is, if the reflectivity of surface is made greater, the amplitude decreases more rapidly as the phase angle is increased from zero. For instance, in Fig. 111(a) the amplitudes measured from the origin O to the ends of the vector additions corresponding to $\delta = 0°$, 45°, and 90° have the relative values of 1.00, 0.78, and 0.64. For the higher reflectivity case the corresponding relative amplitudes are 1.00, 0.34, and 0.19.

8.5 Thin Films for Microwaves

Films of thickness of the order of a wavelength of microwaves are no longer soap bubbles and films of oil on water. They are the walls of a

Figure 112. Transmission of microwaves by a thin film of dielectric.

building, plates of glass, or sheets of lumber the thickness of which can be measured directly on a meter stick.

Figure 112 is an arrangement for the study of transmission of microwaves by a thin film. Thin sheets of glass may be set in front of the intensity meter one at a time and the intensity of transmission plotted against thickness as in

Fig. 110. At least three peaks should be found including the one for zero thickness. Since the peaks are narrow and the valleys wide, the thicknesses corresponding to a maximum of intensity can be determined most precisely.

The hole in the metal screen is to reduce the variable effects of diffraction by the edges of the dielectric. A hole one wavelength in diameter has a maximum in its own diffraction pattern at the center.

The variable reflected wave from the dielectric back to the oscillator will cause a variable output of the oscillator. The beam from the oscillator and that reflected from the dielectric are sufficiently divergent that the effect of the reflected beam on the oscillator will be negligible if the oscillator and intensity meter are 6 ft apart.

Figure 113. Transmission of microwaves by a thin film of air.

The condition for maximum transmission for normal incidence is that the *optical thickness* of the film equals an integer number of half wavelengths. That is,

$$nd = \frac{N\lambda}{2}.$$

From the measured wavelength in air and the thicknesses of the film for maximum transmission, the index of refraction can be calculated.

Figure 113 is an arrangement for studying transmission of microwaves by a thin film of air. The second sheet of dielectric is moved away from the first by steps of 0.1 wavelength or less and the intensity plotted against thickness of the air film.

When a film is sufficiently thin, about one-tenth wavelength for a soap film, the transmission is 100% as nearly as can be observed. This very thin film appears black by reflected light. Two glass blocks can be ground so optically flat that when they are held together the thin film between them is a nearly perfect transmitter of light. The glass blocks are said to be in *optical contact*.

For microwaves two dielectrics in optical contact may still be separated by amounts easily measured on a meter stick. This is indicated in Fig. 114 where a row of dry building bricks serves as a wave guide for microwaves of 12 cm wavelength. The V-shaped gaps are good optical contact. We recall from the treatment of wave guides in Fig. 63 that the electric field must be parallel to the short edge of the brick.

In the study of thin films thus far we have treated the special cases in which there was phase reversal at only one of the two reflecting surfaces. As we treat the modern optical revolution of nonreflecting glass, step gages, and interference filters we shall use methods of the previous sections but not the same formulas.

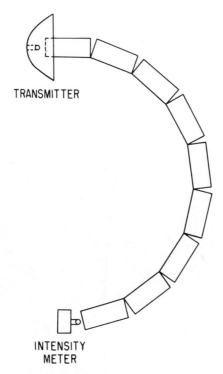

TRANSMITTER

INTENSITY
METER

Figure 114. Row of bricks as wave guide to illustrate optical contact for microwaves.

8.6 Interference Films on Glass

Interference films on glass used either to make the surface nonreflecting or highly reflecting without loss of wave energy to heat are a by-product of research in surface chemistry, a new science for which Irving Langmuir received the Nobel Prize. If certain long-chain molecules such as fatty acids are spread over the surface of water, they form a monomolecular layer, the axes of the long molecules being nearly perpendicular to the water surface and one end being attracted by the water.

The measurement of the lengths of molecules was made quantitative when

Katherine Blodgett[1,2] discovered and developed a method of superposing the monomolecular layers one layer at a time on a clean glass or metal surface, thus producing crystals of a precisely known number of molecular layers. The glass or chromium plates were dipped into the water perpendicularly to the surface and withdrawn taking on a layer each way. The techniques have been described[1] in sufficient detail to be copied in student laboratories of optics and chemistry.

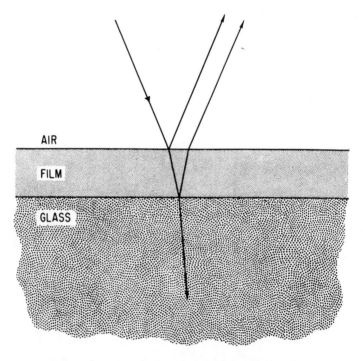

Figure 115. Arrangement for study of interference of light reflected from a thin film on glass.

A barium copper stearate molecule is about 25 A long. Blodgett was able to build 3000 layers of this crystal, a total thickness of about 12 wavelengths of sodium light. At this stage the application of physical optics to surface chemistry became also the application of surface chemistry to optics. The study involved interference in thin films, crystal optics, polarization by reflection, and x-ray diffraction by crystals.

We shall confine our study of Blodgett's crystals in this chapter to interference effects in thin films on solids and to small angles of incidence. At larger angles of incidence polarization effects become prominent. We shall treat them in the chapter on polarization by reflection. Figure 115 is a diagram of a thin crystal on glass. If the thin film of crystal has an index of refraction intermediate between that of air and glass, the reflections at both surfaces will involve phase changes of π, the incidence being from an optically less to an optically more dense medium in each case. Thus the phase difference between the first two reflected rays is due solely to path difference.

Applying the geometry of Fig. 107, we note that, if neither or both of the reflected waves undergo phase reversal on reflection, the amplitude of the first two combined reflected waves is *maximum* when $2n_c d \cos \phi' = N\lambda$, and *minimum* when

$$2n_c d \cos \phi' = (2N + 1)\lambda/2,$$

where n_c is the index of refraction of the crystal and the order N of the spectrum is any integer or zero. In elementary courses it is customary to treat only the first two rays as a good approximation. With the aid of complex algebra we may make an exact solution for an infinite number of reflected rays.

If the reflected parallel rays are focused at a point on the retina, the resultant reflected amplitude u_R may be expressed in terms of u_0 the amplitude of the incident wave, r_{ac} the fraction of the amplitude reflected for incidence from air to crystal, t_{ac} and t_{ca} the fractions of amplitude transmitted from air to crystal and crystal to air, respectively, and δ the phase angle between two consecutive reflected rays caused by path difference only. From Fig. 116, with the history of each ray labeled, we may express the complex amplitude of the resultant of the reflected rays.

$$\frac{u_R}{u_0} = r_{ac} + t_{ac}t_{ca}(r_{cg}e^{-j\delta} + r_{cg}^2 r_{ca}e^{-2j\delta} + r_{cg}^3 r_{ca}^2 e^{-3j\delta} + \cdots). \qquad (8.9)$$

Since the films are transparent we may apply the results of the law of reversibility:

$$r_{ca} = -r_{ac} \quad \text{and} \quad t_{ac}t_{ca} = 1 - r_{ac}^2.$$

Thus Eq. (8.9) becomes

$$\frac{u_R}{u_0} = r_{ac} + \frac{1 - r_{ac}^2}{r_{ac}} [r_{ac}r_{cg}e^{-j\delta} - (r_{ac}r_{cg}e^{-j\delta})^2 + (r_{ac}r_{cg}e^{-j\delta})^3 - \cdots]. \qquad (8.10)$$

Since r_{ac} and r_{cg} are both less than unity,

$$\frac{u_R}{u_0} = r_{ac} + \frac{(1 - r_{ac}^2)r_{cg}e^{-j\delta}}{1 + r_{ac}r_{cg}e^{-j\delta}} = \frac{r_{ac} + r_{cg}e^{-j\delta}}{1 + r_{ac}r_{cg}e^{-j\delta}}.$$

The reflected intensity relative to that of the incident beam is

$$\frac{I_R}{I_0} = \left| \frac{u_R}{u_0} \right|^2 = \frac{r_{ac}^2 + 2r_{ac}r_{cg}\cos\delta + r_{cg}^2}{1 + 2r_{ac}r_{cg}\cos\delta + r_{ac}^2 r_{cg}^2}, \qquad (8.11)$$

where I_R is a minimum when the path difference

$$2n_c d \cos \phi' = \frac{(2N+1)\lambda}{2}.$$

Thus the phase difference is $\delta = (2N+1)\pi$ so that

$$\frac{I_R}{I_0} = \left(\frac{r_{ac} - r_{cg}}{1 - r_{ac}r_{cg}}\right)^2. \tag{8.12}$$

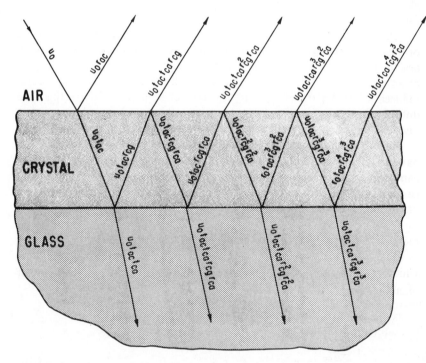

Figure 116. Successively reflected rays within a thin film of crystal on glass.

If $r_{cg} = r_{ac}$, then $I_R/I_0 = 0$ and all the light enters the glass. To obtain no reflection we must adjust the index of refraction of the crystal until $r_{cg} = r_{ac}$.

From Fresnel's law for normal or near normal incidence, the amplitude reflectivity r_{12} at the boundary of two surfaces 1 and 2 of indices of refraction n_1 and n_2

$$r_{12} = \frac{n_2 - n_1}{n_2 + n_1}. \tag{8.13}$$

If the index of refraction of air is n_a, of the crystal n_c, and of the glass n_g,

$$r_{ac} = \frac{n_c - n_a}{n_c + n_a} \quad \text{and} \quad r_{cg} = \frac{n_g - n_c}{n_g + n_c},$$

when $r_{ac} = r_{cg}$,

$$\frac{n_c - n_a}{n_c + n_a} = \frac{n_g - n_c}{n_g + n_c}.$$

Clearing fractions, $n_c^2 = n_g n_a$. If the surface is to be nonreflecting, the index of refraction of the intermediate thin film must be the geometric mean of the indices of refraction of the other two media. If the indices of refraction of glass and air are 1.50 and 1.00, the index of refraction of the film must be 1.22 for zero reflection.

Blodgett developed an ingenious means of reducing the index of refraction of the film to the desired value. Making up the monolayers of 50% cadmium arachidate and 50% arachidic acid, she dissolved out the alternate molecules of arachidic acid with alcohol to leave a skeleton of cadmium arachidate of reduced index of refraction without altering the thickness of the film. X-ray diffraction studies[3] revealed no change in the lattice spacing between the heavy atoms.

Figure 117 is a picture of an electric meter in which half the glass face has been made nonreflecting. Films of fatty acid used in building the crystals can be rubbed from the glass with the fingers and are thus unsatisfactory for some applications.

At the same time that surface chemistry was developing, the art of evaporating metal and dielectric films in vacuum was being perfected. After the method of producing nonreflecting films had been clearly defined by the work of Blodgett, searches were made[4] for dielectrics of the right index of refraction which would be durable and could be evaporated onto glass. At present, coats of magnesium fluoride are evaporated on the glass surfaces of optical instruments.

Although loss of intensity due to reflection from one surface of clean glass is but 0.04, this can be a serious loss in an optical instrument with three lenses, six surfaces. The proof that the same coating on the side of the glass from which the light is leaving will also yield perfect transmission is left for the problems.

We note that the conditions for nonreflection are expressed in wavelengths. The elements of optical instruments are made nonreflecting at the maximum sensitivity of the eye, 5100 A when dark adapted and 5550 A in daylight. One observes a slight purple (mixture of red and violet) reflection from coated optical glass.

[3] Holley and Bernstein, *Phys. Rev.*, **52**, 525 (1937).
[4] J. Strong, *J. Opt. Soc. Amer.*, **26**, 73 (1936).

Two or more coatings of films with geometrically increasing indices of refraction[5] have been used to make nonreflecting glass. If thicknesses of the two or more films are chosen corresponding to quarter wavelengths of properly spaced wavelengths in the visible spectrum, the glass can be made more nearly nonreflecting over the whole visible spectrum.

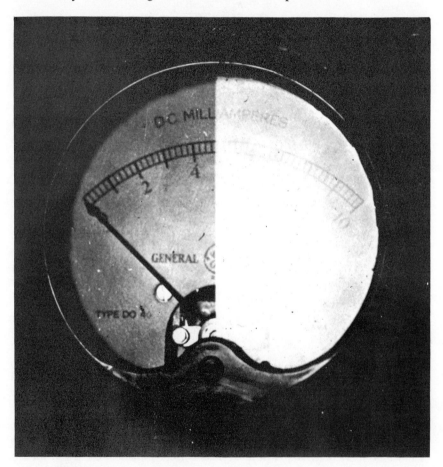

Figure 117. Electric meter on which the left-hand half of the glass face has been made nonreflecting.

8.7 Step Gage

Employing the precise reproducibility of molecular dimensions, Blodgett built a step gage for industrial and research use, shown in the frontispiece.

[5] C. Candler, *Modern Interferometers:* Glasgow, Scotland, Hilger and Watts, The University Press (1951).

Unknown thicknesses of thin films on metal or on other dielectrics of higher index of refraction may be determined by matching colors with those of the step gage. The steps are increments of 10 molecular layers from 20 to 160. A thin metallic lead surface on the glass back produces a phase change equivalent to eight layers of the barium stearate crystal, so that the first layer is counted as number nine.

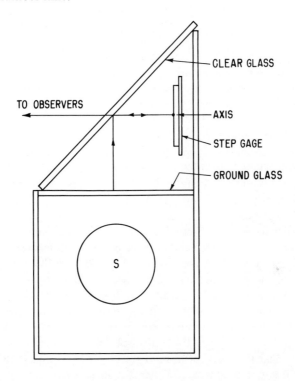

Figure 118. Arrangement for viewing step gage at normal incidence.

We shall be concerned with the step gage for laboratory exercises and quantitative demonstrations of interference in thin films. To observe the interference colors at near normal incidence, we may stand with our backs to a window and look at the film reflecting light from the sky. Figure 118 indicates a method by which a group may observe the interference colors at near normal incidence, where S is a source of either sodium light or white light in a box covered with ground glass which serves as an extended source.

Every thickness of film gives a minimum intensity by reflection for a series of wavelengths. The color observed is the remainder of the spectrum, the complement of the transmitted portion of the spectrum. The transmitted portion is absorbed by the black surface on which the steps are built. The thickness of the metallic lead film on the glass was chosen to make minimum reflection of sodium light by the gage zero.

The condition for an intensity minimum is that the path difference be an odd number of half wavelengths, that is, $2n_c d \cos \phi' = (2N + 1)\lambda/2$. The wavelengths corresponding to the black bands across the reflection spectrum for normal incidence are

$$\lambda = \frac{4n_c d}{2N + 1},\qquad (8.14)$$

n_c being the index of refraction of the barium stearate crystal.

Step 4 on the gage is the thinnest film which will give a black band for the yellow sodium lines at 6000 A. Since the index of refraction of the barium stearate is 1.5, the thickness of the film in step 4 is approximately 1000 A. The series of black bands for this step corresponding to $N = 0, 1, 2$ computed from Eq. (8.14) are 6000 A, 2000 A, 1200 A, and so on. On a frequency scale these waves would be evenly spaced in the spectrum. Since the visible spectrum extends from 4000 A to 7000 A there is but one dark band in the visible region. Step 4 is quite dark under white light because the maximum sensitivity of the eye in daylight is at about 5560 A, which is near the yellow in the spectrum.

Here N is the order of the spectrum. Step 4 is the zero order and step 12 the first order for yellow. Step 12 is thus 3000 A thick and the dark bands in the spectrum of interference colors reflected by this thickness are at 18,000 A in the infrared, 6000 A in the visible, and 3600 A in the ultraviolet. As the thickness of the film increases the dark bands in the spectrum become narrower and more closely spaced. The black band in the spectrum of the first order is narrower than that in the zero order. Thus the colors of the fourth and twelfth steps are not quite the same. When the order number for sodium light is 5 there are three absorption bands in the visible spectrum reflected by that thickness of film. If the step gage were extended, the interference colors would approach white as N increased.

Since the lead glass was so chosen that $r_{ac} = r_{cg}$ and since these amplitude reflectivities are only 0.2, we may neglect the square and fourth power terms in the denominator of Eq. (8.11) as compared to unity with only an 8 % error. Thus Eq. (8.11) becomes

$$\frac{I_R}{I_0} = 2r_{ac}^2(1 + \cos \delta).$$

As indicated in Fig. 119, I_R/I_0 plotted against $n_c d/\lambda$ varies between zero and $4r_{ac}^2$. For sodium light and normal incidence the phase steps are each $\pi/4$. In the photograph of the step gage shown in Fig. 120, as taken under sodium light and normal incidence, the steps in intensity are all distinguished by the human eye. It is interesting to note that since our eye "measures" intensity on an approximately logarithmic scale, the contrast between steps 4 and 5 as observed by the eye is much greater than between 7 and 8. An intensity meter would indicate equal differences in intensity between these two pairs of steps. By rotating the step gage about the axis indicated in Fig. 118, we may

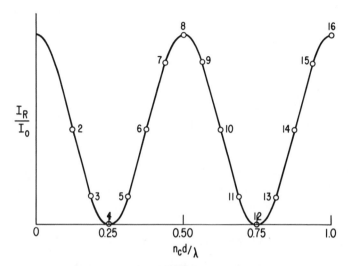

Figure 119. Reflected intensities from steps of a step gage indicated on a continuous graph of reflected intensities against phase decrements.

demonstrate (1) how the intensity of monochromatic light varies with the angle of incidence and (2) how under white light the colors vary with angle of incidence. Actually we have found convenience in expressing the angle of refraction instead of the angle of incidence.

The path difference

$$\Delta = 2n_c d \cos \phi',$$

Figure 120. Step gage observed by reflection of sodium light.

and the phase difference

$$\delta = \frac{2\pi\Delta}{\lambda} = \frac{4\pi n_c d \cos \phi'}{\lambda}.$$

The phase difference δ decreases as ϕ' increases from zero. Equally interesting is the demonstration of how the rate of variation of Δ with ϕ' depends on d.

$$\frac{d\Delta}{d\phi'} = -2n_c d \sin \phi'.$$

The rate of change of path difference of the reflected rays from the two surfaces is proportional to the thickness d. If the step gage is rotated until the intensity null for sodium light at step 4 moves to 5, the null at 12 moves to 15. Similarly, if white light is used, the color complement of yellow will move to the thicker steps as the angle of incidence increases. At still higher orders the colors zip up the crystal stairs with velocities proportional to thickness d.

Applications to research will be found in the instructions accompanying the step gage and in books on interferometry.[6]

8.8 Interference Filters, Transmission

The art of evaporating films of precisely controlled thickness of metal and certain dielectrics in high vacuum for mirrors and nonreflecting glass has also been employed to produce interference filters. Figure 121 indicates the cross section of a single-layer interference filter. A semitransparent metal film is evaporated on a glass plate followed by a film of transparent dielectric with a low index of refraction such as cryolite, $n = 1.36$, and a second film of metal. The glass envelope serves as protection.

An ideal optical filter would transmit 100% of a narrow portion of the spectrum and reject the remainder. Such an ideal filter is approached by curve d in Fig. 110. This is the case in which the reflectivity at the surface of the thin film is high. Many dielectrics have high indices of refraction and corresponding high surface reflectivities for microwaves so that single sheets serve as transmission filters in that range of the spectrum. In the visible part of the spectrum the indices of refraction are not higher than 2.5, so that surface reflectivity must be made sufficiently high by a thin coat of transparent metal. Unfortunately a highly reflecting metal is also an absorber of the portion passing through it, so that a compromise must be made between high reflection and absorption in determining the thickness of the film. The thicknesses of the metal film are chosen to give maximum values of I_T/I_0 for the filter of somewhat less than 50%.

Since the phase change upon reflection is the same at both surfaces, the transmission will be a maximum when the optical path difference between two

---

[6] Candler, *op. cit.*, Chap. IV.

consecutive superposed rays is an integer number of wavelengths, that is, $2nd = N\lambda$ for normal incidence. For a given optical thickness of the dielectric film, there is a series of wavelengths with maximum transmission corresponding to the integers N. If the index of refraction were constant with frequency, the bands of maximum transmission would be uniformly distributed along the frequency scale. As in treating the step gage, we shall find that the thickness of the dielectric must not be more than one or two wavelengths if there are to be but one or two transmitted bands in the visible spectrum. Determination of thicknesses will be retained for the problems.

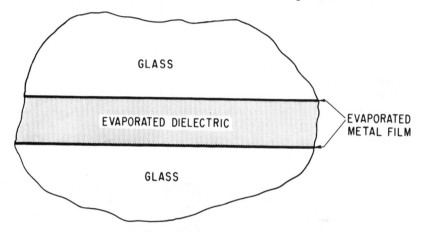

Figure 121. Cross section of a single-layer interference filter.

Single-film absorption filters are made with transmission band widths at half maximum $\Delta\lambda = 15$ A in the visible spectrum. If we define the chromatic resolving power as $\lambda/\Delta\lambda$, such a filter has a chromatic resolving power of 400 at 6000 A. We shall continue to use the concept of chromatic resolving power of interferometers and spectrometers in distinguishing neighboring spectral lines. Student spectrometers have chromatic resolving powers of the order ten times that of the interference filters.

Interference filters have two advantages over absorption filters. (1) They may be made for maximum transmission at any desired wavelength. (2) A true interference filter is not heated but selectively separates the spectrum into reflected and transmitted parts. Wave energy remains constant in pure interference.

We have noted that the single-layer interference filter for the visible spectrum did not achieve the ideal of pure interference. Absorbing metal coats were required. Currently multilayers of dielectric are being developed with reflectivities of over 90% and absorption of less than 1%.[7] Such a

[7] S. Tolansky, *An Introduction to Interferometry:* New York, Longmans (1954) p. 73.

nonabsorbing dielectric mirror will have many applications. Its application to transmission filters is treated in books on interferometry.[8]

8.9 Interference Filters, Reflection

Reflection interference filters were first developed for the microwave portion of the spectrum. They have since been extended to the infrared and

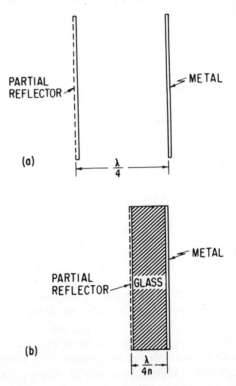

Figure 122. Reflection interference filter for microwaves. (a) Quarter-wave space in air. (b) Quarter-wave space in dielectric.

visible region. Since microwave sources radiate a narrow band of wavelength interference reflectors are designed to absorb all the incident radiation. They are thus called *interference absorbers* in microwave usage. We recall that interference involves no loss of wave energy. The interference absorber combines interference effects with true absorption. The wave energy is converted into thermal energy in the thin partially reflecting sheet.

[8] Candler, *op. cit.*, Chap. IV.

The first interference absorbers for microwaves were made with a plane metal sheet and a sheet of carbon-coated canvas spaced one-quarter wave apart as shown in Fig. 122(a). We shall show that if the partially reflecting coat is of such conductivity as to reflect one-third the amplitude for normal incidence, the net reflection from the interference absorber is zero. Neither can any radiation pass through the metal sheet.

Figure 122(b) shows an interference absorber in which the space is filled with dielectric. Because of the high indices of refraction available for microwaves, the thickness of the microwave absorbers may be thin compared to a

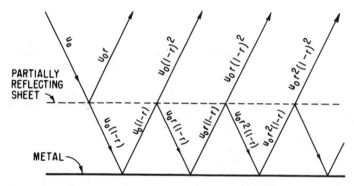

Figure 123. Amplitudes of successively reflected rays from an interference filter for microwaves.

wavelength in air. Derwin[9] has made use of the metal surface of electrically conducting glass to produce highly absorbing thin screens. The reflectivity of the coat can be made to order. The coat is uniform and not subject to humidity effects as is the canvas sheet. The coat on glass is specified in the unit *ohms per square*. The meaning of this unit is recognized when we note that if a square sheet is cut from any conductor of uniform thickness, the electric resistance between two opposite edges is independent of the size of the square. A coat that reflects one-third the amplitude has 377 ohms per square.

Figure 123 is a diagram of the multiple reflections with amplitude reflectivity r at the partially reflecting screen and perfect reflectivity at the metal sheet. Customarily a broad beam is incident normally. The oblique incidence is indicated for ease in labeling the multiple reflections. The resultant amplitude u_R of the infinite number of reflections may be expressed in terms of the amplitude u_0 of the incident wave, the reflectivity r of the space cloth at normal incidence, and δ the phase difference between two consecutive reflected waves.

$$\mathbf{u}_R = \mathbf{u}_0\{r + (1 - r)^2 e^{-j\delta}[1 + re^{-j\delta} + (re^{-j\delta})^2 + (re^{-j\delta})^3 + \cdots]\}.$$

[9] C. Derwin, *J. Appl. Phys.*, June 1958.

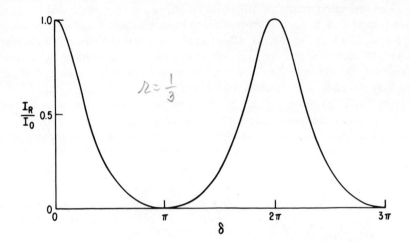

Figure 124. Plot of reflected intensities against phase decrements for microwave interference absorber illustrating large tolerance in spacing.

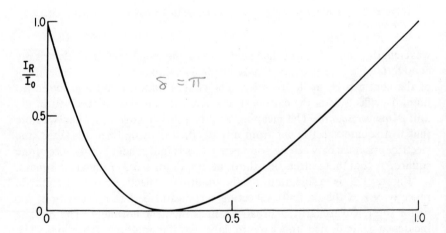

Figure 125. Plot of reflected intensities against reflectivities of the partially reflecting screen of the microwave interference absorber to illustrate large tolerances in the reflectivity.

Since r is less than one,

$$\frac{\mathbf{u}_R}{\mathbf{u}_0} = r + \frac{(1-r)^2 e^{-j\delta}}{1 - re^{-j\delta}} = \frac{r + (1 - 2r)e^{-j\delta}}{1 - re^{-j\delta}}. \tag{8.15}$$

If $\mathbf{u}_R$ is to be zero, the numerator

$$r + (1 - 2r)e^{-j\delta} = 0.$$

The real and imaginary parts must each equal zero. Thus

$$(1 - 2r)\cos\delta = -r,$$
$$(1 - 2r)\sin\delta = 0.$$

If we square and add the two equations, we obtain $r = \frac{1}{3}$. Substituting this value of r in the first of the simultaneous equations, we obtain $\cos\delta = -1$ and $\delta = \pi$. If the combined screens are to make a perfect absorber of a given wavelength for normal incidence, the phase difference δ between consecutive reflections must be π, the spacing $\frac{1}{4}$ wavelength.

The relative intensity for all reflectivities and phase differences is

$$\frac{I_R}{I_0} = \left|\frac{\mathbf{u}_R}{\mathbf{u}_0}\right|^2 = \frac{1 - 4r + 5r^2 + 2r(1 - 2r)\cos\delta}{1 + r^2 - 2r\cos\delta}. \tag{8.16}$$

If we fix $r = \frac{1}{3}$,

$$\frac{I_R}{I_0} = \frac{1 + \cos\delta}{5 - 3\cos\delta}.$$

Figure 124, a plot of I_R/I_0 against δ for $r = \frac{1}{3}$, reveals that δ may vary by 10% on either side of π without the reflected intensity exceeding 1%. Likewise, if we fix $\delta = \pi$,

$$\frac{I_R}{I_0} = \left(\frac{1 - 3r}{1 + r}\right).$$

We find on plotting I_R/I_0 against r in Fig. 125 that r may vary by 10% on either side of $\frac{1}{3}$ without the reflected intensity exceeding 1%. Experiment confirms that the interference absorber for microwaves is not critical in dimensions or in the reflectivity of the partial reflector.

8.10 Newton's Rings

Historically, the first determination of the wavelengths of light was made by Thomas Young using Newton's measurements of diameters of the different colored rings observed in the thin film between a convex lens surface and a flat plate of glass, and the radius of curvature of the lens surface.

No matter how refined may be the research instruments available to a student laboratory in optics, Newton's ring measurements and a series of observations made with the simple equipment serve as an effective survey of the principles and methods of interferometry. Figure 126 is a diagram of an arrangement for observing Newton's rings at normal incidence, where S is an extended source of sodium or mercury. The lens of radius of curvature 1 m or more (Newton used a 50 ft radius) rests on a small optical flat. The reflecting plate set at 45° may be a lantern slide cover glass. A low-power measuring microscope is used in determining diameters of rings in the interference pattern.

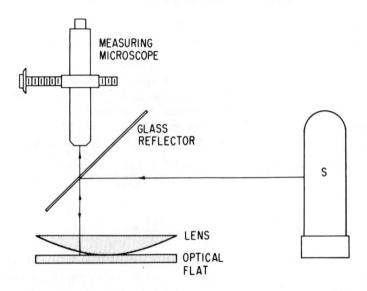

MEASURING
MICROSCOPE

GLASS
REFLECTOR

S

LENS

OPTICAL
FLAT

Figure 126. Arrangement for measuring Newton's rings at normal incidence.

We shall note some of the concepts to be gained in the Newton's ring study. (1) *Localized fringes* are patterns observed in the region of the film[10] when the reflecting surfaces are not parallel. A ray incident normally from a point on the extended source will be split into two rays on reflection from the surfaces bounding the air film. The two diverging rays can be focused by the eye with or without the aid of the microscope upon the retina where the real interference pattern lies. A virtual image lies in the plane of the thin film and may be properly called a contour map of the spherical lens surface. (2) *Optical contact* is more easily obtained between a spherical surface and a flat than between two flats. With a minimum of cutting and trying the surfaces may be cleaned and brought into optical contact with sliding and squeezing motion. When the space is less than 0.1 wavelength a black patch will be noted in the center of the pattern whether the source be monochromatic or white light. On the basis of this observation Thomas Young concluded that the reflected

[10] V. Oppenheim and J. H. Jaffe, *Am. J. Phys.*, **24**, 610 (1956).

wave underwent a π phase change at one of the surfaces. (3) As also observed by Young, if the lower plate is of higher index of refraction than the lens and the space is of index of refraction intermediate between the two, the central patch will be white for optical contact. (4) When the reflectivities are low at the surfaces the pattern observed by reflection has much higher contrast than that observed by transmission as indicated by curve (a) of Fig. 110. (5) Newton's observation that the radii of the rings are as the square roots of the integers may be confirmed. For slightly different reasons this relationship

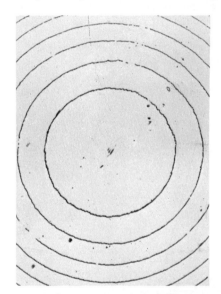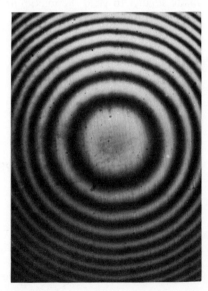

Figure 127. Photographs of Newton's ring interference patterns. (a) Reflection when surfaces are silvered. (b) Reflection when surfaces are unsilvered. (Courtesy of Professor Samuel Tolansky, Royal Holloway College, London.)

between radii and square roots of integers appears frequently in studies of interference and diffraction. (6) The method of Young may be used to measure the wavelength of sodium light. (7) The determination of wavelength difference of neighboring spectral lines may be made by superposition of interference patterns as treated with the Michelson interferometer in the preceding chapter. The two yellow lines of mercury serve well for this introductory study. (8) As demonstrated by Tolansky,[11,12] Newton's rings by transmission become narrow bright rings on a wide dark background when the two surfaces are silvered to 95% reflectivity. Figure 127 shows photographs of patterns taken by reflection when the surfaces are silvered compared to those formed by reflection when the glass is unsilvered.

[11] S. Tolansky, *Nature*, **153**, 195, 314 (1944).
[12] Tolansky, *An Introduction to Interferometry:* Chap. XIII.

When the glass is unsilvered only the first two of the multiple reflections are intense enough to be of importance, as indicated in Fig. 111; when the reflectivity of the surfaces increases the amplitudes of the succeeding multiple reflections are more nearly equal, and a larger number of reflected rays play a part in forming each point in the pattern. When only two reflections are involved the source may be extended. For multiple reflections from a silvered surface, a point source and lens must be used to give a parallel beam. Indeed, as the reflectivity becomes greater the size of "point" source must be made smaller to yield the maximum resolving power.

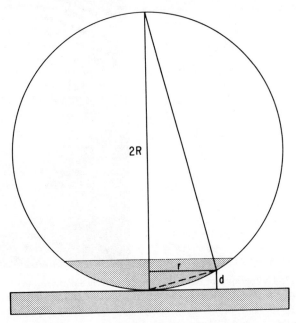

Figure 128. Geometry for finding thickness of thin films between the lens and optical flat.

From Fig. 128 we may determine the thickness d of the thin film of air at a particular ring of radius r in the Newton's ring pattern, where R is the radius of curvature of the lens. Having proved the similarity of two triangles in Fig. 128, we may express the proportion

$$\frac{2R - d}{r} = \frac{r}{d}, \quad \text{and} \quad (2R - d)d = r^2.$$

Since $d \ll R$,

$$r^2 = 2Rd. \tag{8.17}$$

The phase difference of two interfering rays is due to path difference plus the phase reversal for incidence from the less to more dense medium, where

$\delta = [2\pi(2d)/\lambda] + \pi$. For destructive interference, $\delta = (2N + 1)\pi$, N being the order number counting from zero at the center, so that $2d = N\lambda$. Substituting this expression for d in Eq. (8.17) we obtain

$$r^2 = NR\lambda. \tag{8.18}$$

One hundred rings are easily counted under the microscope and a plot of r^2 against N confirms Newton's discovery that the radii are as the square roots of the integers.

8.11 Fabry-Perot Interferometer

The interferometer most widely used for the past 50 years in study of structure of spectral lines and the calibration of standard-length gages consists

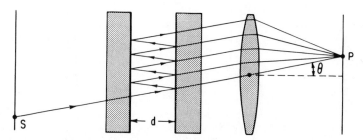

Figure 129. Fabry-Perot etalon.

of two highly reflecting parallel metal films with an air gap between. The air gap of a Fabry-Perot interferometer, often several centimeters wide and approaching one million wavelengths, can scarcely be called thin. However, the principles involved are an extension of the treatment of thin films, so that the Fabry-Perot interferometer properly belongs in this chapter. The original Fabry-Perot interferometer consisted of two glass plates with the parallel silvered surfaces facing each other, one plate fixed and the other driven by a screw between parallel guides as is one plate of Michelson's interferometer.

It was soon found that the driven plate could not be kept as precisely parallel to its mate as could fixed plates with quartz or invar spacing pins. Thus Fabry-Perot etalons with fixed spacing have replaced the moving plate interferometer.

Figure 129 is a diagram of the two plates of an etalon with their two silvered faces separated by spacing d. A ray from point S on an extended source striking the etalon will emerge as a series of parallel rays making angle θ with the principal axis of the lens. They will be brought to a point P in the focal plane of the lens. The intensity at P will be a maximum if

$$2d \cos \theta = N\lambda.$$

If we rotate Fig. 129 about the principal axis of the lens the same conditions will hold. Thus the interference pattern will consist of a set of concentric rings with center on the principal axis of the lens. The radii of the rings of maximum intensity will be proportional to the square roots of the integers counting from zero at the center as for Michelson's interferometer when the mirrors were perpendicular.

The advantage of the Fabry-Perot interferometer over the Michelson interferometer is in its higher chromatic resolving power. The Michelson interferometer involves interference between two rays, the Fabry-Perot

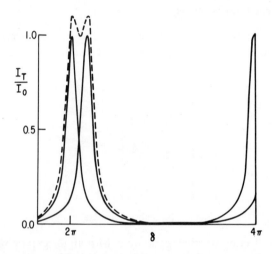

Figure 130. Plot of intensities of two lines in interference pattern that can just be distinguished.

involves a series of rays coming through the thin coat of highly reflecting metal with each multiple reflection. The greater sharpness of the lines in the Fabry-Perot interferometer pattern compare with the circular fringes from Michelson's interferometer as do the Newton's ring patterns of Fig. 127 for silvered and unsilvered surfaces.

Curve d in Fig. 110 indicates the sharpness of the lines in the interference pattern resulting from multiple reflections. Figure 130 indicates two neighboring lines of different wavelength that have the intensity distribution of curve d in Fig. 110. They can just be recognized as separate lines if their intensity curves intersect at one-half maximum. The dotted curve which is the sum of the two intensities has two peaks. If the two curves were closer by a very small amount the two peaks would become one.

Two of the primary uses of the etalon interferometer in spectroscopy are to separate the hyperfine structure in complex spectral lines and to determine intensity distribution in natural single lines. The left-hand side of Fig. 131 is a photograph of a Fabry-Perot interference pattern of the green line of mercury.

Figure 131. Fabry-Perot interference pattern of the green line of mercury. (a) Natural mercury. (b) Mercury 198. (Courtesy of Dr. William F. Meggars, National Bureau of Standards.)

Although no prism or grating spectrometer will separate the green line into its components, the interference pattern indicates several components each radiated by the several "inseparable" isotopes of mercury. Although the isotopes of mercury have not been separated in amounts sufficient to make a mercury lamp, the mercury isotope 198 has been produced by bombarding gold with neutrons from an atomic pile. The right-hand side of Fig. 131 is the interference pattern of the green line of this single isotope of mercury. This green line of mercury 198 was believed to be the ultimate[13] as a standard of length in 1948.

[13] W. F. Meggers, *J. Opt. Soc. Amer.*, **38**, 7 (1948). Address on receipt of the Ives Medal in 1947.

Later the isotope krypton 86 was found to have a sharper orange line at the lowest temperature at which it could be excited. In 1958 The International Committee on Weights and Measures made a resolution[14] to be presented to the General Conference in 1960 that the meter be defined in terms of this line of krypton 86.

We may define the *chromatic resolving power* of a spectrometer or interferometer as $\lambda/\Delta\lambda$ the ratio of the wavelength to the difference in wavelengths of two spectral lines that are just resolved by the instrument.

As we treat the resolving power of a Fabry-Perot etalon we shall use as example the green line of mercury, wavelength 5460 A, and the etalon of spacing 2.5 cm used at the Bureau of Standards in the first study[13] of that line from mercury 198. The wavelength of mercury 198 is standard at 5460.7532 A. The order at the center dot, at angle $\theta = 0$, is

$$N_K = 2d/\lambda = 5.0 \text{ cm}/5.460 \times 10^{-5} \text{ cm} = 9.2 \times 10^4,$$

or nearly 100,000. If for a given wavelength six orders are treated near the center of the plate, the range of order numbers is less than 1 part in 10,000.

Since a lens of longer focal length would merely increase the radius without changing the resolution of the interference pattern, the angle θ is more fundamental than the radius of a ring in the pattern. For a given etalon we wish to find the resolving power $\lambda/\Delta\lambda$ in terms of $\theta/\Delta\theta$, where $\Delta\theta$ is the angular separation of two lines that are just resolved.

We may differentiate the expression $2d \cos \theta = N\lambda$ to find the rate of change of wavelength with θ.

$$\frac{d\lambda}{d\theta} = -\frac{2d}{N} \sin \theta,$$

where N may be considered a constant if we wish to know $d\lambda/d\theta$ to no more than five significant figures. For the small angle employed

$$\sin \theta = \theta \quad \text{and} \quad \frac{d\lambda}{d\theta} = -\frac{2d}{N} \theta.$$

For the small changes $\Delta\lambda$ and $\Delta\theta$ which we wish to consider,

$$\frac{d\lambda}{d\theta} = \frac{\Delta\lambda}{\Delta\theta}$$

to a close approximation, and

$$\Delta\lambda = -\frac{2d}{N} \theta \, \Delta\theta. \tag{8.19}$$

[14] *Resolved*, that the meter is equal to 1,650,763.73 wavelengths in vacuum of the radiation corresponding to the transition between the energy levels of $2p_{10}$ and $5d_5$ of the atom krypton 86. The definition of the meter in effect since 1889 based on a platinum-iridium international prototype is abrogated.

The sign is of no significance since we are not concerned with whether $\Delta\lambda$ is an increase or decrease. If N is but an integer less than N_K, θ is small and $\cos\theta = 1 - \theta^2/2$.

$$\begin{cases} N_K\lambda = 2d \\ (N_K - 1)\lambda = 2d\left(1 - \dfrac{\theta^2}{2}\right). \end{cases}$$

Subtracting, we obtain

$$\lambda = \theta^2 d.$$

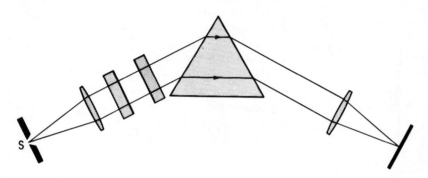

Figure 132. Fabry-Perot interferometer in a spectroscope.

Dividing this expression by Eq. (8.19), we obtain the fractional changes in λ and θ.

$$\frac{\lambda}{\Delta\lambda} = \frac{N}{2}\frac{\theta}{\Delta\theta}.$$

For the etalons with the present reflectivities, two spectral lines can be distinguished if they are separated by 2% of the angular separation of two consecutive orders of the same wavelength. This is for reflectivities somewhat higher than that of Fig. 110 curve (d). The resolving power of the previously mentioned Bureau of Standards etalon of 2.5 cm separation is

$$\frac{\lambda}{\Delta\lambda} = \frac{9.2 \times 10^4 \times 50}{2} = 2.3 \times 10^6.$$

With this etalon we can distinguish green lines differing in wavelength by one part in two million.

If with an etalon of such high resolution we were to observe a portion of the spectrum wider than the components of the green line of mercury, the orders of the different wavelengths would overlap making the pattern too complex to be interpreted. If the etalon is placed after the collimator as in Fig. 132, a cross section of the circular interference fringes will appear in each spectral line of the spectroscope containing only the wavelengths which are components of the spectroscope "line" as indicated in Fig. 133. Using a large quartz spectrograph and Fabry-Perot etalon the Bureau of Standards[15] has measured 26 wavelengths of the spectrum of mercury 198 relative to the green line of 5460.7532 A with probable errors of less than 0.0001 A.

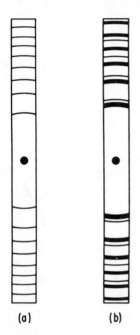

(a)   **(b)**

Figure 133. Two spectral lines from spectroscope with Fabry-Perot interference patterns of the component lines superimposed. Line (a) has one component. Line (b) has two components.

A more complete description of the uses of the Fabry-Perot etalon in spectroscopy, calibration of the standard meter, and determination of indices of refraction is found in books in interferometry.[16,17]

Improvements are expected currently in Fabry-Perot etalons as multilayers of dielectric are being developed to give more nearly perfect reflection without absorption. A Fabry-Perot etalon has been designed for microwaves for which the reflection coefficients of each of the two mirrors is 0.995 and the absorption negligible. Each mirror made is of a series of sheets of one-quarter wave thickness dielectric separated by one-quarter wave thickness of air.[18,19]

8.12 Lummer-Gehrke Plate

If a parallel beam of light enters through a totally reflecting prism into a long glass or quartz plate, Fig. 134, with parallel surfaces, being multiply reflected on each side at slightly less than the critical angle, the reflectivity is nearly 100% without the absorption loss obtained in silver mirrors. For any given wavelength the remaining light passes through the top and bottom to form an interference pattern in the focal plane of the lens. The separation of orders is proportional to the square roots of the integers, like those of Newton's rings. Although the Lummer-Gehrke plate has been replaced by the Fabry-Perot etalon as a research instrument, it still serves because of its simplicity as a student interferometer for the observation of fine structure in spectral lines.

[15] W. F. Meggars and K. G. Kessler, *J. Opt. Soc. Amer.*, **40**, 737–41 (1950).
[16] Candler, *op. cit.*, Chap. IX, XIII.
[17] Tolansky, *An Introduction to Interferometry:* Chaps. XI, XII.
[18] E. L. Ginzton, *Microwave Measurements:* New York, McGraw-Hill (1957) p. 373.
[19] W. Calshaw, *Proc. Phys. Soc. (London)*, **66**, 597 (1953).

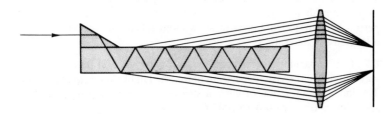

Figure 134. Lummer-Gehrke plate.

PROBLEMS FOR CHAPTER VIII

8.2.1. Derive Eq. (8.2) in a more elegant manner by extending lines AF and DC until they intersect at a point G. Note that AG, the hypotenuse of the triangle ADG, is twice the thickness of the film.

8.2.2. Express the path difference of Eq. (8.2) and Fig. 107 in terms of the angle of incidence ϕ instead of the angle of refraction ϕ'

8.2.3. By redrawing Fig. 107 for angles of incidence of 30° and 60° show that, as the angle of incidence increases, the phase difference of the two reflected rays decreases.

8.4.4. Find the sum of the intensities at points P and P' in the interference pattern of Fig. 106 in terms of the intensity I_0 of the incident beam. What principle is illustrated?

8.4.5. Compare a still pool of water with a black bottom, and a store window with black paint on the opposite side, as mirrors. That is, compare the percentages of intensity reflected by the two mirrors for normal incidence. The index of refraction of the water is 1.33 and of the glass 1.50.

8.4.6. Find the intensities I_T/I_0 of the transmitted interference pattern for nonabsorbing thin films for the cases of r^2 equal to 0.04, 0.18, 0.64, and 0.80 when the phase difference $\delta = \pi$, and check with Fig. 110.

8.4.7. Find the relative transmitted intensity at P', Fig. 106, if four rays are received by the lens when δ is 180° and $r^2 = 0.04$.

8.5.8. The thinnest sheet of glass that transmits a maximum intensity of normally incident microwaves of wavelength 12.5 cm is 2.5 cm thick. Find the index of refraction of that glass for microwaves.

8.6.9. Water has an index of refraction of 9.0 for microwaves of wavelength 12 cm. What must be the index of refraction and thickness of the walls of a container that will permit microwaves to enter the water from air without reflection?

8.6.10. Prove that the coat of dielectric on glass that permits a beam of light to go from air into glass at near normal incidence without reflection will also permit light to go from glass to air without reflection. Include with the proof a labeled ray diagram.

8.7.11. If a barium stearate film on lead glass were 11,000 A thick, at what wavelengths in the visible spectrum of reflected light would black bands appear? The index of refraction of barium stearate is 1.5 and the range of the visible spectrum is from 4000 A to 7000 A.

8.8.12. An interference filter is to be designed for maximum transmission at 5460 A, the wavelength of the green line of mercury. What is the thickest layer of cryolite, $n = 1.36$, that will give maximum transmission of the green line but no other maxima in the visible region 4000 A to 7000 A?

chapter XI

Fraunhofer Diffraction

9.1 Diffraction

Diffraction is the behavior of waves that pass through apertures or by edges of screens of metal or dielectric. Diffracting objects frequently treated .are the edges of lenses, the circular openings known as *stops* in optical instruments, the circular opening of a parabolic reflector, the source slits of spectrometers, the scratches in a metal or dielectric screen that make up a diffraction grating, the array of scattering centers of a crystal for x-rays, and the arrays of reflectors and directors in a microwave antenna.

Diffraction does not include plane waves moving along a transmission line, unobstructed waves in free space, reflection by an infinite plane mirror, or refraction at an infinite plane surface between two dielectrics. These cases of wave propagation not included in diffraction have been treated by use of Maxwell's equations and suitable boundary conditions. There is much current activity to derive the more common cases of diffraction of sound and electromagnetic waves from general differential equations of wave motion. This often involves the fine art of making good approximations in order to make the results meaningful or usable. This theoretical work is being accompanied by experimental checks of special cases particularly with microwaves of the most convenient wavelength for each of the cases. We may expect the subject of diffraction to be in a more satisfactory state within the next generation. In any event the classical cases treated in the following four chapters must be satisfied by any general treatment of diffraction.

Francesco Maria Grimaldi discovered in 1666 that the shadows cast by rods and circular apertures of light from a pinhole source were wider than predicted from the geometry of rays, and that the edges of the shadows had colored fringes. Newton discussed Grimaldi's observations in the queries and proposals for experiment in his *Third Book of Optics*. A century and a half later Young and Fresnel independently explained diffraction on the assumption that light was wave motion. For the past century and a half Fresnel's methods have been in general use. Both Young and Fresnel added the concept of interfering continuous waves to Huygen's principle of secondary wavelets.

9.2 Fraunhofer Diffraction

Fraunhofer diffraction is a special case of Fresnel diffraction in which the source and observer are both an infinite distance from the diffracting object. Thus only plane wave fronts are treated. An effective device for putting the source and observer at opposite infinities is the familiar student spectrometer with its collimator and telescope. We shall obtain a running start in the study of diffraction by treating this very special but practical case of Fraunhofer diffraction. One application is spectroscopy. Joseph Fraunhofer is known to the elementary student as the one who first resolved the yellow lines of sodium, and to the astronomer as the discoverer of the black absorption lines in the continuous spectrum of the sun.

9.3 Diffraction by a Single Slit

We wish to determine the amplitude and phase of the wave at the cross hair of the telescope of a spectrometer when a parallel beam from the collimator falls normally on the plane of the slit of Fig. 135. In Fresnel's theory the secondary continuous waves from every point in the aperture combine to yield the wave at the point of observation. We shall assume an unperturbed wave with constant amplitude and phase over the plane of the aperture. If the slit is infinitely long, the problem is two dimensional and can be represented by plane geometry. We may divide the slit into strips of equal width Δs. From each of these strips is radiated a secondary cylindrical wavelet.

We shall assume as did Fresnel that, if θ is small, the amplitude of the cylindrical wavelet arriving at the point of observation is independent of θ. That is, the obliquity factor is constant. Since the difference in distance that the cylindrical wavelets travel is negligible compared to the total distance, the distance factor in the amplitude is also constant. Thus we may combine the obliquity factor and distance factor in a constant k. The amplitude is proportional to the width of the strip Δs. Since the path differences are of the order of wavelengths, we must express a phase angle δ. If we take a cylindrical wavelet from the center of the slit as reference, δ expresses the lag of the wavelet from strip Δs behind that from the center.

$$\delta = \frac{2\pi s \sin \theta}{\lambda}.$$

The complex amplitude of the cylindrical wavelet arriving at the point of observation is thus

$$\mathbf{du} = ke^{-j\delta}\, ds.$$

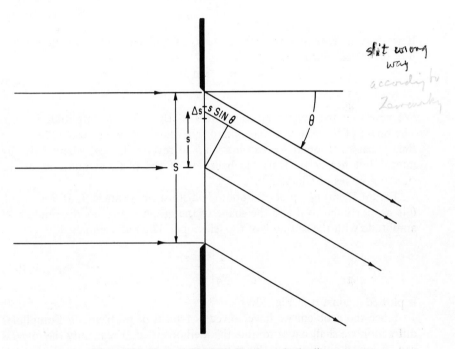

Figure 135. Fraunhofer diffraction by a single slit.

As the number of strips is increased without limit, the width Δs is replaced by the infinitesimal ds. We shall let β be the phase lag of the wavelet from the top of the slit behind that from the center. If S is the slit width,

$$\beta = \frac{\pi S \sin \theta}{\lambda}. \tag{9.1}$$

As in previous problems of interference we shall let the phase angle be the independent variable.

$$d\delta = \frac{2\pi \sin \theta}{\lambda}\, ds.$$

The resultant amplitude of the wave at the cross hair when the axis of the telescope makes angle θ with a ray from the collimator is

$$\mathbf{u} = \frac{k\lambda}{2\pi \sin \theta} \int_{-\beta}^{\beta} e^{-j\delta} \, d\delta = \frac{jk\lambda}{2\pi \sin \theta} (e^{-j\beta} - e^{j\beta}).$$

Expressing in trigonometric form and substituting from Eq. (9.1), we obtain

$$\mathbf{u} = kS \frac{\sin \beta}{\beta}.$$

If we take as reference the amplitude $\mathbf{u}_0$ at the center of the pattern when $\beta = \theta = 0$, $\mathbf{u}_0 = kS$, and

$$\frac{\mathbf{u}}{\mathbf{u}_0} = \frac{\sin \beta}{\beta}. \tag{9.2}$$

We note that the imaginary component of the complex amplitude is zero. The phase of the resultant wave jumps alternately between zero and π every time β passes through $N\pi$ causing $\sin \beta$ to reverse in sign, where N is any integer but not zero. Thus the behavior of the phase reminds us of the standing waves of Chapter V.

Figure 136(a) is a plot of amplitude against phase angle β. If θ is small, θ is proportional to β and the shape of the graph represents distribution of amplitude with the setting θ of the telescope. The relative intensity

$$\frac{I}{I_0} = \left| \frac{\mathbf{u}}{\mathbf{u}_0} \right|^2 = \frac{\sin^2 \beta}{\beta^2} \tag{9.3}$$

is plotted against β in Fig. 136(b).

Since the problem we have solved is typical of problems in Fraunhofer diffraction we shall pause to note the methods used. Frequently the integral can be solved only numerically or by vector addition of complex amplitudes. In numerical integration the number of strips Δs must be finite. Figure 137 indicates the vector sum of the complex amplitudes when the slit is divided into ten strips. If $\beta = \theta = 0$, the ten rotating vectors are in phase and their sum is unity. Thus the lengths of each of the complex amplitudes is 0.1. For the case $\beta = 45°$ the phase of a wavelet from a strip Δs lags 9° behind that from the adjacent strip below it. Note that the reference vector was chosen as the direction of the complex amplitude of a wavelet from the center. The resultant amplitude obtained by adding the ten vectors is in phase with the reference vector which we always choose as real. We see that our arbitrary choice of the wavelet from the center as reference and thus of β as half the phase difference of wavelets from near the two edges was merely a convenience.

In the limit as Δs approaches zero and the number of strips becomes large, the vector addition becomes a smooth curve called a *vibration spiral*. Figure 138 shows the vibration spirals for β equal to $0°$, $45°$, $90°$, and $180°$. The resultant amplitudes are vectors from the origin to the ends of the spirals.

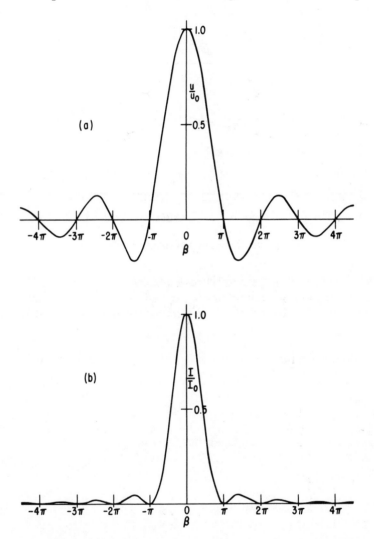

Figure 136. Amplitude and intensity of diffraction pattern of a single slit.

In elementary treatments of diffraction by a single slit we have been concerned only with the positions of the dark bands. This is the case in which the vibration spirals are complete circles. If we number 16 strips from bottom to top of the slit of Fig. 139(a), we note from the complex spiral in Fig. 139(b) that the condition for the first minimum is that wavelet 1 cancel with 9, 2 with 10, 3 with 11, and so on until all the wavelets have canceled. Thus the first minimum occurs when $\sin \theta = \lambda/S$.

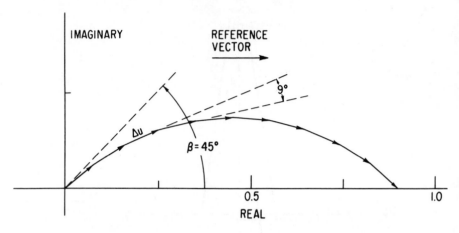

Figure 137. Vector sum of complex amplitudes.

If θ is small and θ_1 is the angular position of the first minimum, $\theta_1 = \lambda/S$. This inverse relation between the angular spread in the diffraction pattern and the width of slit is beautifully illustrated by the diffraction pattern of a

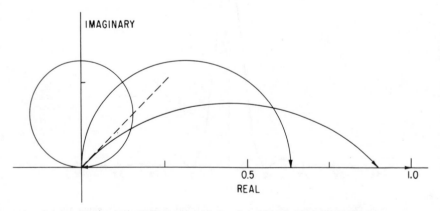

Figure 138. Vibration spirals for $\beta = 0°$, 45°, 90°, and 180°.

rectangular aperture whose height is about twice that of the width. In this case the angular spread of the vertical diffraction pattern will be half that of the horizontal, as shown in Fig. 140.

The relative intensity in the diffraction pattern of a rectangular aperture[1,2] is expressed by

$$\frac{I}{I_0} = \frac{\sin^2 \beta_1}{\beta_1^2} \frac{\sin^2 \beta_2}{\beta_2^2},$$ (9.4)

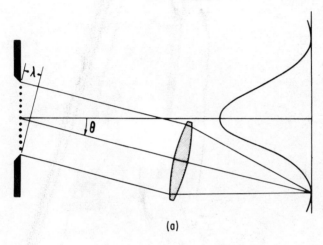

(a)

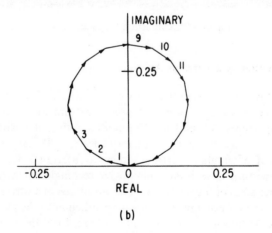

(b)

Figure 139. Treatment of Fraunhofer diffraction by cancellations when the vibration spiral is a complete circle.

where β_1 is half the phase difference between cylindrical wavelets from near the sides of the aperture, β_2 half the phase difference between wavelets from

[1] M. Born, *Optik:* Ann Arbor, Michigan, Edwards Brothers Inc. (1943) Sec. 48.
[2] B. Rossi, *Optics:* Reading, Mass., Addison-Wesley (1956) Secs. 4–5.

near the top and bottom, and I_0 is proportional to the square of the area of the aperture.

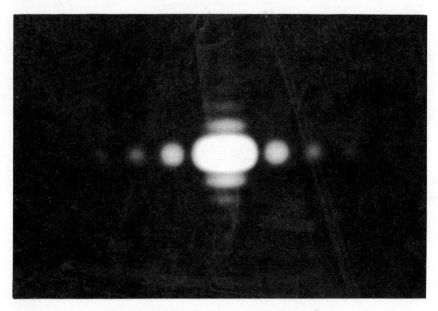

Figure 140. Diffraction by a rectangular aperture.

9.4 Diffraction by a Circular Aperture

One of our concerns in the study of Fraunhofer diffraction of apertures is to find the resolving power of optical instruments many of which have circular apertures. To find the Fraunhofer diffraction pattern of a circular aperture, we may retain the geometry of Fig. 135, Δs being the width of segments of a circular aperture shown in Fig. 141. The segments of the circular aperture have been replaced by rectangles of areas approximately equal to the areas of the segments. The amplitude of a wavelet from a segment reaching a distant point in the plane perpendicular to the plane of the aperture and including line AB is proportional to the area of the rectangular segment. If h_N is the height of one of the segments numbered from left to right, the amplitude of the wavelet from the segment is

$$\Delta u = kh_N e^{-j\delta}\, \Delta s,$$

where δ is defined as in the treatment of the slit in the previous section.

Although this problem has been solved in terms of tabulated Bessel functions of the first order[3,4], it also provides a simple example in numerical integration. Similar cases involving numerical integration are reserved for the problems. The measured heights each times $k \, \Delta s$ of the ten sections numbered from bottom to top of Fig. 141 are as 0.054, 0.090, 0.109, 0.121, 0.126, 0.126, 0.121, and so on. Since the amplitude is to be compared with that at the

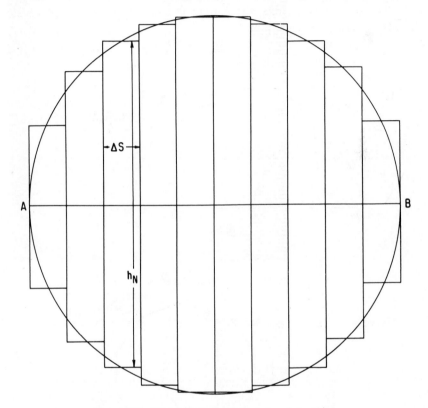

Figure 141. Division of circular aperture into strips.

center of the pattern, the scale is so chosen that the sum of the heights times $k \, \Delta s$ is unity. Figures 142(a) and 142(b) are summations of the complex amplitudes to give the resultant phases and amplitudes for the cases $\beta = \pi/2$ and $\beta = \pi$ compared to the similar summations of complex amplitudes of wavelets from a slit. Since the resultant complex amplitude is real for all values of β, we gain simplicity by adding the real components of each of the elemental amplitudes, or still greater simplicity by adding the real components

[3] Born, *op. cit.*, Sec. 49.
[4] J. Morgan, *Introduction to Geometrical and Physical Optics:* New York, McGraw-Hill (1953) Sec. 13.2.

of the first five elements and multiplying by two. Figure 143 is a plot of the relative intensities against β compared to that of a slit. The intensities are the squares of the amplitudes obtained by the methods indicated. For the circular aperture, the amplitude is zero when

$$\beta = 1.22 \times \pi, \quad 1.11 \times 2\pi, \quad 1.08 \times 3\pi, \quad 1.06 \times 4\pi.$$

Since the aperture is a circle, the pattern is made up of circles of which Fig. 143 is a cross-sectional plot.

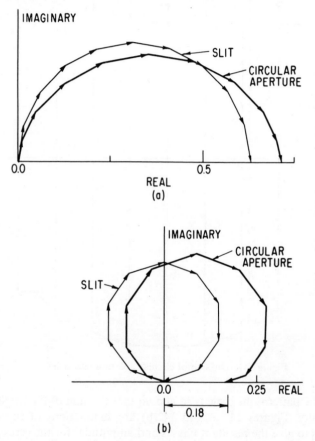

Figure 142. Summation of complex amplitudes for circular aperture compared with that for a slit.

9.5 Minimum Angle of Resolution

If we draw two fine parallel lines 3 mm apart on the blackboard of a lecture room and ask those who see but one line to raise their hands, the hands go up beyond an arc about 8 m from the lines. We shall define the

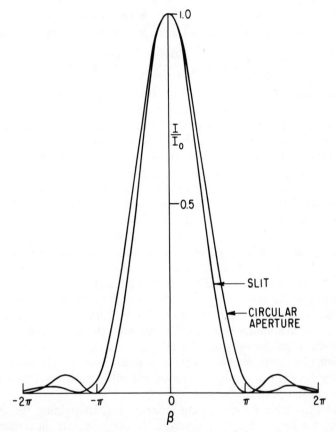

Figure 143. Plot of the relative intensities against β for a circular aperture compared with that for a slit.

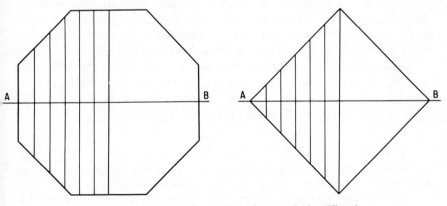

Figure 144. Apertures for problems in Fraunhofer diffraction.

minimum angle of resolution α of the eye as the smallest angle that the line of distance between the two lines subtends at the eye for the lines to be just resolved.

$$\alpha = \left(\frac{0.3}{800}\right) \text{ radians} \frac{360 \text{ deg}}{2\pi \text{ radians}} \times \frac{60 \text{ min}}{\text{deg}} = 1.3 \text{ min.}$$

The minimum angle of resolution is about 1'. Interestingly, 1' is also the approximate angle that the distance between two adjacent cones on the retina of the eye in the region of the fovea subtends at the center of the eye lens. If the images of two sources fall on the same cone, they can not be distinguished. The retinal record is *discontinuous in space*, made up of "grains" like a photographic print. To be sure, in the psychological process of seeing we fuzz the picture over making it continuous. We can not put back details that are not in the retinal record. Sometimes imperfections in the lens are responsible for the limitation on the resolution of the eye. The discontinuity of the retinal record in space as well as the *discontinuity* of the retinal record *in time*, together with the psychological process by which we interpret both as continuous, must be left to textbooks of physiological and psychological optics.[5,6] When the iris is small as in a bright light, the minimum angle of resolution may be limited by the diffraction patterns of the images of the points. It is interesting to note the economy of nature. If the cones which receive the light stimulus were smaller and more closely packed, there would be no gain in resolution since the minimum angle of resolution would be determined by the diffraction patterns of point sources. The lower limit on the minimum angle of resolution of most optical instruments is the diffraction pattern of each point in the source.

Lord Rayleigh set a convenient criterion for determining the minimum angle of resolution due to diffraction. If the principal maximum of the diffraction pattern of one point source falls on the first minimum of the diffraction pattern of another point source, the two points are just resolved. If the sources are brought 20% closer together angularly, the resultant diffraction pattern looks like that of one point source. If they are separated by 20% more than that of the Rayleigh criterion, the diffraction patterns are easily distinguished. The three cases are indicated in Fig. 145.

Figure 146(a) indicates the intensity distribution in the diffraction patterns of two angularly neighboring stars that are just resolved by the telescope with a slit opening of width S. Since angle α is small, $\sin \alpha$ may be replaced by α and $\alpha = \lambda/S$. If the aperture is circular,

$$\alpha = \frac{1.22\lambda}{D} \tag{9.4}$$

[5] Helmholtz, *Treatise on Physiological Optics:* Trans. from German ed. in 1924, Ed. by J. P. C. Southall. Published by the Optical Society of America.

[6] A. L. Linksz, *Physiology of the Eye*, 3 vols.: New York, Grune and Stratton (1952) Vol. II, Sec. II.

as found in the previous section, where D is the diameter of the aperture. Since the central ray through a lens is undeviated, the diffraction pattern in the focal plane of the lens or parabolic reflector is the same as that of the aperture without lens or reflector. The small angle α is equal to x/f. Thus we obtain

$$x = \frac{1.22f\lambda}{D},$$

where f is the focal length of the lens placed in the aperture. Figure 146(b) is a series of photographs of the diffraction patterns of two distant point sources produced by a lens as the distance between the centers of the patterns is increased. Problems are included to indicate the importance of the resolution concept for different parts of the spectrum. Current literature will indicate the increasing resolving power of electron microscopes, x-ray microscopes, and microwave telescopes. The large light telescopes are limited in resolving power by the variable index of refraction in the atmosphere rather than by the diameter of the aperture. The larger lenses and parabolic mirrors are used to gather more light energy.

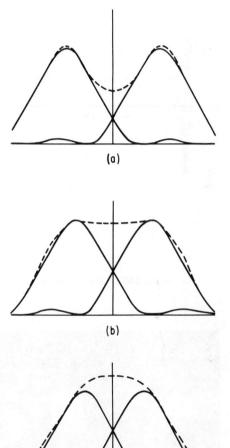

(a)

(b)

(c)

Figure 145. Superimposed diffraction patterns of a single slit. (a) Separated 20% more than Rayleigh criterion. (b) Just resolved by Rayleigh criterion. (c) 20% closer than Rayleigh criterion.

9.6 Chromatic Resolving Power of a Prism

Another application of diffraction by a single slit or rectangular aperture is the determination of the chromatic resolving power $\lambda/\Delta\lambda$ of a prism. The prism is set in the spectrometer in Fig. 147 to give the minimum angle of deviation δ for a given wavelength. Light from the source slit S is focused as an image at point P. The slit image is a diffraction

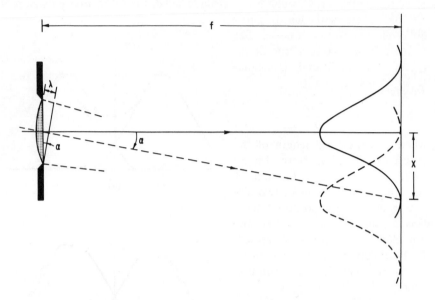

Figure 146(a). Diffraction patterns of two stars that are just resolved.

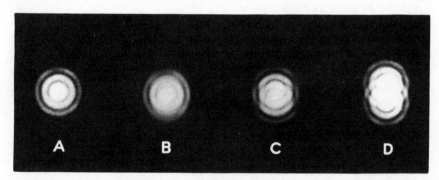

Figure 146(b). Photographs of diffraction images. (a) Single distant point object. (b) Two distant point objects whose diffraction patterns are separated by a distance equal to half the radius of the central disk. (c) Two distant point objects when separation is equal to the radius of the disks. (d) Two distant point objects when separation is equal to twice the radius of the disks. (Hardy and Perrin, *Principles of Optics*: New York, McGraw-Hill Book Company, Inc., 1932. Photographs by A. C. Hall; used by permission.)

pattern with first minimum at P'. Another beam of shorter wavelength will be focused with its maximum at P' and a first minimum at P. By the Rayleigh criterion these two wavelengths are just resolved. The shorter wavelength is deviated more than the other by angle $\Delta\delta$, CE is the wave front for either wavelength entering the prism, and HG and HG' are wave fronts for the longer and shorter wavelengths emerging from the prism. The fronts make the same angle $\Delta\delta$ with each other, as do the rays. The two rays from F reaching P and P' have path differences $HG \times \Delta\delta$, where HG is

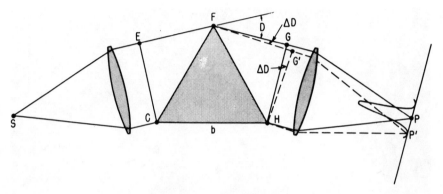

Figure 147. Chromatic resolving power of prism.

an effective slit width. From the treatment of the single slit the path difference $HG \times \Delta\delta$ must be 1 wavelength. The effective slit width may be determined by (1) the size of the lens, (2) the size of an optical stop in the telescope, (3) the dimensions of the prism.

We shall treat the last case. The optical path lengths for any one wavelength are the same for all rays from S to P. Thus

$$nb = EF + FG,$$

where n is the index of refraction of the material of the prism for the longer wavelength, and $n + \Delta n$ for the shorter wavelength. Likewise

$$(n + \Delta n)b = EF + FG + \lambda.$$

Subtracting the first from the second equation, we obtain

$$\Delta nb = \lambda. \tag{9.5}$$

If we divide both sides of the equation by the difference in the two resolved wavelengths $\Delta\lambda$,

$$\frac{\Delta n}{\Delta\lambda} b = \frac{\lambda}{\Delta\lambda}.$$

For the small difference in wavelength the graph of n against λ may be considered a straight line between the two wavelengths so that the chromatic resolving power of the prism is

$$\frac{\lambda}{\Delta\lambda} = b\frac{dn}{d\lambda}. \tag{9.6}$$

The dependence of the chromatic resolving power upon the effective base b of the prism may be demonstrated with a student spectrometer that resolves the sodium D lines. If a vertical adjustable slit is inserted to adjust the width

Figure 148. Microwave spectrometer with prism of polystyrene.

HG, the effective base is proportional to HG. As the width of the slit is decreased the diffraction patterns of the lines widen until they can no longer be resolved.

The rate of change of index of refraction of a medium with wavelength $dn/d\lambda$ is called its *dispersion*. The refractive index and dispersion of materials as they vary throughout the electromagnetic spectrum will be treated in Chapter XV.

Figure 148 is a photograph of a microwave spectrometer with prism of polystyrene, where b is but 4 wavelengths so that the approximations of

Eq. (9.6) do not apply. However, the difference in index of refraction Δn of the two wavelengths that could just be resolved is given by Eq. (9.5).

$$\Delta n = \frac{\lambda}{b} = 0.25.$$

With a monochromatic source this spectrometer serves for measuring indices of refraction to two significant figures. Its value is in demonstrating the low chromatic resolving power as b approaches one wavelength.

9.7 Diffraction by a Double Slit

In performing Young's double-slit experiment in the elementary laboratory, we make the individual slits so narrow that only the central portion of the principal maximum of the diffraction pattern of the individual slits appears in the field of view. In this more general treatment of Fraunhofer diffraction by a double slit, the slits may have any width so that we shall find the single-slit diffraction pattern superposed on the double-slit pattern.

In deriving the intensity distribution we shall employ the methods used in the single-slit study. The reference will be a cylindrical wavelet that would proceed from the center of the system if the center were not covered, where δ expresses the lag of the cylindrical wavelet from strip Δs behind the wavelet from the center of Fig. 149:

$$\delta = \frac{2\pi s \sin \theta}{\lambda}.$$

The complex amplitude of the cylindrical wavelet arriving at the point of observation is

$$\mathbf{du} = k e^{-j\delta} \, ds.$$

The symbols are those used for a single slit, where β is half the phase difference between wavelets from the two edges of a slit and γ is half the phase difference of wavelets from corresponding points distance d apart in the two slits. If a is the slit width,

$$\beta = \frac{\pi a \sin \theta}{\lambda}, \tag{9.7}$$

and

$$\gamma = \frac{\pi d \sin \theta}{\lambda}. \tag{9.8}$$

As in the previous problems of interference, we shall let the phase angle be the independent variable.

$$d\delta = \frac{2\pi \sin \theta}{\lambda} \, ds. \tag{9.9}$$

The resultant complex amplitude at the cross hair when the axis of the telescope makes angle θ with a ray from the collimator is

$$\mathbf{u} = \frac{k\lambda}{2\pi \sin \theta} \int_{\gamma-\beta}^{\gamma+\beta} (e^{-j\delta} + e^{j\delta}) \, d\delta.$$

The first term expresses lag of wavelets from the upper slit and the second the

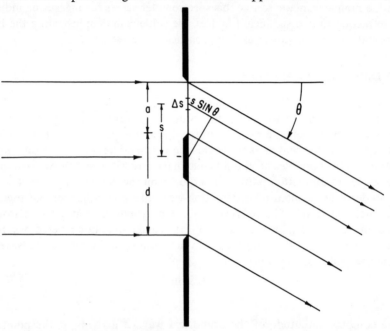

Figure 149. Fraunhofer diffraction by a double slit.

lead of wavelets from the lower slit. If we perform the integration and express the result in trigonometric form,

$$\mathbf{u} = \frac{k\lambda}{\pi \sin \theta} [\sin (\gamma + \beta) - \sin (\gamma - \beta)].$$

Using a trigonometric identity and substituting from Eq. (9.7), we obtain

$$\mathbf{u} = 2ka \frac{\sin \beta}{\beta} \cos \gamma.$$

If we take as reference the amplitude $\mathbf{u}_0$ of the wave from one of the slits at the center of the pattern when

$$\beta = \theta = 0, \qquad \mathbf{u}_0 = ka,$$

and

$$\frac{\mathbf{u}}{\mathbf{u}_0} = 2 \frac{\sin \beta}{\beta} \cos \gamma. \tag{9.10}$$

Equation (9.10) expresses algebraically the vector sum of the complex amplitudes **Δu** reaching the cross hair from each element Δ*s*. This vector addition may be plotted in the complex space of Fig. 150. The arc of the circle is the same vibration spiral as drawn for a single slit in Fig. 138 when the phase difference between wavelets from near the two edges was $\pi/2$. The dotted and solid regions of the arc are proportional to the open and opaque

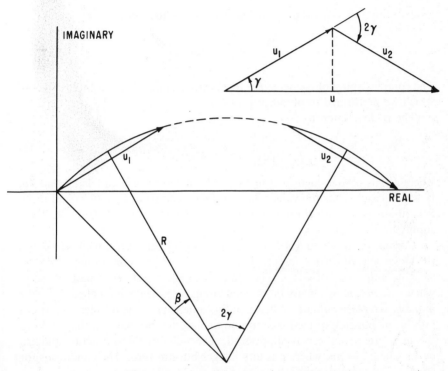

Figure 150. Vibration spirals for a double slit.

widths of the slit system. The vibration spirals for each of the slits are arcs of length $\mathbf{u}_0$. The resultant amplitudes $\mathbf{u}_1$ and $\mathbf{u}_2$ from each of the slits are cords of the two parts of the vibration spiral, where $\mathbf{u}_1$ and $\mathbf{u}_2$ differ in phase by 2γ. The phase of the waves from the two slits is the same as the phases of wavelets from the centers of the corresponding slits. The amplitude **u** of the resultant wave is found in the upper right-hand corner of the figure. Its magnitude is

$$\mathbf{u} = 2\mathbf{u}_1 \cos \gamma,$$

and its phase is γ ahead of $\mathbf{u}_1$ and γ behind $\mathbf{u}_2$. If we construct radii R from the center of the circular vibration spiral, the angles between two radii are the phase angles between elements of complex amplitude Δu represented by small cords of arcs at the outer end of the radii. The arc

$$u_0 = 2\beta R.$$

The cord

$$u_1 = 2R \sin \beta = u_0 \frac{\sin \beta}{\beta} .$$

Substituting this expression for u_1 in the above equation for u, we obtain

$$\frac{u}{u_0} = 2 \frac{\sin \beta}{\beta} \cos \gamma.$$

The complex spiral of elements Δu represents graphically the complex algebra which we performed to obtain Eq. (9.10).

The relative intensity

$$\frac{I}{I_0} = \left| \frac{u}{u_0} \right|^2 = 4 \frac{\sin^2 \beta}{\beta^2} \cos^2 \gamma, \tag{9.11}$$

where I/I_0 is plotted against β in Fig. 151 for the cases γ equals 2β and 4β, in which cases d has the values $2a$ and $4a$ as seen from Eqs. (9.7) and (9.8). Sets of slit pairs with d ranging from $2a$ to $6a$ are available from scientific supply houses.[7,8]

Cosine γ is the Young's *interference* factor in Eq. (9.10), while $\sin \beta/\beta$ is the single-slit *diffraction* factor. The factor $\sin \beta/\beta$ may be thought of as a variable amplitude of $\cos \gamma$. The maxima in the interference pattern occur when $\gamma = m\pi$, m being any integer including zero. Here m is called the *order in the interference pattern*. When a null of intensity in the diffraction pattern falls at the position of the maximum in the interference pattern, that order in the interference pattern is suppressed. The nulls in the diffraction pattern occur when $\beta = p\pi$, where p is any integer but not zero. The conditions for suppressing order m in the interference pattern by minimum p in the diffraction pattern may be obtained by dividing Eq. (9.8) by Eq. (9.7) and substituting the required values of β and γ.

$$\frac{m}{p} = \frac{d}{a} .$$

In Fig. 151(a) the first zero in the diffraction pattern suppresses the second order in the interference pattern when $d = 2a$, and in Fig. 151(b) the first minimum in the diffraction pattern suppresses the fourth order in the interference pattern when $d = 4a$.

[7] Central Scientific Co., Chicago, Ill.

[8] The National Press, Palo Alto, Calif. Designed by Chapman and Meese, *Am. J. Phys.*, **25**, 135 (1957).

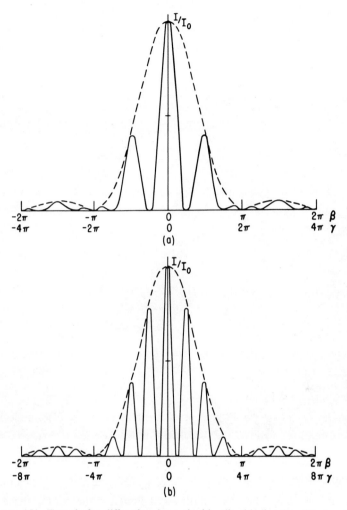

Figure 151. Fraunhofer diffraction by a double slit. (a) $d = 2a$; (b) $d = 4a$. The broken line represents the diffraction envelope.

9.8 Double Slit with Microwaves

Figure 152 is a photograph of a microwave spectrometer with a double slit mounted on the table.[9] Slits are made by painting silver paint or sticking aluminum foil on a manila folder. The dipole antennas of the source and receiver are at the focal points of the parabolic reflectors which serve as

[9] C. L. Andrews, *Am. J. Phys.*, **23**, 495 (1955).

telescope and collimator. The widths of the sources are small compared to a wavelength, which is frequently assumed in diffraction theory but rarely achieved with light. The importance of the size of slit sources will be discussed in Sec. 9.10. Figure 153(a) and (b) are plots of relative intensity I/I_0 for ratios of spacing between common points in the two slits to slit widths equal to 2 and

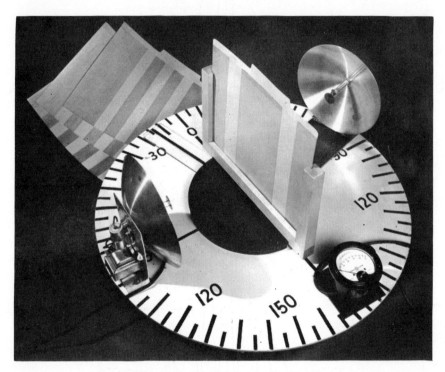

Figure 152. Double slit for microwaves.

4, where I_0 is the intensity at $\theta = 0$ when the slit screen was removed from the spectrometer table. The wavelength was 4.5 cm and the grating space of each 16 cm. The open space was 8 cm wide for the first and 4 cm for the second.

9.9 Two Sources, Michelson's Stellar Interferometer

If light from two distant point sources such as two stars falls on a double slit as in Fig. 154, the intensities of the two interference patterns at any point are added. Since the two primary sources are not coherent the light from these two sources will not interfere. If the distance between the slits is large compared to the slit widths, the intensity of the interference pattern will vary as $\cos^2 \alpha_1$ for a given wavelength. A filter may be used to give a narrow range

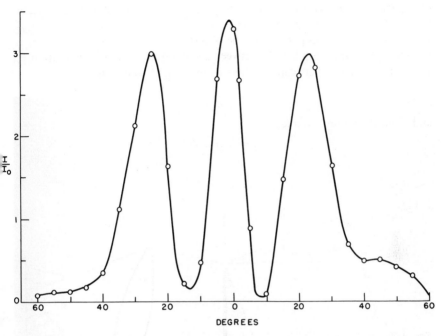

Figure 153(a). Two-slit microwave diffraction pattern $d/a = 2$, open space 8 cm wide.

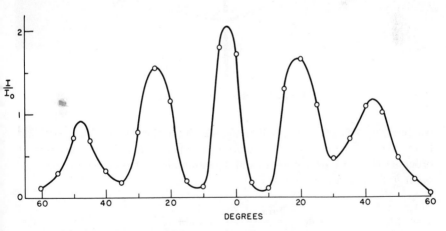

Figure 153(b). Two-slit microwave diffraction pattern $d/a = 2$, open space 4 cm wide.

of spectrum. If the stars are of equal brightness and the maxima of one pattern fall on the minima of the other, the sum of the two intensities will be everywhere constant and no pattern will be observed. Since the rays from the two stars have the same path lengths between a slit and the point of observation P, the path differences between two rays from the first source are

$$\Delta_1 = \alpha_1 d + \theta d,$$

and from the second source

$$\Delta_2 = \alpha_2 d + \theta d,$$

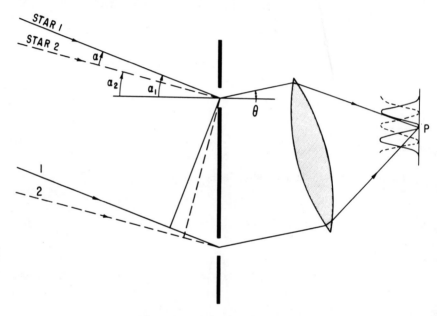

Figure 154. Stellar interferometer.

where α_1, α_2, and θ are the small angles which the rays make with the normal to the plane of the slit, and d is the distance between slits. If the maximum of order m for star 1 falls at point P, and the minimum next after the maximum of order m for star 2 also falls at P,

$$\delta_1 = \frac{2\pi(\alpha_1 + \theta)d}{\lambda} = m2\pi,$$

$$\delta_2 = \frac{2\pi(\alpha_2 + \theta)d}{\lambda} = (2m + 1)\pi.$$

Subtracting the first equation from the second, we obtain

$$\frac{2\pi d}{\lambda}(\alpha_2 - \alpha_1) = \pi.$$

Here $\alpha_2 - \alpha_1$, which is the angle between rays from two stars reaching a slit, we shall call α. Thus

$$\alpha = \frac{\lambda}{2d}. \qquad (9.12)$$

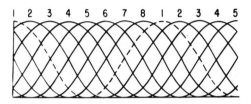

Figure 155. Superposition of diffraction patterns from a continuous source.

If the minimum next beyond $m + N$ in pattern 2 falls at the maximum of order m of pattern 1,

$$\delta_2 = \frac{2\pi(\alpha_2 + \theta)d}{\lambda} = (2m + 2N + 1)\pi,$$

and $$\alpha = \frac{(2N + 1)\lambda}{2d},$$

where N is an integer or zero.

The method may be used to measure the angular separation of double stars if the two stars lie in a plane perpendicular to the slits. The distance d between slits is made adjustable and d reduced to the smallest value that will cause fadeout, so that Eq. (9.12) for which $N = 0$ is employed.

Fizeau (1868) suggested that the method be used to measure stellar diameters by placing the two slits over the objective of a telescope, but it remained for Michelson to perform the first measurements on stars after practicing on Jupiter's moons.

We wish to determine the conditions for fadeout of the superposed interference patterns if the source is continuous as is the surface of a moon of Jupiter. May we first consider a moon that presents a square face with two sides parallel to the slits. If the surface of the satellite is divided into eight strips parallel to the double slits, and the interference pattern by the double slits for each of the eight sources is considered, the peaks of intensity must be evenly spaced as indicated in Fig. 155. The peaks are numbered corresponding to the sources. Note that peak 8 lies close to peak 1. As the surface of the source is divided into more strips, the maximum corresponding to a strip source near one edge must lie on the maximum for a strip source from the opposite edge. Thus the angular separation of the edges to produce fadeout for the continuous source must be twice as great as for the two point sources. Thus the smallest angle that will give fadeout is

$$\alpha = \frac{\lambda}{d}. \qquad (9.13)$$

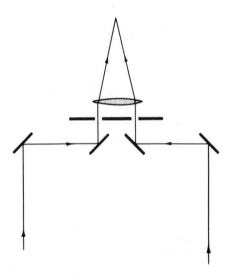

Figure 156. Michelson's stellar interferometer.

For a circular disc presented by a star the strips of different length do not each give the same intensity, so that the angle α which the diameter subtends at the earth is

$$\alpha = 1.22\frac{\lambda}{d}.$$

Assuming that the near stars are not much larger than our sun and knowing their distance from the earth by parallax methods, Michelson estimated that the largest angular diameters were less than 0.1″, so that the required spacing d would be greater than the diameter of the largest telescope. Michelson ingeniously devised the mirror system shown in Fig. 156 to increase the distance d.

Michelson's 20 ft stellar interferometer and the later 50 ft stellar interferometer at Mt. Wilson are described in books of interferometry.[10,11] Angular diameters of many stars which are near enough that interferometry may be employed have been measured to thousandths of seconds.

9.10 Size of Source

In making studies of diffraction by a slit or sets of slits, the observer soon learns to adjust the primary source slit until the pattern is most satisfactory. A compromise is made between sufficient illumination and sharpness of pattern. We are prepared now to explain these cut-and-try adjustments. In the previous section we showed that the first fadeout occurs when

$$\alpha = \frac{\lambda}{d}.$$

This is true for the small angles involved in Fraunhofer diffraction. In general, whether the angles be large or small,

the first fadeout occurs when the maximum of order m of the interference pattern of light from one edge of the primary slit falls on the maximum of order m + 1 in the interference pattern of light from the other edge.

These observations of Fraunhofer diffraction may be made either with a spectrometer or long optical bench. A spectrometer is more convenient since the observer may adjust the hand screw of the source slit while looking into the eyepiece. If with a double slit on the spectrometer table we slowly open the slit of the collimator from the closed position, the interference pattern first becomes brighter, and then when $\alpha = \lambda/d$ the bright field becomes continuous. If the slit is opened still farther, the interference pattern appears again, though not so distinct as before because it is superimposed upon a uniform light background. As the slit source is opened still farther the illumination becomes uniform again. The second and third appearance of the interference patterns are largely academic. The source width for best visual measurements is roughly half that for the first fadeout.

Figure 157 is a diagram of an optical bench arrangement for which the distance D from the source to the double slit is 1000 times greater than the width S of the source and the distance d between the double slits. This is a good approximation of Fraunhofer diffraction. The rays are all nearly normal to the slit plane so that $\alpha = S/D$. Since $\alpha = \lambda/d$ for the first fadeout,

$$\frac{S}{D} = \frac{\lambda}{d}.$$

[10] C. Candler, *Modern Interferometers:* Glasgow, Scotland, Hilger and Watts, Ltd. (1951) Chap. X.

[11] W. E. Williams, *Applications of Interferometry:* London, Methuen and Co., Ltd, (1930).

The inverse relation between the width of the source slit and the spacing of the double slit may be tested with the standard sets of double slits or with a variable-spacing double slit cut as a small angle V.

When we studied standing microwaves at oblique incidence with the electric field polarized perpendicular to the plane of incidence, Sec. 5.6, we found no limit to the angle of convergence of interfering rays. If the source and point of observation of Fig. 157 are brought near the double slit as shown in Fig. 158, there is no limit to the angle ϕ for which secondary rays with electric field polarized perpendicularly to the plane of the intersecting

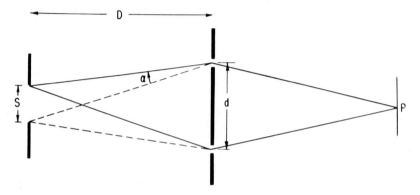

Figure 157. Arrangement for studying effect of size of primary slit.

rays will interfere. However, because of overlapping of interference patterns of light from the extended source S, there are limits to the angle of divergence θ of rays from a point on the source for which an interference pattern can be observed. This limit in θ is dependent on the width S of the source. To insure that there be no coherence between points in the source, we shall use a self-luminous source instead of a slit. We wish to express the conditions for the first fadeout at P in terms of S and θ. The condition for fadeout of the superposed interference patterns is that the minima in the interference pattern of waves from near one edge of the source fall upon the maxima in the pattern of waves from the center. Let P be the position of the central maximum in the interference pattern of light from the center of the source. For the first fadeout to occur at P, the path difference $D_2 - D_1 = \lambda/2$. For a clear interference pattern, $D_2 - D_1 = \lambda/4$. If we construct a perpendicular from the upper edge of the source to the line of length D between the center of the source and the upper slit, the angle between this perpendicular and plane of the source is $\theta/2$. If S is small compared to D, D_1 is less than D by $S \sin (\theta/2)$ and D_2 is greater than D by $S \sin (\theta/2)$. Thus $D_2 - D_1 = 2S \sin (\theta/2)$. The condition for a sharp interference pattern is that $2S \sin (\theta/2)$ be not greater than $\lambda/4$. If S is less than $\lambda/8$, an interference pattern may be observed when the angle of divergence θ approaches 180°. The cross-sectional diameter of a microwave dipole is usually less than 0.1 wavelength. Microwave interference patterns at P are readily demonstrated when θ is 170°.

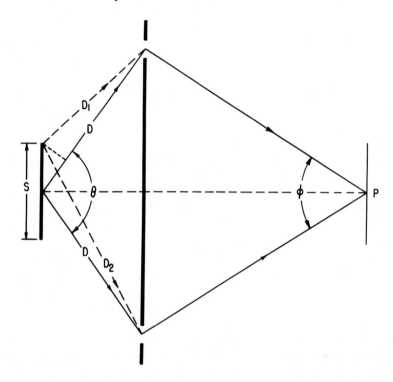

Figure 158. Effect of angle of divergence from primary source upon clarity of interference pattern.

PROBLEMS FOR CHAPTER IX

9.3.1. Prove that the maxima in the intensity of the diffraction pattern of a single slit occur when $\tan \beta = \beta$.

9.3.2. Interpret Eq. (9.2) to explain why the two minima nearest the center of the pattern are twice as far apart as any other consecutive minima.

9.3.3. Construct the vibration spiral and determine the amplitude of the resultant wave of a long slit for the cases β equal to 30° and 60°.

9.4.4. Find the relative amplitude u/u_0 of the Fraunhofer diffraction pattern of the octagonal aperture of Fig. 144(a) in a plane perpendicular to the plane of the aperture and including line AB for the case $\beta = \pi$. Divide the area into 12 strips of equal width Δs by lines perpendicular to AB.

9.4.5. Find the relative amplitude u/u_0 of the Fraunhofer diffraction pattern of the square aperture of Fig. 144(b) in a plane perpendicular to the plane of the aperture, and including the line AB for the case $\beta_d = \pi$. Define β_d as one-half the phase difference between wavelets from the ends of the diagonal. Divide the area of the aperture into twelve strips of width Δs.

9.5.6. At what distance can the human eye resolve the millimeter marks on a white plastic ruler?

9.5.7. Haga and Wind found that x-rays were waves and measured the approximate wavelength by passing a parallel beam through a slit about 0.001 mm wide. If the angular width of the central maximum was about 50″, what was the wavelength?

9.5.8. If a light telescope with a 10 cm aperture were mounted on a space platform above the atmosphere, what would be its minimum angle of resolution for light of wavelength 6×10^{-5} cm?

9.5.9. What must be the diameter of a microwave telescope for studying the shape of the spirals of our galaxy by the famous 21 cm wavelength line of hydrogen if the minimum angle of resolution is to be $1.0°$?

9.6.10. If the dispersion $dn/d\lambda$ for crown glass in the region of the sodium D lines is -0.43×10^{-5} A^{-1}, what size $60°$ prism must be used in a student spectrometer to resolve those two spectral lines? Their wavelengths are 5890 A and 5896 A.

9.7.11. A double slit is desired for Young's experiment in the elementary laboratory for which the single-slit diffraction pattern will not appear in the field of the eyepiece. What must be the ratio of width of slit to distance between centers of slits in order that the sixth order be the first to be suppressed?

9.9.12. A two-slit screen with adjustable space between slits is placed in front of the objective of a small telescope and the space adjusted for the first fadeout of the interference patterns of two distant automobile headlights. The headlights are 4 ft apart. A yellow filter transmitting a maximum intensity at 6000 A is placed in front of the slits. The first fadeout of the interference patterns occurs when the distance between slits is 1.8 cm. How far away is the automobile?

chapter X

Diffraction Grating

10.1 Measurement of Wavelengths with Gratings

Fraunhofer (1823) extended Young's double-slit experiment to many slits in parallel, and measured wavelengths to one part in 2000. He showed experimentally that the angular deviation of a spectral line was independent of the width of either the open or opaque space, but only on the sum of the two widths. He found the wavelengths proportional to the deviations of the spectral lines for small angles in what we now call the *linear spectrum*, but the wavelengths were proportional to the sine of the angle in the more general case including large angles. These relations, discovered experimentally by Fraunhofer, we shall derive in the following sections. Fraunhofer's first gratings were made by winding fine wire closely on two screws and removing every other wire. He also ruled gratings on glass.

Sixty years later Henry Rowland performed an engineering feat in building a ruling engine for cutting gratings on glass and metal with which wavelengths could be measured to another order of magnitude. The mechanical details and development of the theory of aberrations by Rowland are described in detail with photographs by Candler.[1] Harrison[2] has introduced a revolutionary technique of letting the interference pattern of a Michelson interferometer continuously control the ruling engine.

[1] C. Candler, *Modern Interferometers:* London, Hilger and Watts, Ltd, (1951) Chaps. XV–XVIII.

[2] G. R. Harrison, N. Sturgis, S. C. Baker, and G. W. Stroke, *J. Opt. Soc. Amer.*, **47**, 15 (1957).

Figure 159 indicates the use of gratings across the spectrum: (1) reflection gratings at glancing angle or crystals for x-rays, (2) curved gratings to focus as well as diffract the ultraviolet, (3) transmission gratings ruled on glass for the visible, (4) wire transmission gratings for the far infrared, (5) microwave gratings of metal strips, and (6) evenly spaced parabolic receivers in a row a few hundred feet long with cables of adjustable length to lead the radio waves to a common point. We shall consider the common features of these gratings in the following sections.

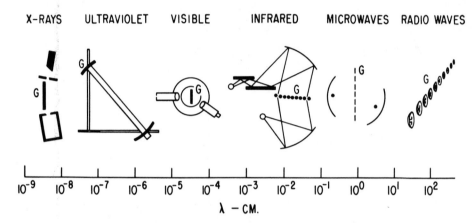

Figure 159. The use of gratings across the spectrum.

10.2 Fraunhofer Diffraction by a Grating

In deriving the intensity distribution produced by a grating at the cross hair of the telescope we shall employ the methods used in the double-slit study. We shall treat an even number of slits. The reference will be a cylindrical wavelet that would proceed from the center of the system if the center were not covered, where δ expresses the lag of the cylindrical wavelet from strip Δs behind the wavelet from the center of Fig. 160.

$$\delta = \frac{2\pi s \sin \theta}{\lambda}.$$

The complex amplitude of the cylindrical wavelet arriving at the point of observation is $du = ke^{-j\delta}\, ds$ as in Chapter IX. As the number of strips is increased without limit the width Δs is replaced by the infinitesimal ds. The symbols are those used for the double slit, where β is half the phase difference between wavelets from the two edges of a slit and γ is half the phase difference of wavelets from corresponding points distance d apart in the two slits. If a is the slit width,

$$\beta = \frac{\pi a \sin \theta}{\lambda}, \tag{10.1}$$

and

$$\gamma = \frac{\pi d \sin \theta}{\lambda}. \tag{10.2}$$

We shall let the phase angle be the independent variable.

$$d\delta = \frac{2\pi \sin \theta}{\lambda} ds. \tag{10.3}$$

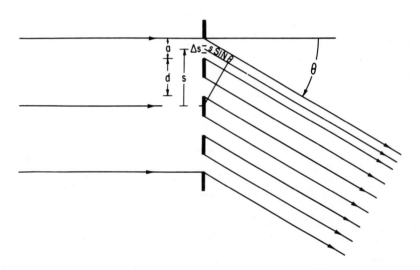

Figure 160. Fraunhofer diffraction by a grating.

The resultant complex amplitude at the cross hair when the axis of the telescope makes angle θ with a ray from the collimator is

$$\mathbf{u} = \frac{k\lambda}{2\pi \sin \theta} \sum_{n=1}^{n=N/2} \int_{(2n-1)\gamma-\beta}^{(2n-1)\gamma+\beta} (e^{-j\delta} + e^{j\delta}) \, d\delta. \tag{10.4}$$

The letter n is used to number the slit pairs from the center outward, and N is the total number of slits in the grating. The first term expresses the lag of wavelets from slits above the center and the second the lead of wavelets from slits below the center. If we integrate and separate the factors involving β and γ and substitute the value of β from Eq. (10.1),

$$\mathbf{u} = ak \frac{\sin \beta}{\beta} \sum_{n=1}^{n=N/2} (e^{j(2n-1)\gamma} + e^{-j(2n-1)\gamma}). \tag{10.5}$$

The two series may be expressed as a simple ratio,

$$\mathbf{u} = ak \frac{\sin \beta}{\beta} \left(\frac{e^{jN\gamma} - e^{-jN\gamma}}{e^{j\gamma} - e^{-j\gamma}} \right).$$ (10.6)

Expressing in trigonometric form and noting that ak is u_0 the amplitude of the wave from any one of the slits when $\theta = 0$ as defined in Eq. (9.2), we obtain

$$\frac{\mathbf{u}}{\mathbf{u}_0} = \frac{\sin \beta}{\beta} \frac{\sin N\gamma}{\sin \gamma}.$$ (10.7)

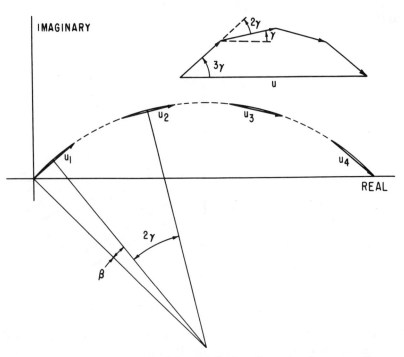

Figure 161. Summation of complex amplitudes of wavelets from a grating.

The complex amplitude is always real. The phase jumps alternately between zero and π every time the amplitude passes through zero.

Each step of the complex algebra which we have performed may be represented by geometry in complex space. We shall treat as example the case of four slits with the transparent and opaque portions of equal width. The four complex amplitudes represented by the cords $\mathbf{u}_1$, $\mathbf{u}_2$, $\mathbf{u}_3$, and $\mathbf{u}_4$ in Fig. 161 each have magnitude $u_0(\sin \beta/\beta)$ as proven from geometry in the treatment of the single slit. If we pair the wavelets from slits equidistant from the center of the grating, their phases with respect to a reference wavelet from the center of the system are odd multiples of γ. The phases of $\mathbf{u}_2$ and $\mathbf{u}_3$ are γ and $-\gamma$, and those of $\mathbf{u}_1$ and $\mathbf{u}_4$ are 3γ and -3γ.

Equation (10.4) from which Eq. (10.7) was derived was written for an even number of slits. The proof that Eqs. (10.6) and (10.7) also apply for an odd number of slits is retained for the problems.

The relative intensity is

$$\frac{I}{I_0} = \left|\frac{\mathbf{u}}{\mathbf{u}_0}\right|^2 = \frac{\sin^2 \beta}{\beta^2} \frac{\sin^2 N\gamma}{\sin^2 \gamma}. \tag{10.8}$$

We see that this checks with the special cases for one and two slits Eqs. (9.2) and (9.10) of the previous chapter.

10.3 Diffraction Pattern of a Grating

Equation (10.8), like its special case for two slits, is made up of two factors. The first factor represents the diffraction pattern of any one of the individual slits, and the second the interference of wavelets from all the slits as if they were each line sources. Figure 162 is a plot of the second factor $(\sin^2 N\gamma)/(\sin^2 \gamma)$, a case closely approximated when the slits are narrow compared to the space between them and $(\sin \beta)/\beta$ is approximately unity. Here $\sin \gamma$ becomes zero whenever $\gamma = m\pi$, m being an integer or zero. The numerator $\sin N\gamma$ becomes zero N times as frequently. When both numerator and denominator are zero the ratio is indeterminate and can be evaluated only in the limit as $\gamma \to m\pi$. By L'Hôpital's rule the limit of the ratio equals the limit of the ratio of the derivatives of the numerator and denominator with respect to the independent variable. Thus

$$\lim_{\gamma \to m\pi} \frac{\sin N\gamma}{\sin \gamma} = \lim_{\gamma \to m\pi} \frac{N \cos N\gamma}{\cos \gamma} = N.$$

Every time

$$\gamma = m\pi, \qquad \frac{\sin^2 N\gamma}{\sin^2 \gamma} = N^2,$$

where m expresses the order of the *principal maxima* for the particular wavelength. We recall that γ is half the phase difference between wavelets from corresponding points in adjacent slits

$$\gamma = \frac{\pi d \sin \theta}{\lambda} = m\pi.$$

Thus $m\lambda = d \sin \theta.$ \tag{10.9}

In elementary courses this expression for the angular positions of the orders was sufficient for an introduction to the diffraction grating.

Figure 162 indicates that the intensities of the principal maxima are proportional to N^2 and that the widths of the spectral lines at half maximum

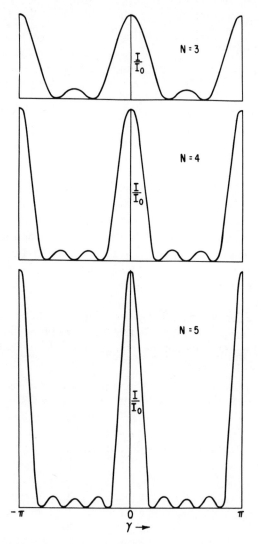

Figure 162. Diffraction patterns of gratings with 3, 4, and 5 narrow slits.

are inversely proportional to N. The latter will be a basis for the determination of the chromatic resolving power of a grating.

We are prepared to look at some secondary features to which a spectro-scopist must be alert. Here $\sin N\gamma$ passes through the value zero N times as frequently as sin γ so that there are $N-1$ zero values of intensity between the consecutive principal maxima. Between these zeros lie $N-2$ *secondary maxima* as seen in Fig. 162 for gratings of three, four, and five slits. These primary and secondary maxima are, of course, all of the same wavelength. A spectroscopist searching for very faint lines of other wavelengths close to a strong line must be certain that he is observing another wavelength and not a secondary maximum of the wavelength that is more intense. Since the principal maximum is roughly N^2 times as intense as the secondary maxima,

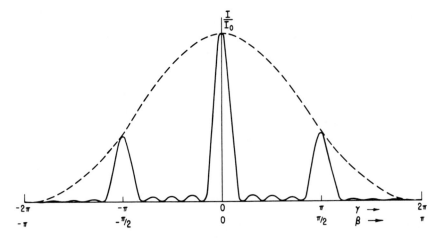

Figure 163. Second-order interference pattern suppressed by the diffraction pattern.

we can not expect to observe secondary maxima visually with gratings of 1000 lines. Sets of gratings on one plate ranging from two to six lines per grating are available from educational scientific supply companies. They are slid in succession across a student spectrometer or given in a kit to each of the students in a class to hold in front of the eye while looking at an incandescent lamp with straight filament covered with a red filter in the front of the room. They reveal clearly the secondary maxima. Computations of the intensities of a few secondary maxima either algebraically or by vector addition of amplitudes from each slit is retained for the problems.

Finally we must consider the diffraction factor $(\sin \beta)/\beta$ of Eq. (10.8). We have treated the case in which the width of open slit was small compared to the opaque space. Such a grating has low percentage transmission. The other extreme is a grating in which open and opaque spaces are equal when $d = 2a$ and $\gamma = 2\beta$. This is the case employed with wire gratings in the far infrared. The even orders in the spectrum are suppressed. Figure 163 is a plot of I/I_0 against both γ and β. We see how completely the first zero in the diffraction pattern of the single slit cancels the second order of the interference pattern. At each point in the curve the two factors of Eq. (10.8) are multiplied.

We note the wastefulness of the grating compared to a coated non-reflecting prism. The prism puts all the light in one spectrum. The grating not only splits the light between the right- and left-hand spectra for each order, but puts even greater intensity in the zero order where the wavelengths remain combined.

10.4 Chromatic Resolving Power

Figure 162 reveals how the spectral lines become narrower with increasing number of lines in the grating. The width of a line at half maximum is equal

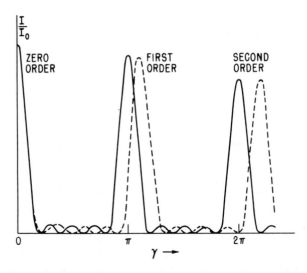

Figure 164. Spectral lines of second-order spectrum just resolved.

to the separation of the center of the principal maximum and an adjacent zero on the phase angle scale γ. The separation $\Delta\gamma$ of a principal maximum and adjacent zero is π/N, irrespective of the order of the spectrum. By the Rayleigh criterion two spectral lines are just resolved when the maximum of one falls on the adjacent zero of the other as shown in Fig. 145(b).

In Fig. 164 the second orders of two wavelengths, one indicated by solid and one by broken lines, are just resolved. The first order is not resolved. It appears from the graphs of Fig. 162 that the resolving power is proportional to the number of lines N in the grating, and from Fig. 164 that it is proportional to the order m. We shall proceed on this graphical hunch to solve for the chromatic resolving power $\lambda/\Delta\lambda$.

Taking the derivative of γ with respect to θ in Eq. (10.2), we obtain

$$\frac{d\gamma}{d\theta} = \frac{\pi d \cos \theta}{\lambda}.$$

If N is large, the finite elements $\Delta\gamma$ and $\Delta\theta$ between the two spectral lines are sufficiently small compared to γ and θ that

$$\frac{\Delta\gamma}{\Delta\theta} = \frac{\pi d \cos \theta}{\lambda} \tag{10.10}$$

to a good approximation. Taking the derivative of λ with respect to θ in the elementary grating expression of Eq. (10.9), we obtain

$$m \frac{d\lambda}{d\theta} = d \cos \theta.$$

Since the wavelength difference between the spectral lines that are just resolved when $\Delta\gamma = \pi/N$ is small compared to the wavelengths

$$m \frac{\Delta\lambda}{\Delta\theta} = d \cos \theta \tag{10.11}$$

to a good approximation. Solving for λ and $\Delta\lambda$ from Eqs. (10.10) and (10.11) and dividing, we obtain the chromatic resolving power of the grating

$$\frac{\lambda}{\Delta\lambda} = mN.$$

To attain high chromatic resolving power, we must make either the order m or the number of grating lines N large.

Because of the confusing overlapping of higher orders, large values of m are not employed in grating spectroscopy. For instance, in using a spectrometer for visible light, we note that the third-order green lines lie at larger angles θ than the second order of red. In using photographic methods outside the visible spectrum where color can not be distinguished, we find the overlap of orders even more confusing. Thus high resolving power in gratings is attained by making the number of lines N large. Gratings have been ruled with as many as 100,000 lines, giving in the second order a resolving power 200 times that needed to separate the D lines of sodium.

We might expect to eliminate the overlap of orders from a grating by studying only a narrow portion of the spectrum obtained from a prism spectrograph. Because of the depth of grooves of ruled gratings the intensity of the higher orders is even less than predicted from our simple slit theory. In succeeding sections of this chapter we shall study some ingenious devices related to the grating with which greater intensity is concentrated in a few higher orders.

10.5 Echelon Gratings, Use of High Orders

Michelson designed an echelon grating or stairs of glass blocks which concentrated the intensity in one or two high orders. The steps indicated in Fig. 165 were of thickness t 1 to 2 cm and grating space d about 0.1 cm. The

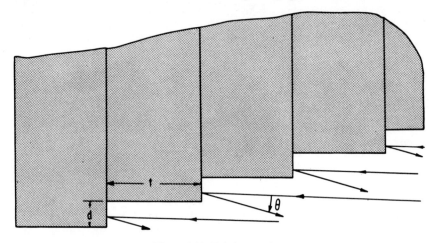

Figure 165. Echelon grating.

optical path differences of reflected beams from consecutive steps are many wavelengths, so that lower orders do not appear. We shall consider a modern echelon.

Williams[3,4,5] converted Michelson's echelon into an instrument that was useful from the far ultraviolet through the infrared by evaporating aluminum on the steps and making it a reflection instead of a transmission grating. To reduce effects of expansion due to temperature the blocks are made of fused quartz. They are ground as optical flats to 0.1 wavelength and made of uniform thickness to one part per million, all pieces being cut from the same flat. After they are squeezed together as clean optical flats and heated to near the fusion point they can not be separated, but behave like a solid block of quartz. Incidence is near normal and the angle θ is so small that the path difference between consecutive rays may be expressed

$$m\lambda = n_a(2t - \theta d),$$

[3] W. E. Williams, *Applications of Interferometry*, 4th ed.: London, Methuen (1950) p. 27.
[4] S. Tolansky, *An Introduction to Interferometry:* New York, Longmans (1954) Chap. XVI.
[5] Candler, *op. cit.*, Chap. XI.

where n_a is the index of refraction of the air. If λ is 5×10^{-5} cm and t is 1.0 cm, the order m observed is about 40,000. The number of steps N in echelon gratings is about 25. Thus resolving powers approaching 1 million are attained.

The advantage of the echelon grating over other instruments of high resolving power is the high intensity of the spectral lines. The diffraction pattern of a step of width d corresponds to the diffraction pattern of individual slits of a grating. This large width yields a narrow diffraction pattern that can contain in the envelope of its central maximum only one order of the interference pattern at its center. The interferometer is placed in a partially evacuated chamber. A change in the air pressure is used to change the optical path difference by small amounts so that one order in the interference pattern may be placed precisely in the center of the maximum of the diffraction pattern or two consecutive orders may be placed in the central diffraction envelope at the positions of half maximum. If the gas pressure is maintained constant, the optical air path is independent of temperature.

The Michelson-Williams echelon grating is more expensive and less flexible than the Fabry-Perot etalon. Echelons must be built for a particular portion of the spectrum. The spectral range of the etalon is changed by merely changing the length of the spacer pins. Thus the echelon may never compete with the etalon in the visible or near visible spectrum.

The reflection echelon has been used to measure wavelengths in the ultraviolet to as low as 1500 A to eight significant figures. Other interferometers can not be used in this region.

R. W. Wood[6] has shown how the transmission echelon may be transformed stepwise into a series of prisms of the same chromatic resolving power as the echelon. Unification of treatment of seemingly diverse instruments is desirable in a basic course. In the following section we shall note a similarity in the behavior of the plane grating and prism.

10.6 Oblique Incidence, Minimum Deviation

Thus far we have treated the diffraction grating for normal incidence. The succeeding sections of this chapter will include oblique incidence as well. If we watch a spectral line as the plane grating on the table of a spectrometer is rotated, we note one striking similarity to the spectrum of a prism. Any line on the side toward which the grating is being rotated will move through an angle of *minimum deviation* just as does a spectral line formed by a prism. The graphical plot of the angle of deviation δ against the angle of incidence i is similar to that for a prism. Figure 166 is a graph of the angle of deviation against the angle of incidence for the cases $d/m\lambda = 1$, 2, and 3. If the order $m = 1$, the grating spaces are 1, 2, and 3 wavelengths for the three curves.

[6] R. W. Wood, *Physical Optics,* 3rd ed.: New York, Macmillan (1934) p. 287.

We shall solve for the condition of minimum deviation. If a parallel beam is incident obliquely on a grating, the path difference through corresponding points of adjacent slits as they travel from collimator slit to cross hair is

$$m\lambda = d(\sin i + \sin \theta). \qquad (10.12)$$

As indicated by Fig. 167, i and θ are the angles which the incident and diffracted beams make with the normal to the grating. The angle of deviation

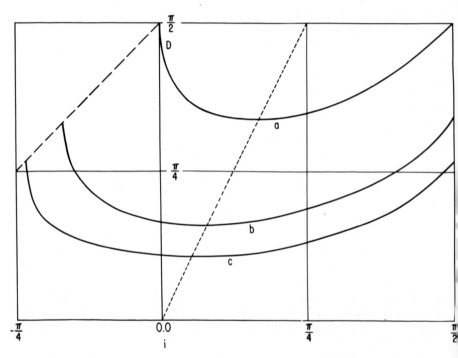

Figure 166. Minimum angle of deviation against angle of incidence for cases (a) $d/m\lambda = 1$, (b) $d/m\lambda = 2$, (c) $d/m\lambda = 3$.

δ is measured from the line of the incident beam, that is, the zero order, and θ is positive if it is in the direction the grating has been rotated from its position of normal incidence. We note from the geometry that

$$\delta = i + \theta. \qquad (10.13)$$

We may eliminate θ from the simultaneous Eqs. (10.12) and (10.13), and obtain

$$\frac{m\lambda}{d} = \sin i + \sin (\delta - i). \qquad (10.14)$$

If we take the derivative with respect to i and let $d\delta/di = 0$, we obtain the condition for the minimum angle of deviation

$$\delta = 2i \quad \text{and} \quad \theta = i.$$

The dotted line in Fig. 166, whose equation is $\delta = 2i$, intersects each of the graphs at the angle of minimum deviation.

The use of minimum deviation has two advantages. (1) It is experimentally simpler to set the grating for minimum deviation than at right angles to the

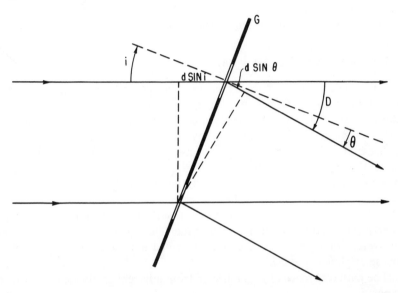

Figure 167. Oblique incidence on a grating.

beam. (2) Orders which are too faint to be seen when θ approaches $\pi/2$ under normal incidence can be observed easily at minimum deviation. In practice, only the middle two thirds of the curves of Fig. 166 are useful. At the extreme end the intensity is too faint and the chromatic resolving power is not so good as predicted from theory due to effects of depth in the ruling of the grating. A ruling with spacing d equal to a wavelength indicated by curve a of Fig. 166 would throw all its intensity in the zero order at normal incidence, but may be used to observe the first order on one side at minimum deviation.

Although minimum deviation is of academic interest in comparison of the grating and prism, it is not used by spectroscopists. In spectroscopy measurements of unknown wavelengths are made by comparison with standard spectral lines, in which case a spectrum is needed in which the wavelength varies linearly with distance along the photographic plate. Such a linear spectrum is attained most closely when the beam is incident normally on the grating.

The plane gratings of 10,000, 15,000, and 25,000 lines per inch for use in student spectrometers are all replica gratings made by spreading collodion or formvar over the grating as a mold and peeling it off. Since the coat shrinks, replica gratings have more lines per inch than the originals. The skill required in making good replicas is such that replicas are known by the names of the men who developed them, such as Wallace and Ives.

In this section we have discussed plane gratings for light which were of little value when angles i or θ were greater than 75°. In the next section we shall treat the opposite extreme of reflection gratings for x-rays which are useful only at angles of incidence close to 90°.

10.7 Reflection Gratings for X-Rays

Since the discovery of x-rays there have been continuous attempts to apply optical methods to that part of the spectrum. One feature of x-rays is different from that generally observed for light. Its index of refraction is less than unity. It differs from one by less than two parts per million. Each material has a critical angle for x-rays as it does for light. If light is incident internally on a clean glass to air surface at greater than the critical angle of incidence, the light is totally reflected internally. If x-rays are incident on a smooth surface at greater than the critical angle, they are totally reflected externally. Working with x-rays of wavelength 0.7 A, Compton and Doan[7] observed specular reflection at angles of incidence greater than 89.5°. Having discovered total external reflection, they ruled a grating on speculum metal for use at glancing angle.

The path difference of rays reflected from adjacent grating spaces distance d apart is

$$m\lambda = BD - AC = d(\cos \alpha - \cos [\alpha + \beta])$$

as indicated in Fig. 168, where m is the order of the spectrum, α the glancing angle of incidence, and β the angle which a ray of that order makes with the specularly reflected ray of order zero. Since α and β are small, we may use the first two terms of the Maclaurin series expansion of $\cos \alpha$ and $\cos(\alpha + \beta)$ to obtain

$$m\lambda = d\left(\alpha\beta + \frac{\beta^2}{2}\right). \tag{10.15}$$

X-ray spectroscopy is usually performed with crystals, nature's own three-dimensional gratings, which we shall treat in a later section. The determination of the grating or lattice spaces of a crystal can not be performed with a microscope, but is made indirectly from fundamental constants of

---

[7] A. H. Compton and S. K. Allison, *X-Rays in Theory and Experiment:* New York, Van Nostrand (1935) pp. 22, 40, 690.

nature. The number of molecules in a crystal such as calcium carbonate is determined from Avogadro's number N, the number of atoms in a mole of the substance, and the molecular weight. Here N is in turn most precisely determined as a ratio

$$N = \frac{Q}{e},$$

where Q is the amount of electricity required to deposit 1 gram molecular weight in electrolysis, called the *faraday* of electricity, and e is the charge on the electron. Thus the determination of an x-ray wavelength with a crystal is dependent on the knowledge of the charge on the electron. If the x-ray

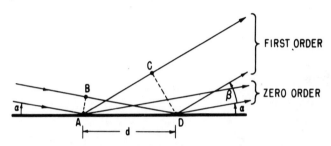

Figure 168. Grazing incidence of x-rays on a grating.

wavelength is measured with a grating, the calculations for the crystal measurements may be used to make an independent check of the charge on the electron. Currently the measurement of the charge on the electron by x-ray spectroscopy is determined to about one part in 5,000.

Osgood[8] extended the glancing angle grating method from 40 A to 200 A using a curved grating of glass. The curved gratings were like those developed by Rowland, which we shall discuss in the next section. Thus the method of the focusing reflection grating extends from x-rays to light. Osgood used glass because it is not so easily corroded as metals. A few irregular monolayers of corrosion would cause hills higher than a wavelength, greatly impairing the spectrum of the grating at glancing angle.

10.8 Focusing Reflection Gratings for the Ultraviolet

A major step in spectroscopy of the ultraviolet was taken when Rowland developed a spherical concave reflection grating. If we note that much of spectroscopy is performed by comparing higher orders of shorter wavelengths with first orders of longer wavelengths such as the red cadmium line or green line of the artificial iosotope of mercury, we appreciate two advantages of the

[8] T. H. Osgood, *Phys. Rev.*, **30**, 567 (1927).

concave grating. (1) The focusing grating replaces the two lenses of the plane grating spectrometer which are absorbers in the ultraviolet. For wavelengths shorter than 2000 A, lenses of quartz are too absorbing. (2) Concave mirrors have no chromatic aberration. Even the slight chromatic aberration of the best lens combinations is a serious handicap in spectroscopy, because neighboring lines of different orders and widely different wavelengths can not be focused simultaneously.

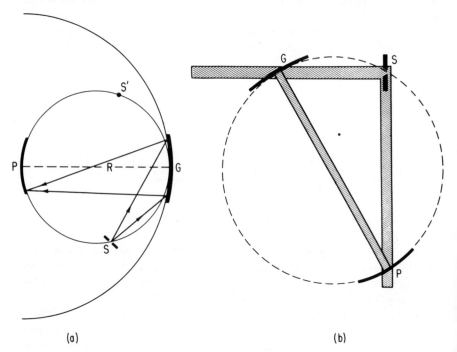

(a)   (b)

Figure 169. (a) Focusing reflection grating. (b) Rowland mount.

From geometrical optics we know that, if an object is placed at the center of curvature of a spherical concave mirror, the image also falls at the center and, if the arc of the mirror is large, the only positions of object which will not yield an image with spherical aberration is on a sphere whose diameter is the radius of curvature of the curved mirror indicated in Fig. 169(a). The image of a point source S falls on a circle obtained by intersecting the sphere with the plane of incidence. The image S' of slit S is the zero-order spectrum formed by the grating. Rowland showed by consideration of interference that all the orders of the diffraction pattern fall on this same circle, now known as the *Rowland circle*. That portion of the spectrum which falls near the normal to the center of the grating at position P of the photographic plate in Fig. 169(a) is a linear spectrum and thus convenient in spectroscopy for interpolating unknown wavelengths from standard wavelengths. Figure 169(b) is a sketch of the Rowland mount with grating G and photographic plate P mounted on opposite ends of a beam. The ends of the beam rest on carriages which move along two beams at right angles to each other. The source slit S is at a fixed position at the corner. The grating and photographic plate are moved together so that the plate falls at any order of spectrum on the Rowland circle. Thus with the Rowland mount any order taken is a linear spectrum. To yield sufficient dispersion so that the resolving power will not be limited by the grain of the photographic plate, Rowland mounts are often 20 ft long.

More compact spectrographs for reflection gratings mounted in evacuated chambers for use in the extreme ultraviolet are described in books of spectroscopy.[9,10] We have noted in the previous section a reflection grating developed by Osgood for use at glancing angle in the extreme ultraviolet and soft x-rays. Such a system would employ but a small portion of the Rowland circle, so that the spectrum would not be linear.

10.9 Echelette Gratings for the Infrared

A problem in infrared spectroscopy is to obtain sufficient intensity in a spectral line. A wire grating with spaces between the wires equal to the diameters of the wires transmits 50% of the incident light and suppresses all the even orders of the spectrum. However, as indicated in Fig. 163, the first order on one side is only 40% as intense as the useless zero order. We ask the question, "Does nature require as an immutable law that the zero order be more intense than the others, and that the intensity be equally divided between the right- and left-hand orders?"

In 1888 Lord Rayleigh showed how a reflection grating should be shaped to throw most of the energy in one order on one side. Twenty years later Wood[11] built such a grating for the infrared where the rulings are coarse and their shapes can be more easily controlled. Far infrared gratings have about one tenth as many lines per inch as those for light.

Figure 170 indicates such a grating. Corresponding points on the reflecting faces are distance d apart measured in the plane of the grating. The orders appear in the same angular positions for a grating with any shape of groove having the same periodicity of groove, index of refraction, or reflectivity. The width of face a determines the angular width of the single-slit diffraction pattern. Its center lies in the direction of the reflected ray, reflected by the law of specular reflection from a plane mirror. Angle ϕ is chosen to throw the

[9] R. A. Sawyer, *Experimental Spectroscopy*, 2nd ed.: Englewood Cliffs, N.J., Prentice-Hall (1951) Chap. 7.

[10] Candler, *op. cit.*, Chap. XVII, XVIII.

[11] R. W. Wood, *Phil. Mag.*, **20**, 770 (1910).

position of the central maximum in the diffraction pattern at the first order on one side in the interference pattern. The region of the central maximum in the diffraction pattern is called the *blaze* and the gratings sometimes called *blazed gratings*.

The best gratings for the infrared are ruled on gold with diamond. On such a soft metal the diamond point keeps its shape throughout the ruling process. The diamond moulds the gold instead of scratching out chips as it does on glass.

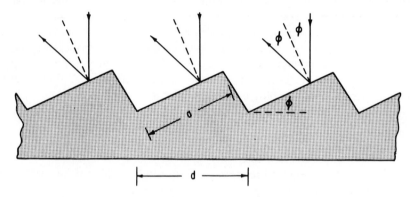

Figure 170. Echelette grating.

With the development of techniques of evaporation of aluminum films that adhere to glass, Wood[12] has ruled gratings with grooves of controlled shape for use in the visible spectrum which concentrate 75% of the incident mercury green light in the first order on one side. As a result of this gain in intensity, gratings have replaced prisms in astronomy for studying spectra of faint stars.

This blazed grating is generally called an *echelette*. We have noted three French names for interference devices sounding somewhat alike: the *étalon*, which is a French word for standard of length; *échelon*, which means stairs; and *échelette*, a word which has been coined for "little échelon" because it is somewhat like a miniature Michelson echelon. Harrison[13] has ruled blazed gratings of 100 lines per inch which he calls *échelles* because they are intermediate between the échelon and échelette.

It is a simple matter to demonstrate a blazed grating with microwaves. A Venetian blind with alternate slats removed is used with wavelengths of about 4 cm. The intensity meter is placed at the position of the first order on one side and the intensity plotted against the angle which the reflecting surfaces make with the grating plane.

[12] R. W. Wood, *J. Opt. Soc. Amer.*, **34**, 509 (1944).
[13] G. R. Harrison, *J. Opt. Soc. Amer.*, **39**, 522 (1949).

10.10 Fraunhofer Diffraction by Two-dimensional Gratings

We find by analysis of two- and three-dimensional gratings that we may generalize some of the conclusions from our study of one-dimensional gratings. For instance, an array of identically shaped and oriented transmitting apertures, reflecting objects, or phase altering objects will produce identical superposed Fraunhofer diffraction patterns. If a very large number of identical rectangular apertures with identical orientation in a plane screen

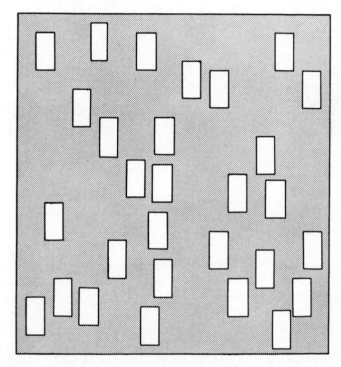

Figure 171. Randomly scattered identical apertures.

are randomly scattered about on the screen as indicated in Fig. 171, the interference pattern of the combination will be smoothed out to constant intensity, but the diffraction pattern will be identical with that of Fig. 140.

If the apertures are not quite identical in size or shape, the minima in the diffraction patterns are not zero. The blood corpuscles of a human are sufficiently uniform in diameter that Thomas Young was able to design a clinical device known as *Young's Eriometer*,[14] with which the mean diameters of blood corpuscles of different individuals are compared by measuring their diffraction rings.

[14] R. W. Ditchburn, *Light:* New York, Interscience Publishers, Inc. (1953) p. 171.

When identical diffracting holes or objects are periodically distributed in space, the interference pattern appears with the diffraction pattern as envelope. Beautiful Fraunhofer diffraction patterns of crossed gratings may be observed by looking through fine silk or bolting cloth, held close to the eye, at a point source such as an automobile headlight bulb a few feet away, first with white

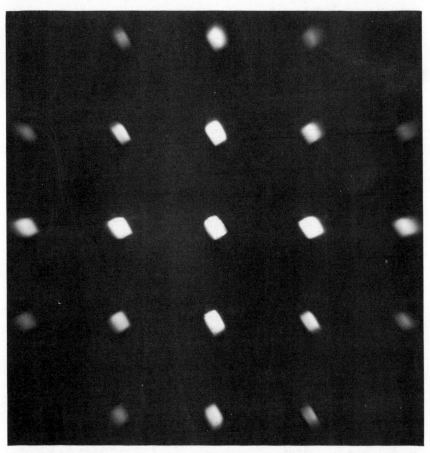

Figure 172. Diffraction pattern of the crossed grid of a microwave triode.

light and then with a red filter. Two diffraction gratings may be superposed in front of the eye, and one rotated with respect to the other so as to slowly change the angle between the rulings. Figure 172 is a photograph of the diffraction pattern of a crossed grid[15] for experimental high-frequency microwave triodes. The grids have 1000 lines per inch and 50% transmission.

[15] Grids may be obtained from Buckbee Mears Co., Saint Paul, Minnesota.

They are made by photographing precise drawings and nickel-plating the photographs.

For some years it has been engineering practice to use pairs of crossed photogrids coarser than diffraction gratings as a sensitive means of measuring (1) linear displacement, (2) rotation, and (3) strain in stress-strain relations.

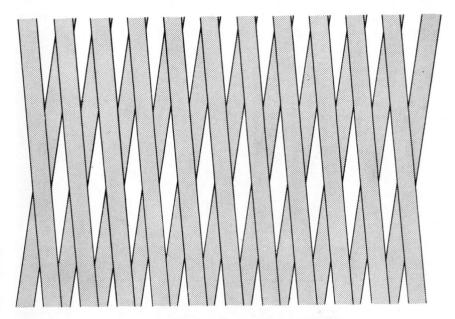

Figure 173. Shadow pattern of crossed photogrids.

With coarse gratings the patterns were essentially shadowgraphs, and only geometrical optics was employed. The patterns for perfect grids look like that of Fig. 173. If they are less perfect the lines of intersection are wavy, presenting the appearance of watered silk or two loosely mounted picket snow fences, one behind the other. Currently, finer gratings are being used for engineering problems, and physical optics of diffraction replaces geometrical shadow optics. Guild[16] has given a perspective of the scientific and engineering possibilities of crossed gratings in an analytical treatment of pairs of gratings crossed at all angles. The present most urgent use of crossed gratings is in an attempt to improve and rapidly test the best research gratings so that grating production may be taken out of the academic laboratory to large scale production in industrial laboratories. Guild treats the methods by which two replicas of a grating are superposed to study (1) progressive errors

[16] J. Guild, *The Interference Systems of Crossed Diffraction Gratings:* New York, Oxford University Press (1956).

in the ruling, (2) periodic errors, (3) accidental errors, (4) defects in parallelism, (5) defects in straightness of ruling, and (6) nonparallelism of surfaces.

We shall analyze only the special case of normal incidence upon a two-dimensional rectangular array of diffracting holes or objects. Figure 174 is a diagram of a portion of a rectangular crossed grating, the circles being transparent portions. These transparent portions lie along lines parallel to the Cartesian coordinates y and z. The incident rays are in the positive x direction. Instead of expressing the direction of the diffracted ray with

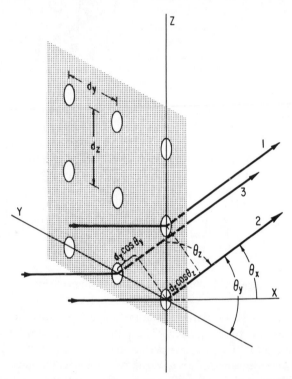

Figure 174. Normal incidence on a two-dimensional rectangular lattice.

respect to the normal as we did in treating a one-dimensional grating, we shall use the two-direction cosines between the rays and the y and z directions. The two-direction angles are θ_y and θ_z indicated in Fig. 174. Parallel diffracted rays on the opposite side of the screen from the observer are indicated by three heavy broken lines. Ray 2 lags ray 1 by $d_z \cos \theta_z$, and ray 3 lags ray 2 by $d_y \cos \theta_y$, where d_y and d_z are the lattice spaces.

From any row of secondary sources parallel to the y axis there are angles θ_y at which a set of parallel rays is all in phase as defined by the equation

$$d_y \cos \theta_y = m_y \lambda, \tag{10.16}$$

where m_y is any integer positive, negative, or zero. If the secondary wavelets are radiated in all directions, the plane of the parallel rays 2 and 3 may be rotated about the y axis to form cones. Any two parallel rays in the cones satisfy Eq. (10.16). Likewise, for any row of secondary sources parallel to the z axis there are angles θ_z at which a set of parallel rays are all in phase, defined by the equation

$$d_z \cos \theta_z = m_z \lambda, \tag{10.17}$$

m_z being any integer positive, negative, or zero. Also θ_z defines cones which

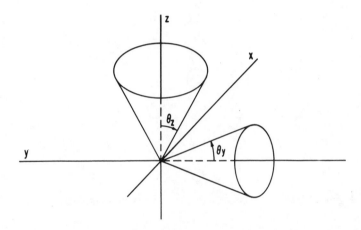

Figure 175. Cones defined by the direction angles.

are generated when the plane of the parallel rays 1 and 2 is rotated about the z axis. We shall now apply the two conditions simultaneously. If we simultaneously require that ray 1 be parallel to 2 and 2 parallel to 3, 1 is parallel to 3. However ray 1 may be parallel to 3 only if the two cones intersect. They can intersect if $\theta_y + \theta_z > \pi/2$, as seen from Fig. 175. These parallel rays from the secondary sources are in phase if they satisfy the simultaneous equations

$$\begin{cases} d_y \cos \theta_y = m_y \lambda \\ d_z \cos \theta_z = m_z \lambda. \end{cases}$$

For a given lattice and wavelength the directions in which the rays will be in phase are determined by a pair of integers m_y and m_z.

Figure 176 is a diagrammatic sketch near the normal of the diffraction pattern of the rectangular two-dimensional grating. The integers m_y are indicated at the tops of the columns and m_z at the right-hand side of the rows. Since the ratio d_z/d_y in the lattice was $\frac{4}{3}$, the ratio of z to y spacings in the diffraction pattern is inversely $\frac{3}{4}$. The sizes of the circles are a convenient way

of representing the relative intensities at the points of constructive interference. The relative intensities of the interference maxima are determined by
the diffraction pattern of the circular apertures. The transparent circles are
small enough that the suppressed orders lie outside the region shown in
Fig. 176.

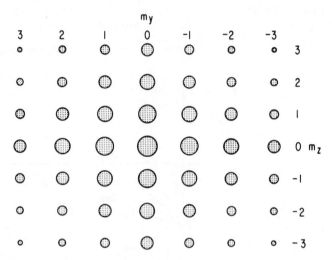

Figure 176. Diffraction pattern of a rectangular two-dimensional grating.

10.11 Fraunhofer Diffraction by Three-dimensional Gratings

The study of diffraction by three-dimensional gratings began on the day
that von Laue proposed to Friedrick and Knipping[17] that they look for an
interference pattern of x-rays transmitted through a natural crystal. Von Laue
analyzed diffraction by the three-dimensional lattice and laid the background
for x-ray crystallography.

He generalized the equation for the one-dimensional grating, showing
that there will be constructive interference between rays from the lattice of
scattering centers of a rectangular lattice if three simultaneous equations are

$$\left\{ \begin{array}{l} d_x(\cos \theta_x - \cos \phi_x) = m_x\lambda, \\ d_y(\cos \theta_y - \cos \phi_y) = m_y\lambda, \\ d_z(\cos \theta_z - \cos \phi_z) = m_z\lambda. \end{array} \right. \tag{10.18}$$

The cosines of ϕ_x, ϕ_y, and ϕ_z are the direction cosines of the incident beam of
x-rays made approximately parallel by collimating slits. Likewise θ_x, θ_y, and
θ_z are the angles between the diffracted beam and the rectangular coordinates;

[17] W. Friedrick, P. Knipping, and M. von Laue, *Ber. bayer. Akad. Wiss.*, 303 (1912).

d_x, d_y, and d_z are the lattice spacings; and m_x, m_y, and m_z are integers. When we treated the two-dimensional grating, the simultaneous equations were applicable only if the two cones of Fig. 175 defined by the direction angles intersected. For a three-dimensional grating the requirements are much more stringent. The three cones defined by the three direction angles θ_x, θ_y, and θ_z of the diffracted beam must not only intersect, they must intersect in a common line. This is possible only for special angles of incidence. Only then will Eqs. (10.18) have a common solution. From the one- and two-dimensional gratings we obtain diffraction patterns for any angle of incidence.

Figure 177 is a photograph of a Laue diffraction pattern. Since the Laue pattern is an array of points, photographic methods of detection are employed in crystallography. The kinds of lattice systems, their analysis, and the methods of x-ray crystallography are found in textbooks on x-rays.[18,19,20]

X-ray spectroscopy, which has revealed the energy levels of the inner, more closely bound electrons of the atoms, was introduced by W. H. Bragg, who first succeeded in obtaining reflection of x-rays from a cleavage face of a crystal. His son, W. L. Bragg, devised a simpler means of analysis of x-ray diffraction by crystals equivalent to that of von Laue.

There are but two conditions for Bragg diffraction. (1) Any set of equally spaced planes in a crystal, each containing a sufficient number of atoms as scatterers, acts as a set of mirrors for x-rays. Figure 178(a) shows a cross section of a cubic crystal with four series of planes.

The reflection is like that of geometrical optics in that the reflected ray is in the plane of incidence, and the angle of refraction equals the angle of incidence. It is unlike the reflections of geometrical optics in that reflection occurs only for discrete angles of incidence. (2) For constructive interference the beam must be incident on the set of planes at such a glancing angle θ indicated in Fig. 178(b) that

$$2d \sin \theta = m\lambda,$$

where d is the distance between planes and m is an integer.

Figure 179 is a diagram of a Bragg spectrometer. Since lenses can not be used with x-rays, collimation is accomplished with slits. The detector is an ionization chamber treated in Sec. 1.7.

Rock salt, calcite, gypsum, and mica are the commonly used crystals of x-ray spectroscopy. Cleavage faces of a few square centimeters are easily obtained. We note in Fig. 178(a) that those sets of planes with the greatest spacing d between planes have the greatest density of points in each plane. These are also the cleavage planes of the above four crystals and the planes

[18] B. D. Cullity, *Elements of X-Ray Diffraction:* Reading, Mass., Addison-Wesley (1956).

[19] A. H. Compton and S. K. Allison, *X-Rays in Theory and Experiment*, 2nd ed., New York, Van Nostrand (1934).

[20] W. H. Bragg and W. L. Bragg, *The Crystalline State*, 3 vols.: London, G. Bell (1953).

Figure 177. Laue diffraction pattern of magnesium oxide. (Courtesy of General Electric Research Laboratory.)

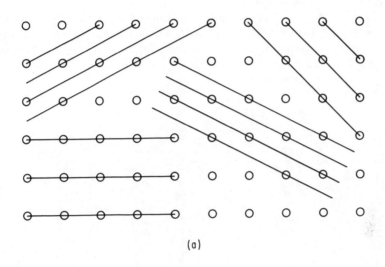

(a)

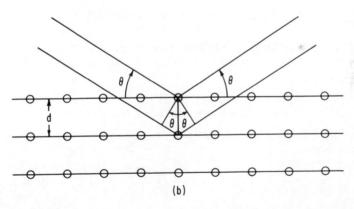

(b)

Figure 178. (a) Cross section of cubic crystal showing four sets of reflecting planes. (b) Condition for constructive interference of rays reflected from Bragg planes.

used in spectroscopy. The corresponding spacings for these crystals are 2.8 A, 3.0 A, 7.7 A, and 10.0 A, respectively, which are of the order of magnitude of the wavelengths of x-rays.

Scaling up a rock salt crystal by a factor of 1 billion to a cubical array of metal-covered balls held in the lattice by wooden dowels, Allen[21] developed a laboratory experiment in Bragg diffraction with microwaves of 12 cm wavelength. His measured Bragg angles for the first and second orders were within 1° of the calculated values.

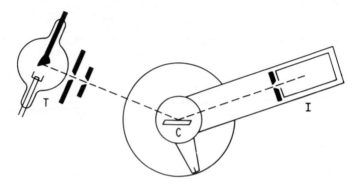

Figure 179. Bragg spectrometer.

PROBLEMS FOR CHAPTER X

10.2.1. Show that Eqs. (9.2) and (9.10) for the diffraction patterns of single and double slits are special cases of the diffraction pattern of a grating given by Eq. (10.7).

10.2.2. Perform the division $(e^{jN\gamma} - e^{-jN\gamma})/(e^{j\gamma} - e^{-j\gamma})$ for the case $N = 4$ and show that it is equal to the summation of Eq. (10.5).

10.2.3. The Fraunhofer diffraction pattern of a grating with an odd number of slits is given by

$$\mathbf{u} = \frac{k\lambda}{2\pi \sin \theta} \left[\int_{-\beta}^{\beta} e^{-j\delta} \, d\delta + \sum_{n=1}^{n=(N-1)/2} \int_{2n\gamma - \beta}^{2n\gamma + \beta} (e^{-j\delta} + e^{j\delta}) \, d\delta. \right]$$

The reference wavelet is taken at the center of the system. The first term is for the central slit, and the two summation terms for the slits above and below center. Show that Eq. (10.6) is equivalent to this relationship. Obtain a running start by first solving the special case when the number of slits N is 3.

10.3.4. Plot graphs for comparison of the interference patterns of two and three slits when $(\sin \beta)/\beta = 1$ similar to the graphs of Fig. 162.

[21] R. A. Allen, *Am. J. Phys.*, **23**, 297 (1955).

10.3.5. Plot a graph of the diffraction pattern of five slits between $\gamma = -3\pi$ and 3π for the case $d = 3a$.

10.3.6. Prove that the intensity of the secondary maximum for a grating of three slits is one-ninth that of the principal maximum.

10.3.7. Prove that for gratings with an odd number of slits the ratio of the intensity of the principal maximum to that of the secondary maximum midway between consecutive principal maxima is N^2.

10.3.8. Find the intensities of the secondary maxima for a grating of four slits relative to that of the principal maxima.

10.4.9. A grating of 15,000 lines/in. is used to observe the sodium D lines in the second order. How many lines of grating are required to just resolve these two yellow lines?

10.6.10. If the grating space d is one wavelength, what is the angle of minimum deviation for the first order?

10.7.11. A ruled grating on glass of 2000 lines/cm is used as a grazing angle grating for soft x-rays of 80 A. If the grazing angle α is zero, what angle does the first order make with the surface of the grating?

10.11.12. What must be the Bragg angle of glancing incidence of the aluminum K line, wavelength 8.320 A, upon mica to produce the first order? The lattice space of mica is 9.845 A.

chapter XI

Fresnel Diffraction

11.1 The Fresnel Method

In the previous two chapters we considered Fraunhofer diffraction, the effect of apertures and objects on waves when the source and point of observation were both an infinite distance from the diffracting object. In Fresnel diffraction the source and point of observation are in any position. Fraunhofer diffraction is a special case of Fresnel diffraction.

Observation of Fresnel diffraction does not require lenses. With a bright point source in one end of a dark room and needles, razor blade edges, and apertures mounted in the middle, we may observe their diffraction patterns on a ground-glass screen at the opposite end of the room. With no apparatus at all, we may squint between almost closed eyelids at the sky, and the corpuscles which are always floating across the front surface of the eyeball will cast diffraction rings on our retina giving the impression of "flying saucers" dashing across the sky.

Building upon Huygens' principle, Fresnel added the concept of continuous wavelets. He explained quantitatively many of his own observations on the assumption that

every point on an unperturbed wavefront is a source of continuous wavelets traveling out in all directions to determine the amplitude and phase at any point.

256

Diffraction in Fresnel's theory is not caused by the edge. The edge of the aperture in the hemispherical absorbing screen that fits over the spherical wave front of Fig. 180(a) is but the boundary of secondary sources. Fresnel's

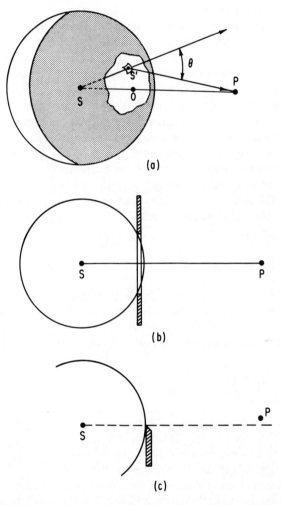

Figure 180. Fresnel diffraction. (a) Portion of wave front uncovered by an aperture. (b) Circular aperture. (c) Straight edge.

methods check with experiment satisfactorily if the angle θ between the direction of propagation of the wave to the secondary source S' and the direction of the wavelet from the secondary source to the point P of observation is small. It is particularly successful in two cases. (1) If source S lies on the axis of a circular aperture of Fig. 180(b) and $OP \gg D \gg \lambda$, Fresnel's

method predicts correctly the diffraction pattern on and near the axis, where
OP is the distance from the center of the aperture to the point of observation
and D is the diameter of the aperture. (2) His method yields the intensity near
the geometrical shadow of a straight edge, Fig. 180(c), at distances from the
edge which are large compared to a wavelength.

For many years Fresnel's methods were satisfactory for practical problems
with light. With the development of wide angle lenses for light, and the
advent of microwave optics with wavelengths so convenient that diffraction
patterns can be measured near and in the apertures themselves, we shall use
the more exact solution of Kirchhoff of which Fresnel's solution is a special
case. Kirchhoff solved the differential equation for scalar waves such as
longitudinal sound waves, letting the boundaries be the edges of an absorbing
screen. Kirchhoff's equation for scalar waves is applicable to electromagnetic
waves in those cases of symmetry in which polarization will not affect the
intensity such as positions along the axis of a circular aperture. Solutions for
transverse electromagnetic waves will be made in Chapter XII, employing the
methods of Thomas Young. Young treated the diffraction pattern as the
resultant of the unperturbed wave and continuous Huygens' wavelets
reradiated from the edges.

11.2 Kirchhoff's Method

Employing Green's theorem, Kirchhoff developed an exact formulation
of Fresnel's theory of diffraction. (See Appendix II.) For the case in which
the source S and point of observation P lie on the axis of a circular aperture
of a plane absorbing thin screen Kirchhoff's equation becomes

$$\frac{\mathbf{u}_P}{\mathbf{u}_0} = \frac{1}{4\pi} \int \int \left[\frac{2\pi j e^{-j\alpha}(1 + \cos\theta)}{\lambda r} + \frac{e^{-j\alpha}}{rr_S} + \frac{e^{-j\alpha}\cos\theta}{r^2} \right] d\sigma. \quad (11.1)$$

The complex amplitude of the unperturbed wave that has just reached the
boundary of the aperture, Fig. 181, is $\mathbf{u}_0$ and the resultant complex amplitude
at P is $\mathbf{u}_P$. The distance from the source to the wavefront is r_S. The distance
from the element of surface $d\sigma$ to the point P is r, where α is the phase lag of
the wavelet from element $d\sigma$ behind that from point O where the spherical
wavefront is intersected by the line SP, and θ is the angle between the ray
from S through $d\sigma$ and the ray from $d\sigma$ to P.

The terms of Eq. (11.1) represent three Huygens' wavelets spreading out
from each point. The amplitude of the first wavelet depends on three factors,
the area of element $d\sigma$, inversely as the distance r, and an obliquity factor
$1 + \cos\theta$. The second wavelet depends on the area $d\sigma$ and inversely on the
distance r. The third wavelet depends on area $d\sigma$, inversely as the square of r,
and on an obliquity factor $\cos\theta$. Figures 182(a) and (b) indicate by thickness

of the fronts the amplitudes of the first and third Huygens' wavelets in all directions.

When $r_S \gg \lambda$ and $r \gg \lambda$ the second and third terms may be omitted. If θ is always near zero as in the cases treated by Fresnel, the obliquity factor $1 + \cos\theta$ becomes 2. Fresnel's equation consisted of the phase factor and an amplitude factor, the latter being made up of area $d\sigma$, the inverse r, and a constant factor.

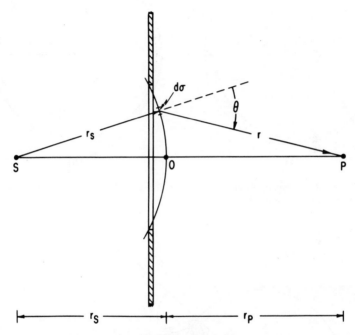

Figure 181. Geometry for determination of the diffraction pattern along the axis of a circular aperture by Kirchhoff's method.

Since we are concerned with all values of θ and r, we shall make a general solution for the intensity on the axis of a circular aperture by including all terms of the integral. As in previous interference studies, we shall let the phase angle α be the independent variable. From the symmetry we find it convenient to divide the area of the spherical wavefront into narrow zones by constructing spheres with centers at P to intersect the wavefront as indicated in Fig. 183. The area $d\sigma$ of this narrow ring surface or zone is the product of its circular length $2\pi r \sin\theta_P$ and its width $dr/\sin\theta$, where θ_P is the angle between SP and r.

$$d\sigma = \frac{\sin\theta_P}{\sin\theta} 2\pi r \, dr. \tag{11.2}$$

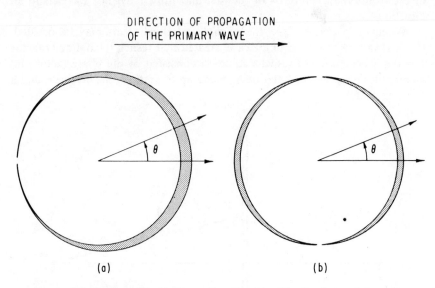

Figure 182. Huygens-Kirchhoff wavelets for (a) obliquity factor $1 + \cos\theta$, (b) obliquity factor $\cos\theta$.

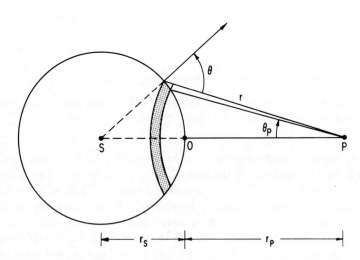

Figure 183. Secondary radiation from a narrow zone of a spherical wave.

From the sine law for triangles

$$\frac{\sin \theta_P}{\sin \theta} = \frac{r_S}{r_S + r_P}, \tag{11.3}$$

where r_S is the radius of the sphere about the source S, and r_P the radius of a sphere about P tangent to the spherical wavefront from S. The phase angle

$$\alpha = \frac{2\pi}{\lambda}(r - r_P), \tag{11.4}$$

and

$$d\alpha = \frac{2\pi}{\lambda} dr. \tag{11.5}$$

Substituting from Eqs. (11.3) and (11.5) in Eq. (11.2), we obtain

$$d\sigma = \left(\frac{r_S}{r_S + r_P}\right) \lambda r \, d\alpha. \tag{11.6}$$

Substituting this value for $d\sigma$ in Eq. (11.1) and letting α range from zero to β, which is determined by the circular aperture, we obtain the somewhat simpler expression

$$\frac{\mathbf{u}_P}{\mathbf{u}_0} = \frac{1}{2}\left(\frac{r_S}{r_S + r_P}\right) \int_0^\beta e^{-j\alpha} \left\{ j(1 + \cos \theta) + \frac{\lambda}{2\pi r_S} + \frac{\lambda \cos \theta}{2\pi r} \right\} d\alpha. \tag{11.7}$$

We note how the distance factor and area factor have cancelled from the first term leaving the obliquity factor as the only variable. This cancellation of the distance and area factors which appears so simply in Kirchhoff's equation was one of the theorems in Fresnel's original work.

Before we can integrate Eq. (11.7) analytically we must express the variables r and $\cos \theta$ in terms of the phase angle α. For convenience we shall replace the distances r, r_S, and r_P by phase angles of the expressions

$$\gamma = \frac{2\pi r}{\lambda}, \qquad \gamma_P = \frac{2\pi r_P}{\lambda}, \qquad \gamma_S = \frac{2\pi r_S}{\lambda}.$$

The phase angle

$$\gamma = \alpha + \gamma_P,$$

and

$$d\gamma = d\alpha.$$

If we let γ be the independent variable, the limits of integration are γ_P and $\beta + \gamma_P$. To determine $\cos \theta$, we may replace the triangle of distances of Fig. 184(a) by a triangle of phases, Fig. 184(b). From the cosine law for triangles,

$$\cos \theta = \frac{2\gamma_S\gamma_P + \gamma_P^2 - \gamma^2}{2\gamma_S\gamma}. \tag{11.8}$$

For simplicity we shall replace complicated constant factors by letting

$$A = \frac{1}{2}\frac{\gamma_S}{\gamma_S + \gamma_P}, \qquad B = \frac{\gamma_P(2\gamma_S + \gamma_P)}{2\gamma_S}, \qquad C = \frac{1}{2\gamma_S}, \qquad (11.9)$$

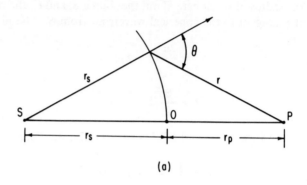

(a)

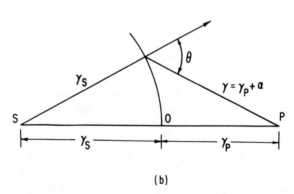

(b)

Figure 184. (a) Triangle of distances. (b) Triangle of phases.

so that Eq. (11.7) becomes

$$\frac{\mathbf{u}_P}{\mathbf{u}_0} = Ae^{j\gamma_P}\int_{\gamma_P}^{\beta+\gamma_P} e^{-j\gamma}\left[j\left(1 + \frac{B}{\gamma} - C\gamma\right) + \frac{B}{\gamma^2} + C\right]d\gamma. \quad (11.10)$$

Equation (11.10) may be most conveniently treated as three integrals,

$$\frac{\mathbf{u}_P}{\mathbf{u}_0} = A\left[e^{j\gamma_P}\int_{\gamma_P}^{\beta+\gamma_P} je^{-j\gamma}\,d\gamma + Be^{j\gamma_P}\int_{\gamma_P}^{\beta+\gamma_P}\left(\frac{j}{\gamma} + \frac{1}{\gamma^2}\right)e^{-j\gamma}\,d\gamma\right.$$

$$\left. + Ce^{j\gamma_P}\int_{\gamma_P}^{\beta+\gamma_P}(1 - j\gamma)e^{-j\gamma}\,d\gamma\right]. \quad (11.11)$$

The first integral becomes

$$A(1 - e^{-j\beta}).$$

The second may be integrated by parts. It is made up of two integrals of such form that if $w = e^{-j\gamma}$ and $v = -1/\gamma$,

$$\int v \, dw + \int w \, dv = vw.$$

Thus the second integral becomes simply

$$AB\left(\frac{1}{\gamma_P} - \frac{e^{-j\beta}}{\beta + \gamma_P}\right),$$

and the third yields

$$AC[(\beta + \gamma_P)e^{-j\beta} - \gamma_P].$$

We note that the second integral, which was integrated by parts, permitted cancellation of integrals. This cancellation could be performed only if all the terms of Eq. (11.7) were retained. The first term could be solved alone only by resort to infinite series and special cases. This is an example of a problem of which the whole is simpler than its parts.

Adding the results of integration, we obtain

$$\frac{\mathbf{u}_P}{\mathbf{u}_0} = A\left\{1 - e^{-j\beta}\left[1 + \frac{B}{\beta + \gamma_P} - C(\beta + \gamma_P)\right] + \frac{B}{\gamma_P} - C\gamma_P\right\}. \quad (11.12)$$

If we let ϕ, Fig. 185, be the upper limit of the variable direction angle θ as set by a circular aperture in a thin, absorbing spherical shell that just fits the wave, and replace the values of constants A, B, and C, we obtain

$$\frac{\mathbf{u}_P}{\mathbf{u}_0} = \frac{r_S}{r_S + r_P}\left[1 - \frac{1}{2}(1 + \cos\phi)e^{-j\beta}\right], \quad (11.13)$$

and the relative intensity is

$$\frac{I_P}{I_0} = \left|\frac{\mathbf{u}_P}{\mathbf{u}_0}\right|^2 = \left(\frac{r_S}{r_S + r_P}\right)^2\left[1 + \frac{1}{4}(1 + \cos\phi)^2 - (1 + \cos\phi)\cos\beta\right].$$

$$(11.14)$$

If Huygens-Kirchhoff wavelets are received at P from the whole spherical wave from S, then ϕ, the limiting value of θ, is π, and

$$\frac{I_P}{I_0} = \left(\frac{r_S}{r_S + r_P}\right)^2. \quad (11.15)$$

Since I_0 is the intensity of the unperturbed wave front shown in Fig. 182 and I_P is the intensity of an unperturbed spherical wave reaching P, Eq. (11.15) is simply an expression of the inverse square law for intensities from a point source. Indeed, if we wished to take as reference the intensity of an unperturbed wave reaching P, the factor $r_S/(r_S + r_P)$ could be omitted from Eq. (11.13).

The simplicity of Eq. (11.13) is surprising when we consider the complexity of the Kirchhoff integral involving three kinds of Huygens wavelets. The simple results suggest that there might be a simpler approach. In the succeeding chapter we shall obtain the same results by the simpler method of Young.

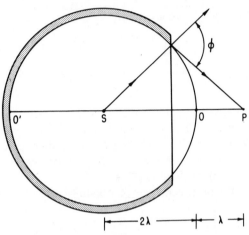

Figure 185. Spherical wave bounded by a circular aperture at the obliquity angle ϕ.

11.3 Diffraction of Spherical Waves by a Circular Aperture

We are prepared to find the intensity in the diffraction pattern of a circular aperture of a thin absorbing screen along the axis of the aperture when the source lies on the axis. A convenient interpretation is made of Eq. (11.13) if we let the radius of the spherical wave r_S and the distance r_P be constants. The circular aperture of Fig. 185 with $O'P$ as its axis may be increased from zero diameter when its plane is through point O to the diameter of the spherical wave when its plane is through S and diminished to zero again as its plane approaches O'. As the aperture is thus moved back along its axis, ϕ will increase from zero to π.

We may interpret Eq. (11.13) for the case $r_S = 2\lambda$ and $r_P = \lambda$. For simplicity we shall let the reference amplitude be the amplitude at point P when there are no screens or obstacles in the region so that the equation may be expressed simply

$$\frac{\mathbf{u}_P}{\mathbf{u}_0} = 1 - \frac{1}{2}(1 + \cos \phi)e^{-j\beta} \tag{11.16}$$

represented by the spiral of Fig. 186. Equation (11.16) represents two vectors, the first term expresses the vector OA of unit length and phase angle zero, the second the vector AB. The resultant amplitude and phase relative to that of OA is the vector OB. The factor $-e^{-j\beta}$ represents a rotating vector whose arrow sweeps in a negative or clockwise direction, having the value -1 when $\beta = 0$. The factor $\frac{1}{2}(1 + \cos \phi)$ causes the length of the vector to decrease as β increases so that AB shrinks from unity to zero as β increases from zero to

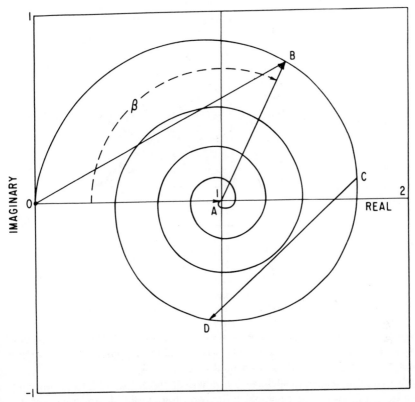

Figure 186. The amplitude and phase are represented by a vector which is the resultant of a fixed vector and a shrinking, rotating vector.

8π. The factor $1 + \cos \phi$ depends on β. By the expression of the cosine law for triangles, when r_P is positive,

$$1 + \cos \phi = \frac{(4\pi r_P + \beta\lambda)(4\pi r_S - \beta\lambda)}{4\pi r_S(2\pi r_P + \beta\lambda)} .$$ (11.17A)

When r_P is negative,

$$1 + \cos \phi = \frac{\beta\lambda(4\pi r_S - 4\pi|r_P| + \beta\lambda)}{4\pi r_S(2\pi|r_P| + \beta\lambda)} .$$ (11.17B)

The proof is retained for the problems.

If ϕ is needed to only two figures, it may be determined more quickly by construction. In Fig. 187, ϕ has been constructed for all the integer values of β/π when $r_S/\lambda = 2$ and $r_P/\lambda = 1$.

The amplitude is a maximum and the phase zero when β/π is an odd integer and a minimum when β/π is an even integer. The intensity of radiation I/I_0 for β/π from zero to 8 is plotted in Fig. 188, where I/I_0 may be calculated from Eq. (11.14) or by measuring and squaring the amplitudes on the vibration spiral of Fig. 186. The scale of intensity of Fig. 188 is for I_0 taken as the

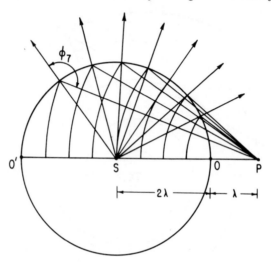

Figure 187. Determination of the obliquity angle by construction.

intensity of an unperturbed spherical wave reaching P. If the reference I_0 is taken at the surface of the spherical wave reaching the edge of the aperture from S, the intensity scale should be divided by 9/4.

If two absorbing thin shells fit the spherical wave, Fig. 189, to permit only reradiation from a zone to reach P, the resulting amplitude and phase at P is represented by vector CD on the vibration spiral of Fig. 186.

We have treated graphically only the case in which $r_S/\lambda = 2$. For larger values of r_S/λ, the spiral closes less rapidly with β and the number of turns is equal to $2r_S/\lambda$. We shall treat next the case of an incident plane wave, for which r_S/λ is infinite.

11.4 Diffraction of a Plane Wave by a Circular Aperture

When light or microwaves from a distant source fall on a telescope objective the diffraction pattern is that of a plane wave falling normally on a circular aperture. The length of a light telescope compared to the diameter

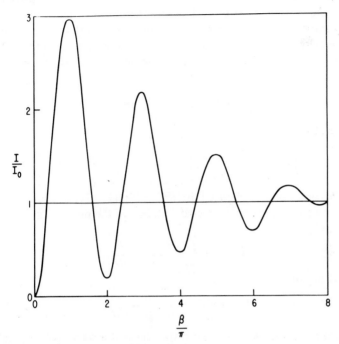

Figure 188. The relative intensity of radiation against phase angle β/π, determined by squaring the amplitudes of Fig. 186.

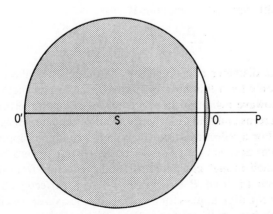

Figure 189. Thin absorbing shells fitting the wave front to permit only reradiation from a zone.

of its objective is often so large that Fraunhofer methods can be employed to determine the diffraction pattern. The focal length of a microwave telescope is usually shorter than the diameter of the objective, so that Fresnel methods must be employed. When the incident wave is plane, r_S is infinite and the ratio $r_S/(r_S + r_P)$ becomes unity. The complex amplitude of Eq. (11.13) becomes

$$\frac{\mathbf{u}_P}{\mathbf{u}_0} = 1 - \frac{1}{2}(1 + \cos \phi)e^{-j\beta}, \qquad (11.18)$$

and the relative intensity

$$\frac{I_P}{I_0} = 1 + \frac{1}{4}(1 + \cos \phi)^2 - (1 + \cos \phi) \cos \beta. \qquad (11.19)$$

Since $\beta\lambda$ becomes small compared to $4\pi r_S$ in Eq. (11.17) as r_S becomes large, the obliquity factor may be expressed in terms of the phase angle β. If r_P is positive,

$$1 + \cos \phi = \frac{4\pi r_P + \beta\lambda}{2\pi r_P + \beta\lambda}. \qquad (11.20)$$

If r_P is negative,

$$1 + \cos \phi = \frac{\beta\lambda}{4\pi|r_P| + \beta\lambda}. \qquad (11.21)$$

We recall that the phase angle β is the phase of a wave from a point near the edge of the aperture relative to a wavelet reaching P from O of Fig. 190, so that

$$\beta = \frac{2\pi}{\lambda}(r - r_P) = \frac{2\pi}{\lambda}(\sqrt{r_P^2 + R^2} - r_P). \qquad (11.22)$$

A convenient form for calculations is

$$\left(\frac{D}{\lambda}\right)^2 = \left(\frac{\beta}{\pi}\right)^2 + 4\left(\frac{\beta}{\pi}\right)\left(\frac{r_P}{\lambda}\right), \qquad (11.23)$$

D being the diameter of the aperture. Although Kirchhoff's equation was developed only for a thin absorbing screen, the results check experimentally in the microwave region of the spectrum for circular apertures in both thin reflecting screens and thin absorbing screens of the interference absorber type (Sec. 8.9). For a reflecting screen Kirchhoff's equations apply along the axis of the circular aperture for r_P of any positive value or zero, and for negative values r_P small enough compared to D that reflection from the back surface of the screen to point P is negligible. For a perfectly absorbing screen, Kirchhoff's equation applies for all points on the axis of the circular aperture. Here r_P may have both positive and negative values.

Figures 191(a) and (b) are plots from Eq. (11.19) of intensities against position along the axes of apertures of fixed diameters, $D/\lambda = 2$ and 3. We note that the oscillating intensity on the side of incidence damps toward unity, the intensity of the unperturbed incident beam, as the direction angle ϕ approaches π. The measured intensities of the microwave diffraction pattern along the axis of a circular aperture near the aperture agree with Kirchhoff's equation within the limits of experimental error.[1,2]

The largest intensity gradients in the diffraction pattern of a circular aperture are near the center. We shall treat the variation of intensity with diameter for the cases $r_P = \pm 1$, and finally the limiting case as r_P approaches zero. If the fixed position on the axis, distance r_P from the center of the

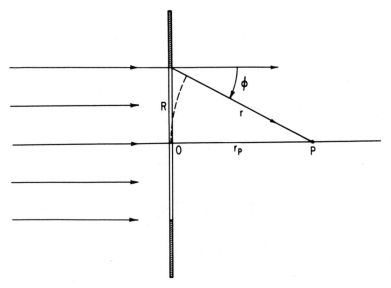

Figure 190. The limiting phase angle β may be determined in terms of the radius of the aperture, and the distance of the point of observation from the center, each expressed in wavelengths.

aperture, is positive, the limiting direction angle ϕ, Fig. 190, has values ranging from 0 to $\pi/2$ as the diameter increases from zero to large values. Thus the obliquity factor $1 + \cos \phi$ decreases from 2.0 to 1.0 as the diameter of the aperture increases. Figure 192 is the vibration spiral in complex space which gives the amplitude and phase at a point on the axis at distance $r_P/\lambda = 1$. The rotating vector $\frac{1}{2}(1 + \cos \phi)e^{-j\beta}$ approaches the dotted circle of radius $\frac{1}{2}$ as asymptote. Thus for apertures large compared to r_P the resultant amplitude at P oscillates between 0.5 and 1.5 as the diameter increases.

[1] H. Severin, Z. Naturforsch., **1**, 487 (1946).
[2] C. L. Andrews, J. Appl. Phys., **21**, 761 (1950).

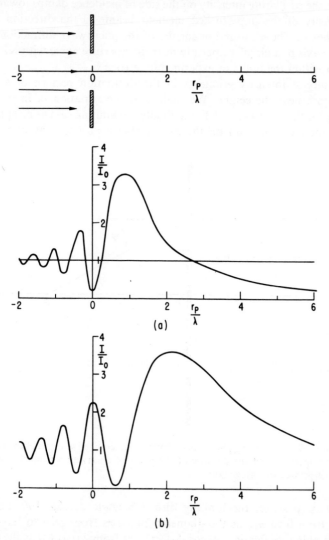

Figure 191. Plots of relative intensity against distance along the axis of a circular aperture on which a plane wave is incident when (a) $D/\lambda = 2$, (b) $D/\lambda = 3$.

Figure 193 is a similar vibration spiral giving the amplitude and phase at a point on the axis 1 wavelength toward the source, $r_P/\lambda = -1$. The screen is perfectly absorbing. As the diameter of the aperture is increased from zero the direction angle varies from π towards $\pi/2$. The amplitude of the rotating vector $\frac{1}{2}(1 + \cos \phi)$ increases from zero toward 0.5 as the vector rotates in a clockwise direction. The spiral for negative values of r_P approaches the broken circle of radius 0.5 from within. For apertures large compared to r_P the resultant amplitude at P oscillates between 0.5 and 1.5 as the diameter increases.

Figures 194(a) and (b) are plots of the intensities against D/λ at the two positions r_P/λ equal to 1.0 and -1.0, obtained by squaring the amplitudes given by the two vibration spirals. We note that when D/λ is small, the

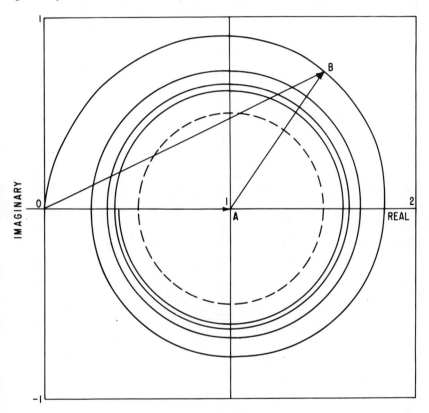

Figure 192. Vibration spiral for determining the amplitude and phase at the position $r_P = \lambda$ as the diameter of the aperture is varied.

intensity on the source side of the absorbing screen is very near that of the unperturbed incident beam. As the diameter becomes large the minimum and maximum values of the intensities approach asymptotes of 0.25 and 2.25, indicated by broken lines.

The simplest case to treat is that of the center of the aperture itself, where ϕ remains constant at $\pi/2$ and the complex amplitude is

$$\frac{\mathbf{u}}{\mathbf{u}_0} = 1 - \frac{1}{2} e^{-j\beta}. \tag{11.24}$$

Thus the vibration spiral is the circle in complex space which was the asymptote for the spirals corresponding to all other points on the axis of the circular aperture. The intensity becomes

$$\frac{I}{I_0} = 1.25 - \cos \beta,$$

(11.25)

and

$$\beta = \frac{2\pi R}{\lambda}.$$

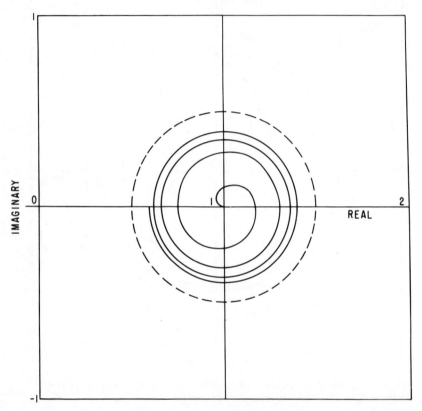

Figure 193. Vibration spiral for determining the amplitude and phase at the position $r_P = -\lambda$ as the diameter of the aperture is varied.

Kirchhoff's equation does not apply at the center of apertures less than 1 wavelength in diameter. We shall treat this case in the succeeding chapter.

11.5 Microwave Demonstrations of Fresnel Diffraction

Diffraction patterns of light made by small apertures may be observed by one person at a time on a ground-glass screen in a dark room. If we use microwaves of 12 cm wavelength, the apertures may be cut in a 2 ft square screen and the intensities of points in the pattern read on the intensity meter used as a probe. Figure 195 shows an arrangement for studying diffraction by a circular aperture.

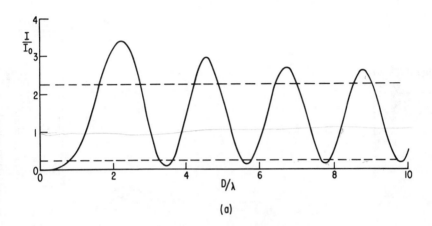

(a)

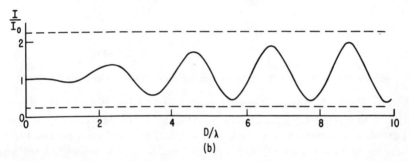

(b)

Figure 194. Plots of intensities against diameters of aperture at positions (a) $r_P/\lambda = 1$, and (b) $r_P/\lambda = -1$.

The extremes of intensity are observed when the phase angle is an integer multiple of π.

$$\left(\frac{\mathbf{u}_P}{\mathbf{u}_0}\right)_n = 1 - \frac{1}{2}(1 + \cos \phi_n)e^{-jn\pi}. \qquad (11.26)$$

If n is odd, $e^{-jn\pi} = -1$ and the amplitude is a maximum. If n is even, $e^{-jn\pi} = 1$ and the amplitude is a minimum. For these extreme cases the phase is always zero and only real algebra is employed.

The sizes of circular apertures for these extreme cases may be obtained by constructing spheres about the point P to intersect the plane wavefront that is to fill the aperture. The first sphere is tangent to the wavefront with center at P as shown in Fig. 196. The set of concentric spheres about P with increments of radius of $\frac{1}{2}$ wavelength, numbered from the center outward with the tangent point numbered zero, intersects the wavefront in circles. The zones between the circles, numbered from the center outward beginning with one, are called *Fresnel zones*.

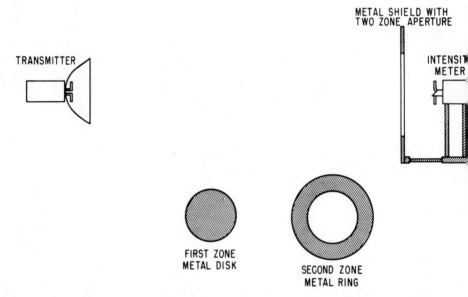

Figure 195. Arrangement for demonstrating diffraction by a circular aperture.

The first zone disc and second zone ring of Figs. 195 and 197 are cut relative to a point 1.5 wavelengths from the center of the aperture. We may calculate the diameters to be 2.64λ and 4.00λ. The amplitudes obtained from the one- and two-zone apertures are 1.87 and 0.20. The intensities are 3.52 and 0.04. In spite of the difference in the obliquity factors the intensity from two zones is only about 1% of that from the first zone alone. The effects of the two zones have nearly cancelled.

The amplitude from the second zone is the difference of the amplitudes from the circular apertures of two and one zones. Thus from Eq. (11.26) we obtain

$$\left(\frac{\mathbf{u}_P}{\mathbf{u}_0}\right)_{\text{zone 2}} = \left(\frac{\mathbf{u}_P}{\mathbf{u}_0}\right) - \left(\frac{\mathbf{u}_P}{\mathbf{u}_0}\right)_1 = -\frac{(1 + \cos\phi_1) + (1 + \cos\phi_2)}{2}. \quad (11.27)$$

The amplitude from a single zone is equal to the average of the obliquity factors of wavelets from the inner and outer edges of the zone.

The amplitude from the second zone, when the first is covered by the disc, is 1.7 and the intensity 2.8. We note the effectiveness of this latter demonstration as an introduction to diffraction. When the first two zones are uncovered the intensity is 0.04. If the disc is placed over the first zone, it does not cast a geometrical shadow but increases the intensity by a factor of 70. The effects from the first two zones nearly cancel.

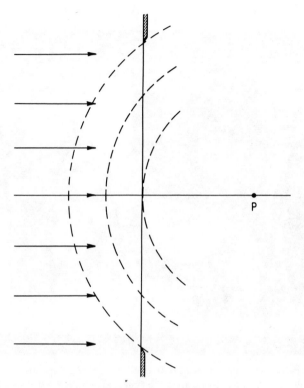

Figure 196. Determination of zone sizes.

We recognize a fundamental fact of interference. None of the wave energy is destroyed. It is redistributed in space. Thus, when the first two zones are uncovered and there is a dark spot at *P*, we are not surprised on moving the intensity meter radially outward from the axis to find a bright ring around the black spot.

We must stress that the zones are constructed relative to a fixed point. As we move the intensity meter in along the axis we find the points relative to which the aperture uncovers one, two, and three Fresnel zones. Relative to the center of the aperture, this aperture 4λ in diameter uncovers four Fresnel zones, and the intensity will have a minimum value of 0.25 as shown in the previous section.

The treatment of the diffraction pattern across the whole face of the aperture is retained for the succeeding chapter in which polarization will be included in the diffraction study.

In view of the observations in the plane of the aperture made possible by the convenient wavelength of microwaves, we shall give a new emphasis to the Fresnel-Kirchhoff principle.

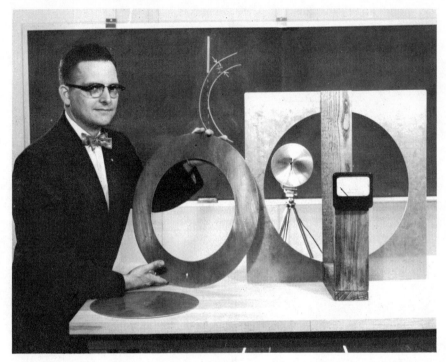

Figure 197(a). Demonstration of diffraction by a circular aperture. The disc and ring have been cut to uncover the first and second Fresnel zones taken relative to the position of the intensity meter. (a) The amplitudes from the first two zones nearly cancel.

The amplitude and phase of the diffracted wave at any point P beyond, in, or behind the plane of the aperture may be found by adding the continuous wavelets reaching the point P from every point of an imagined unperturbed wave over the surface of the aperture.

Microwave measurements have extended the experimental confirmation of the Fresnel-Kirchhoff principle to the near region where the obliquity factor extends over the whole range from 2 to zero.

11.6 Far Field Diffraction, Fresnel Zone Methods

If the distances r_S and r_P of the source and point of observation from the diffracting aperture are large compared to the diameter of the aperture, and if

u_0 is the amplitude of an unperturbed wave reaching P, Eq. (11.13) reduces to

$$\frac{\mathbf{u}_P}{\mathbf{u}_0} = 1 - e^{-j\beta}. \tag{11.28}$$

This is the equation of a circle with radius 1.0 and center at position 1.0 on the real axis. The circle extends from the origin in a clockwise direction. Even

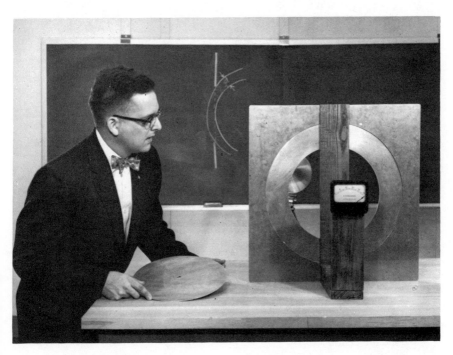

Figure 197(b). When only the first zone is uncovered, the intensity meter indicates full scale.

for this simple case Kirchhoff's equation yields two new facts not in Fresnel's equation. (1) Kirchhoff expresses the amplitude in terms of the amplitude of the unperturbed wave $\mathbf{u}_0$. (2) The amplitude reaching P from a very small aperture is represented by a vector extending in the positive direction along the imaginary axis. The wavelet from the center thus leads the phase of an unperturbed wave reaching P by $\pi/2$. This phase advance of a wavelet from a source that is small compared to a wavelength is in agreement with the experimental observation by Gouy which we treated in Chapter VI. A spherical wave spreading out from a "point" source advances by $\pi/2$.

Fresnel recognized that the effects from succeeding zones on a spherical wavefront must diminish with the zone number, even though he did not discover the obliquity factor. Equation (11.28) is a circle inside which lie all the vibration spirals for finite distances of observation r_P. If the distances of the source of light and point of observation are each 1 m from the circular aperture which is continuously expanded up to a few millimeters, the succeeding turns in the vibration spiral are so close to each other that they can not be distinguished from a circle in a textbook drawing.

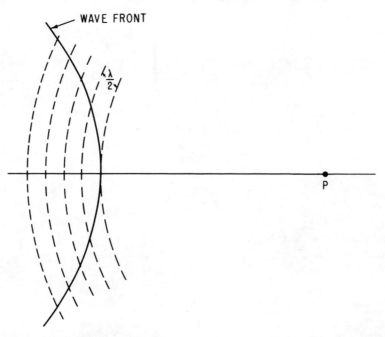

Figure 198. Division of spherical wave front into Fresnel half-period zones with respect to point P.

The success of Fresnel's methods in solution of optical problems over the past century lies largely in his clear models and construction techniques. Being a mathematician, Fresnel was able to devise qualitative construction techniques for the layman. Constructing a set of concentric circles about the point of observation P, the inner of which is tangent to the spherical wave, and succeeding spheres separated by increments of one-half wavelength, he divided the wavefront into a set of zones as shown in Fig. 198. They are often called *Fresnel half-period zones*. The zones themselves may be thousands of wavelengths wide. The expression "half-period" zone refers to the method of constructing the zones. Since the waves from successive zones arrive at P with opposite phase, this subdivision of the wave front is sufficient to predict the positions of maximum intensity along the axis.

To introduce the vibration spiral without the use of algebra, we shall divide the half-period zones into six subzones. The path difference of wavelets from two successive subzones is $\frac{1}{6}$ of $\lambda/2$ or $\lambda/12$, and the phase difference is 30°. Figure 199 is a vector summation of the shorthand rotating vectors that represent the wavelets reaching P from the 12 subzones. The vector from the origin O to the end of vector number 5 represents the resultant amplitude and phase of the wave reaching P from the first five subzones. For every subzone in the first Fresnel zone there is a corresponding subzone in the second Fresnel zone from which the wavelets cancel. Thus vector 1 cancels 7, 2 cancels 8, and so forth, so that the wavelets from two successive zones cancel or nearly cancel if the obliquity angle is greater than zero. As the number of subzones is increased the summation becomes the smooth vibration spiral which we obtained from Kirchhoff's equation.

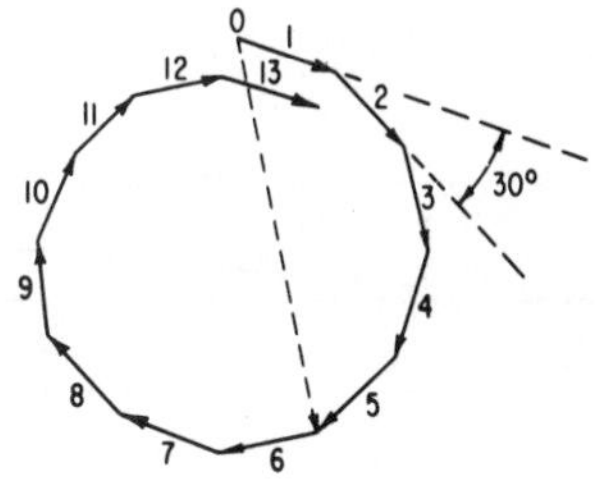

Figure 199. Summation of amplitudes and phases from six subzones per half-period zone.

No matter how versed we may be in mathematics, we shall frequently find it convenient to employ Fresnel's approximate construction methods. For instance if the aperture or object is irregular as in Fig. 200, the amplitudes from the partially uncovered zones may be found by measuring the areas. If we wish to determine the intensity in the far field of a circular aperture a short distance from the axis, the Fresnel methods for scalar waves

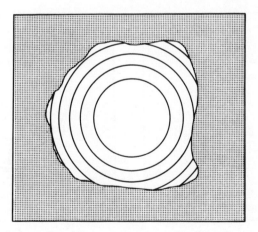

Figure 200. Formation of zones of an irregular aperture.

still apply to good approximation. Figure 201 indicates the construction of zones relative to a point P' off the axis. Figure 202(a) shows the zones relative to a point P on the axis where $n = 2$ and the intensity is a minimum. Figure 202(b) shows the uncovered zones constructed relative to point P'. Since the

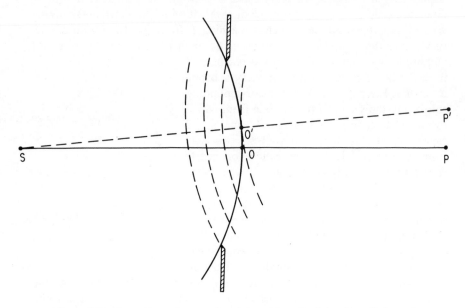

Figure 201. Formation of zones for determining the intensity off the axis.

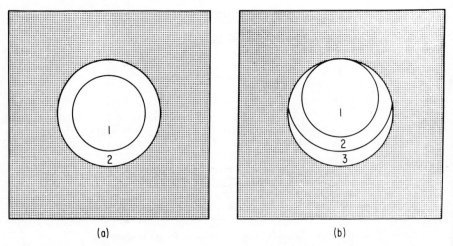

(a)   (b)

Figure 202. Portions of zones uncovered by an aperture. (a) The zones are
constructed relative to a point on the axis. (b) The zones are constructed relative
to a point off the axis.

amplitudes from a zone are approximately proportional to the fraction of the zone uncovered, the vector summation of Fig. 203(a) is obtained. More precisely the zones may be divided into subzones and a vibration spiral drawn as in Fig. 203(b).

No other Fresnel diffraction pattern gives the series of contrasting jet black nulls as does the diffraction pattern of a circular aperture. Sanderman

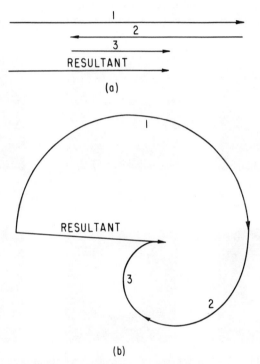

Figure 203. (a) Vector addition of complex amplitudes reaching a point off the axis. (b) Vibration spiral for a point off the axis.

and Bradford[3] have described a widely used elementary laboratory experiment for which a dozen points corresponding to integers n are obtained. The art of producing sharp patterns such as those of Fig. 204 lies in the use of very perfect smooth-edged apertures in a thin screen kept free of dust particles. If the incident wave is plane, as in Fig. 190,

$$r_P^2 + R^2 = \left(r_P + \frac{n\lambda}{2} \right)^2,$$

(11.29)

[3] L. A. Sanderman and R. S. Bradford, *Am. J. Phys.*, **17**, 514 (1949).

where R is the radius of the aperture. Squaring the right-hand side, we obtain

$$R^2 = r_P n\lambda + \left(\frac{n\lambda}{2}\right)^2$$

If $r_P \gg n\lambda$,

$$R^2 = r_P n\lambda. \qquad (11.30)$$

A graph of R^2 against n has a slope of $r_P\lambda$, from which the wavelength may be determined. We may note the several times since we met Newton's rings that we have observed sets of rings for which the radii increase as the square roots of the integers.

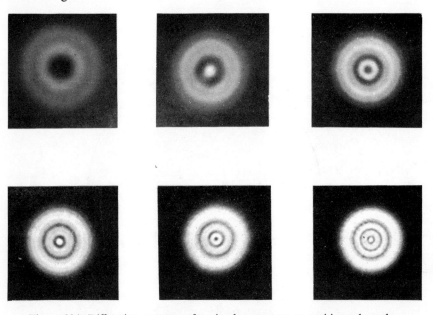

Figure 204. Diffraction patterns of a circular aperture at positions along the axis relative to which the aperture uncovers 2, 3, 4, 5, 6, and 7 Fresnel zones. (Photographs by J. J. Carmichael and L. Merrill.)

If we treat only waves from Fresnel half zones, the vectors are all added along the same line. If we make alternate zones opaque as in Fig. 205, all the vectors add arithmetically so that high concentration may be obtained at P. Indeed, the *Fresnel zone plate* satisfies the elementary lens equation for conjugate foci. Its chromatic aberration is much greater than that of any lens. Some of the intensity is lost to higher orders at larger distance than P. At a larger distance can be found a point P_3 on the axis relative to which three constructed zones cover a single zone opening on the zone plate. The odd number of zones yield at P_3 intensity $\frac{1}{9}$ that at P.

Along the axis of a zone plate we may observe brightly colored images of a

C-shaped filament of a 200 w incandescent lamp. Although the author has made photographic reductions of large drawings of Fresnel zone plates, none of them approaches in resolving power the zone plate obtained by making a lantern slide from the print in Wood's textbook.[4]

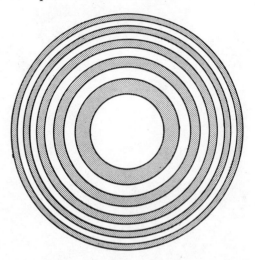

Figure 205. Fresnel zone plate.

11.7 Diffraction Pattern of a Cylindrical Wave by a Straight Edge

Another illustration of Fresnel diffraction is the pattern of the straight edge of a razor blade of Fig. 206. Straight-edge diffraction patterns of the sharp jaws of a slit of an optical instrument for light or the edge of an airplane wing for microwaves are of practical importance. In this chapter we shall use the classical Fresnel method of finding the diffraction pattern under restricted but useful conditions. The following approximations are made. (1) The second of Kirchhoff's wavelets, Fig. 182(b), is ignored. (2) The obliquity factor $1 + \cos \theta$ of the first wavelet will be considered constant. (3) We shall treat only the far-field pattern at distances from the straight edge which are large compared to a wavelength. (4) The distance of the point of observation from the straight edge must be very large compared to its distance from the geometrical shadow. For the study of light diffraction these restrictions are not serious since the observable diffraction pattern lies in this region. For man-sized wavelengths, however, the near field on all sides of the straight edge is an interesting part of the pattern.

Figure 207 indicates a long slit source S of coherent light, P is a line of observation of the resultant of the secondary wavelets arriving from the primary cylindrical wavefront, O is the intercept of SP with the wavefront, and

[4] R. W. Wood, *Physical Optics*, 3rd ed.: New York, Macmillan (1934) p. 38.

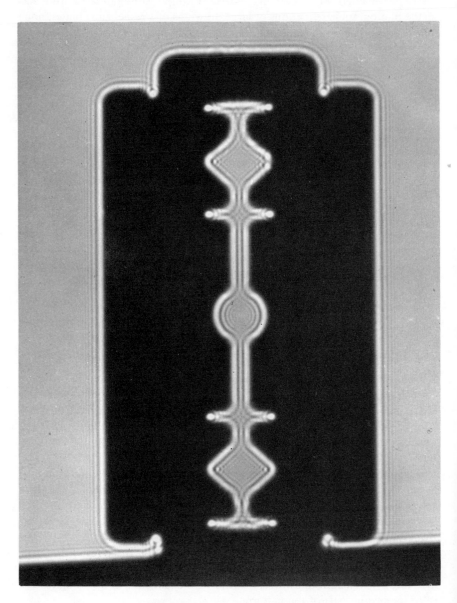

Figure 206. Diffraction pattern of a razor blade.

s is the distance measured along the front from line O to a strip of wavefront of width Δs. We shall treat only values of s that are small compared to r_S and r_P. The strip is cut in the wavefront by cylinders concentric about line P in the manner that zones of spherical wavefronts were cut by concentric spheres. The amplitude of the cylindrical wavelet reaching line P from Δs is proportional to the area per unit length which is Δs. Since the distances from the secondary sources to P are very large compared to the difference in distance of P from the different strips of the wavefront, we shall consider the effect of the

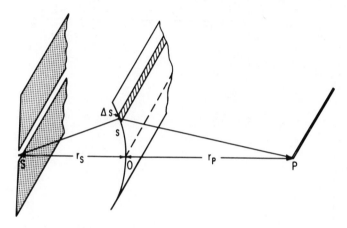

Figure 207. Reradiation from a strip on a cylindrical wavefront.

distance factor on the amplitude to be a constant. If we take the phase of an unperturbed wave reaching line P from source S as reference, the phase of a wavelet will be determined by two factors, (1) the path difference Δ, and (2) the Gouy phase advance $\pi/4$ of a cylindrical wavelet from secondary source Δs which is narrow compared to a wavelength.

We may divide the cylindrical wavefront into a set of half-period Fresnel strips, Fig. 208, by constructing a set of concentric cylinders about the line P to intersect the wavefront, each successive cylinder being one-half wavelength greater in radius. If the increments in radii are $\frac{1}{20}$ wavelength, we divide each half-period strip into ten substrips and may construct the vibration spiral. Each cylindrical wavelet reaching line P has an amplitude proportional to the width of the substrip. The distances of the strip boundaries from O are as the square roots of the integers. The wavelet from a substrip lags by 18° that from the preceding substrip.

We shall take as reference the phase of the unperturbed wave arriving at P. From our experience with the Gouy effect we conclude that the wavelet from a narrow strip at O will lead the unperturbed wave by $\pi/4$. The vibration spiral is plotted in Fig. 209 for wavelets from three Fresnel half-period strips above

O. If we uncover an equal number of strips below zero, the amplitudes are doubled and the phases remain the same. Thus if we include strips equally spaced on either side of *O*, the dimensions of the spiral are doubled. We shall

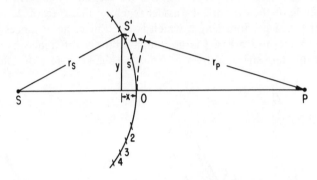

Figure 208. Construction for determination of Δ in terms of r_S, r_P, and s.

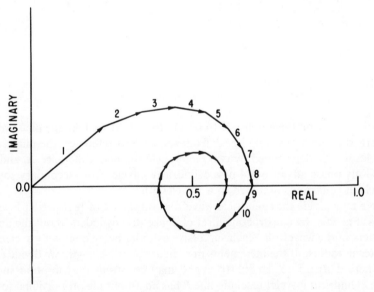

Figure 209. Vibration spiral for wavelets from three Fresnel half-period strips.

let the point of convergence of the larger spiral be 1.0 since it is the amplitude of the unperturbed wave. Our anticipation of the Gouy effect has led to a phase of zero of the resultant wave from all the strips. This is a confirmation of the Gouy effect. To obtain a more precise vibration spiral, we must let the substrips become infinitesimal in width Δs.

The approximation of small values of s is poorer as strips farther from O are included and the obliquity factor becomes appreciably less than 2. However, in that case the substrips will have become so narrow and the spiral will have converged so close to the limiting value that the effect of the obliquity factor is trivial.

We shall now express the integral for the summation of the cylindrical wavelets. We wish to express the phase in the most meaningful and simple form. The arc s of the wavefront of Fig. 207 is approximately equal to the cord. We shall drop a perpendicular of length y from S' to the line SP, Fig. 208. Let the distance from O to the foot of the perpendicular be called x. Using the Pythagorean theorem, we may write three simultaneous equations corresponding to three triangles.

$$\left\{ \begin{array}{l} r_S^2 = y^2 + (r_S - x)^2 \\ (r_P + \Delta)^2 = y^2 + (r_P + x)^2 \\ s^2 = y^2 + x^2. \end{array} \right.$$

If we neglect the squared terms in x and Δ and eliminate y, we obtain

$$\left\{ \begin{array}{l} s^2 = 2r_S x \\ 2r_P \Delta = s^2 + 2r_P x. \end{array} \right.$$

Eliminating x and solving for Δ, we obtain

$$\Delta = \frac{r_S + r_P}{2r_S r_P} s^2, \tag{11.31}$$

and the phase angle

$$\delta = \frac{\pi}{\lambda} \left(\frac{r_S + r_P}{r_S r_P} \right) s^2. \tag{11.32}$$

If we let a new quantity

$$v^2 = \frac{2(r_S + r_P)}{\lambda r_S r_P} s^2, \tag{11.33}$$

the solution will be for all values of r_S and r_P within the limits of our approximations. Here $ds = k_1 dv$, and $\delta = \pi v^2/2$. The constant k_1 includes r_S, r_P, and λ. The complex amplitude of a wavelet reaching point P from a small strip Δs, Fig. 207, is

$$\Delta \mathbf{u}_P = \Delta u e^{-j(\delta - \pi/4)}.$$

Of the three factors (1) distance, (2) obliquity, and (3) area of wavefront that affect the amplitude of the wavelets, the obliquity factors and distance factors are constant so that Δu varies only with Δs. Since Δs is proportional to Δv, the amplitude of the wavelet may be expressed $\Delta u = k_2 \Delta v$, where k_2 is a constant. Integrating the complex amplitudes of wavelets reaching P from a strip of width s extending upward from O, we obtain

$$\mathbf{u}_P = k_2 \int_0^v e^{-j(\pi v^2/2 - \pi/4)} \, dv.$$

Since $\pi/4$ is a constant,

$$\mathbf{u}_P = k_2 e^{j(\pi/4)} \int_0^v e^{-j(\pi/2)v^2} \, dv. \tag{11.34}$$

The integral

$$\int_0^v e^{j(\pi/2)v^2} \, dv,$$

known as the *Fresnel integral*, differs from the integral of Eq. (11.34) only by the sign of the exponent. This merely reverses the direction of the spiral which represents the integral, and does not affect the values of computed intensities. The complex spiral that represents the Fresnel integral is named for Marie Alfred Cornu. The Cornu spiral is defined by the fact that the angle which the tangent to the curve at any point makes with the real axis is proportional to the square of the distance measured along the curve from the origin to the point. In other words, the angle $\delta = (\pi/2)v^2$. The factor $e^{j(\pi/4)}$ in Eq. (11.34) merely rotates the Cornu spiral through the angle $\pi/4$ about the origin, and does not affect the computed intensities. We note that the distance v along the curve from the origin is proportional to the distance s along the wavefront. Instead of doubling the dimensions of the spiral to include strips below the line O on the front, we shall find it more convenient to use the Cornu spiral, Fig. 210, which has symmetry of the parts in the first and third quadrants with respect to the origin. The Cornu spiral of mathematics corresponds to a positive exponent instead of the negative phase angle of Eq. (11.34). The curve in the third quadrant is the complex spiral for wavelets from below line O of Fig. 207. The vector $J'O$ represents the amplitude at P from the lower half of the cylindrical wavefront and OJ from the upper half, $J'J$ represents the amplitude of the unperturbed wave, and $\mathbf{u}_0$ has the value $\sqrt{2}$ on the scale commonly used for the spiral and expressed in mathematical tables. Thus to express $\mathbf{u}/\mathbf{u}_0$ we must divide $\mathbf{u}$ by $\sqrt{2}$.

Using the Cornu spiral we may plot the amplitude of the diffraction pattern of a straight edge along a line perpendicular to SP, Fig. 207. Instead of moving P we may move the straight edge in the opposite direction. When P is on the edge of the geometrical shadow, the amplitude $\mathbf{u}$ is OJ on the spiral and the relative amplitude $\mathbf{u}/\mathbf{u}_0$ is 0.5. If the straight edge is moved upward as in Fig. 211, P is in the region of the shadow. The arrow of the amplitude vector remains at J and the tail moves along the scale v of the spiral. We note that the size of the amplitude diminishes continuously as P is moved into the region of the geometrical shadow. If the straight edge is moved downward from O, P is on the light side of the geometrical shadow, and the tail of the

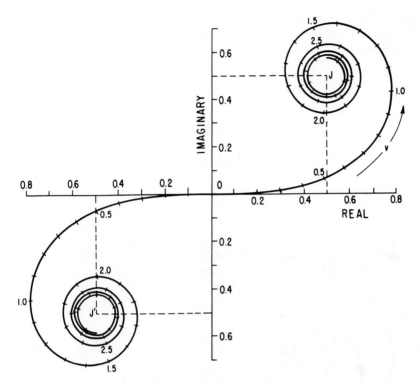

Figure 210. Cornu spiral.

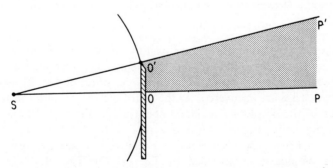

Figure 211. Determination of the diffraction pattern in the shadow of a straight edge.

amplitude vector moves from the origin along the spiral in the third quadrant. The amplitude reaches its maximum value AJ considerably before $v = \sqrt{2}$ when the first half-period strip is uncovered as indicated in Fig. 212. When the first Fresnel half-period strip is uncovered the phase of an elemental wavelet

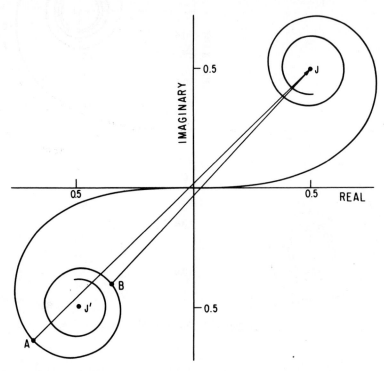

Figure 212. Determination of first maximum and first minimum from the Cornu spiral.

from near the edge has increased by π over that of a wavelet from the origin O, and the tangent to the spiral is horizontal again. The first minimum occurs when the amplitude is represented by BJ on the spiral of Fig. 212 somewhat before two strips are uncovered. As the tail of the vector spirals in toward J' the value of the amplitude oscillates about unity, the maxima and minima approaching unity. Figure 213(a) is a plot of the relative amplitude $\mathbf{u}/\mathbf{u_0}$ against v, and Fig. 213(b) is a plot of the relative intensity I/I_0 against v. We note the simplification provided by Eq. (11.33). The plots of complex amplitude in the Cornu spiral and of amplitude and intensity in Fig. 213(a) and (b) are universal, applying to all values of r_S, r_P, and λ. Plots of amplitude and intensity against distance of P from the edge of the shadow instead of against v are retained for the problems.

The use of the photomultiplier tube with a fine slit to scan the pattern has extended the precision of measurement of the straight-edge diffraction pattern to another significant figure.[5] This precision is higher than can be measured on the spiral. The integral of Eq. (11.34) can not be solved in

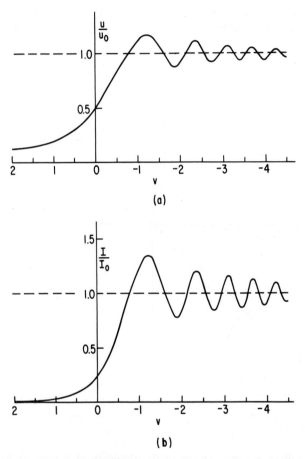

Figure 213. Plots of (a) amplitude and (b) intensity of the diffraction pattern of a straight edge in the far field.

closed form, but in terms of an infinite series. A table of three columns, (1) the distance v along the spiral from the origin to any point on the spiral, (2) the real, and (3) the imaginary values of the point are given to four significant figures in Table I in the back of the book. In expressing four significant figures we must recall the limitation that r_S and r_P be large compared to s. In the

[5] K. L. McDonald and S. Harris Jr., J. Opt. Soc. Amer., **42**, 321 (1952).

next chapter we shall determine *how large* the ratios r_S/s and r_P/s must be to keep the error below the current errors in measurements.

11.8 Diffraction Patterns of Slits

When the jaws of a slit for x-rays or the metal barn doors for microwaves are pushed back, how does the intensity at P vary? As we ask this question of

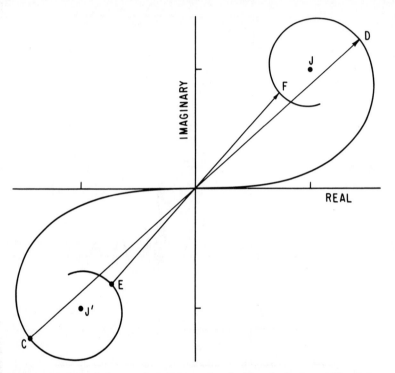

Figure 214. Use of Cornu spiral to determine the intensity in the middle of the beam of a slit.

the Cornu spiral, we may compare the intensity at P midway between the geometrical shadows with that on a point on the axis of a circular aperture. As the slit jaws are moved back, the positive and negative values of v move from the origin of the Cornu spiral with equal velocity until the amplitude reaches a maximum indicated by the vector CD on the spiral of Fig. 214, where EF is the amplitude of the first minimum as indicated on the spiral. Figure 215 is a plot of the intensity I/I_0 at P against the value of Δv measured along the spiral between the two points on the spiral; P is midway between the edges of the geometrical shadow.

If we wish to plot the pattern of a slit of fixed width taken along a line at right angles to the geometrical beam, we obtain the same result whether we move P or move the slit in the opposite direction along the cylindrical wave. When the slit width is constant, the length Δv along the spiral is fixed by

$$\Delta v = \sqrt{\frac{2(r_S + r_P)}{\lambda r_S r_P}} \, \Delta s.$$

If the Cornu spiral is mounted as a wire on a laboratory wall, a rubber tube

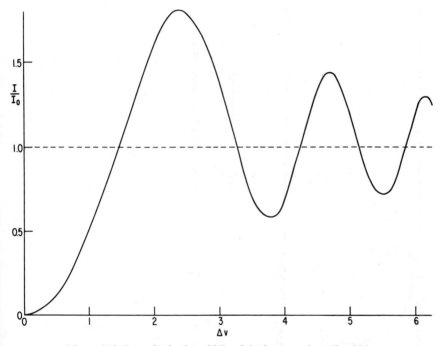

Figure 215. Intensity in the middle of the beam against slit width.

of length Δv may be slid along the spiral as the slit is moved along the wavefront. The resultant amplitude is the cord AB, Fig. 216, between the ends of the tube. If the slit width is small compared to the width of the Fresnel half-period strip so that Δv is less than 0.1, the cord nearly equals the arc as the tube is slid around several turns of the spiral. As the width of the slit approaches zero the intensity becomes equal in all directions, except for the effect of the obliquity factor which we ignored. When the slit uncovers less than half a Fresnel strip the pattern is of the Fraunhofer type of Fig. 136.

If, in the other extreme, the slit is wide enough to uncover many of the central Fresnel half-period strips, the ends of the rubber tube on the wire spiral lie close to J and J', and, as we scan this central portion of the pattern, the intensity will vary by a very small amount about unity. However, as one end of the tube moves out of the last few large turns about J' and the other end approaches J, the pattern becomes that of a straight edge. The slit pattern of a wide slit becomes the pattern of two straight edges with the intensity of the unperturbed wave between.

For intermediate cases of fixed slits with Δv ranging from 2 to 10 the pattern has complex detail. If the rubber tube extends much farther into one spiral than the other, the off-center portion of the pattern contains a coarse

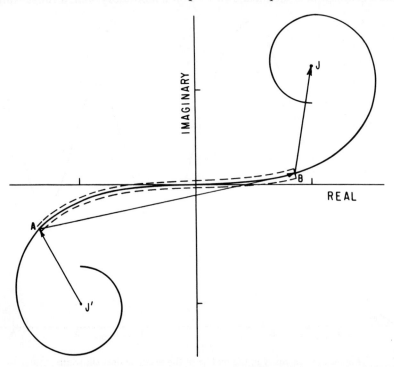

Figure 216. Use of Cornu spiral to determine the diffraction pattern of a slit or opaque strip.

part as one end swings around a large turn of the spiral and a fine structure as the other moves around the small spirals more rapidly. In terms of Fresnel half-period strips, one edge of a moving slit is covering fine off-center strips rapidly while the other uncovers coarse strips slowly. One side of the slit is producing the coarse pattern while the other produces the fine. The intensity of the diffraction pattern for $\Delta v = 3$ is shown in Fig. 217.

11.9 Diffraction Pattern of an Opaque Strip

The diffraction pattern of a fine wire for x-rays, a needle for light, or a hidden metal conduit in a wall for microwaves may be found by use of Cornu's spiral. The length of rubber tube on the wire spiral now corresponds to the covered portion of the cylindrical wavefront given by Eq. (11.33). The amplitude is the resultant of two vectors. The first is from J' to A at one end of the tube along the spiral, and the other vector from the other end B of the tube to J as indicated in Fig. 216.

As the width of a strip covering the middle Fresnel half-period strips is increased in width from zero, the intensity diminishes from unity and

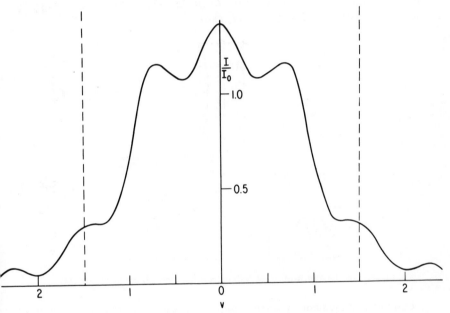

Figure 217. Fresnel diffraction pattern of a slit, $\Delta v = 3$.

approaches zero asymptotically. The intensity plot is similar to that for a straight edge extending from the edge of the geometrical shadow into the shadow region. We note that the vector sum of the complex amplitudes of the waves reaching point P for the slit and strip of the same width is equal to $\mathbf{u}_0$, the amplitude of the unperturbed wave. This conclusion may be drawn for any two complementary screens of any shapes that fit together to just cover the wavefront without overlapping.

11.10 Babinet's Principle

The fact that the sum of the complex amplitudes from complementary screens reaching a point P equals the amplitude of the wave at P when both screens are removed has wide application when the resultant amplitude $\mathbf{u}_0$ is zero. For instance, in regions near the focal point of the lens combination of Fig. 218 the intensity is zero. Thus the amplitudes due to the two complementary screens placed between the lenses must be equal and opposite in order to add to zero at points in those regions. Since the absolute values of the amplitudes are identical, the intensities at P due to each of the complementary screens must be identical.

The intensities of the diffraction patterns of complementary screens are identical everywhere far enough from the focal point that the intensity of a wave unperturbed by either screen is zero.

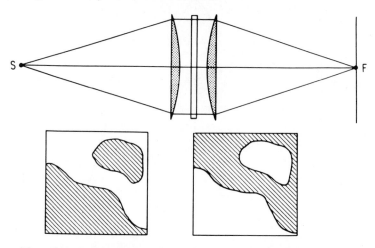

Figure 218. Demonstration of Babinet's principle with conjugate screens.

Pairs of complementary screens may be made as positives and negatives on lantern slides. We note that the case treated in Fig. 218 is of Fraunhofer diffraction. Babinet's principle applies at all points in the Fraunhofer diffraction pattern except near the first-order maximum.

An application of Babinet's principle to Fresnel diffraction previously treated is that of positive and negative zone plates. In this case the intensity of the unperturbed wave is very small compared to the intensities of the images of the lamp filaments formed by the zone plates so that Babinet's principle applies with good approximation in this case.

We may apply Babinet's principle in the design of diffraction gratings. By Babinet's principle, complementary diffraction gratings give identical diffraction patterns except at the zero order where the intensity is not zero when the grating is removed. For instance, if we wish a diffraction grating to suppress the third order, we recall from Secs. 10.2 and 10.3 that we can let the open slits be one-third as wide as the distance between corresponding points in consecutive slits. Thus the opaque portions must be twice as wide as the open ones. Using Babinet's principle, we could obtain the same diffraction pattern with suppression of the third order if the transparent portions of the grating were twice as wide as the opaque portions. In this case the second minimum in the single-slit diffraction pattern suppresses the third-order line.

The surprising discovery which we probably would not have surmised without the use of Babinet's principle is that the intensities obtained with the complementary gratings are identical in both the first and second orders. The amplitudes of the zero orders, on the other hand, are proportional to the widths of slit. We shall leave for the problems the confirmation of Babinet's principle for this special case.

11.11 Geometrical Optics, a Special Case of Physical Optics

Physical optics necessarily becomes geometrical optics whenever the structure of the diffraction pattern is finer than the smallest detectors man can produce. When the diffraction pattern of a strip or slit is finer than the grain in the photographic plate, the slit of a multiplier tube, or the cross hair of a telescope, the optics is geometrical. As closely as we can detect under these conditions rays of light travel in straight lines in a uniform medium.

If the distance PP', Fig. 211, contains the diffraction pattern of a straight edge but all our detectors are coarser than PP', the straight edge casts a geometrical shadow. From geometry,

$$PP' = \frac{r_S + r_P}{r_S} s. \tag{11.35}$$

Substituting from Eq. (11.33), we obtain

$$PP' = v\sqrt{\frac{r_P \lambda(r_S + r_P)}{2r_S}}. \tag{11.36}$$

As r_S approaches infinity, the incident wave becomes plane and

$$PP' = v\sqrt{\frac{r_P \lambda}{2}}. \tag{11.37}$$

In the limit as the product $r_P \lambda$ approaches zero, optics becomes geometrical. Pinhole images of x-ray targets are geometrical except under the severest conditions of fineness of grain of the photographic emulsion and large distances r_P. The diffraction pattern of light becomes difficult to observe at points a few wavelengths from the diffracting object. With man-sized microwaves and radio waves we may observe the diffraction pattern when r_P is a fraction of a wavelength.

In the following chapter we shall treat some empirical equations of diffraction patterns revealed by these man-sized wavelengths. These equations are general enough to include the near as well as far-field diffraction patterns.

PROBLEMS FOR CHAPTER XI

11.2.1. Compare the absolute values of the amplitudes of the two Huygens-Kirchhoff wavelets $1 + \cos \theta$ and $\lambda \cos \theta/2\pi r$ of Eq. (11.7) for the cases $r/\lambda = 0.1$, 1, and 10, and $\theta = 0$.

11.3.2. Plot the first turn of the complex spiral

$$1 - \tfrac{1}{2}(1 + \cos \phi)e^{-j\beta}$$

for the case $r_S/\lambda = r_P/\lambda = 8$. Ten points for equally spaced values of β will be sufficient. If unit length on the complex scale is 10 cm, the measurements of amplitudes for use in the following problem will be simplified.

11.3.3. Plot the intensity at point P against β for the range β equals zero to 2π for the case $r_S/\lambda = r_P/\lambda = 8$.

11.3.4. As a means of expressing the obliquity factor $1 + \cos \phi$ in terms of β and the constant distances r_S and r_P, prove that

$$2r_S\left(|r_P| + \frac{\beta\lambda}{2\pi}\right) \cos \phi = 2r_S r_P - 2|r_P|\frac{\beta\lambda}{2\pi} - \left(\frac{\beta\lambda}{2\pi}\right)^2,$$

and solve for Eq. (11.17), where r_P is negative when P is between S and O. However, when r_P is a term in the distance r, Fig. 183(a), it is always positive and expressed as an absolute value.

11.4.5. Prove that, if a plane wavefront is divided into Fresnel half-period zones relative to a point P which is distance r_P from the front, the radii of the zone boundaries are as the square roots of the integers for $r_P \gg n\lambda$.

11.4.6. Prove that, if a plane wave is incident normally on a circular aperture, the distance r_P from the aperture to point P on the axis is much larger than D, and D in turn is much larger than λ, the areas of two adjacent zones are approximately equal. This is the usual case of far-field light optics.

11.4.7. On the same complex coordinates plot two vibration spirals for the range $\beta = 0$ to 2π for the two cases $r_P/\lambda = 0.01$ and -0.01 when a plane wave is incident on the aperture. Note that this is an approach to the special case of solving for the amplitude and phase at the center of the aperture.

11.5.8. The frequency of 2450 megacycles per second has been allocated by the Federal Communications Commission for educational purposes. If we use this frequency, what must be the diameter of a circular hole in a metal screen to uncover two Fresnel zones in a plane wave relative to a point on the axis two wavelengths away from the center of the aperture?

11.6.9. An aperture near one end of a long dark room is to be illuminated by a parallel beam of sodium yellow light. What must be the diameter of aperture that will uncover two Fresnel zones on a wavefront relative to a point of observation 10 m away?

11.6.10. A circular aperture of 0.04 mm diameter is illuminated by a parallel beam of x-rays of the $K\alpha$ line of aluminum, wavelength 8 A. How far from the aperture is the point on the axis relative to which the aperture uncovers two Fresnel zones?

11.7.11. Making use of Fig. 213(b), find the distance between the first two minima in the straight-edge diffraction pattern at a distance of 1 m from the edge when sodium light is incident as a plane wave normally on the edge.

11.8.12. Make a plot of I/I_0 against v for the diffraction pattern of a slit for the case $\Delta v = 2.5$.

11.9.13. Make a plot of I/I_0 against Δv for the intensity in the middle of the geometrical shadow of a strip, as the width of strip is increased so that Δv increases from zero to 2. Compare this plot with that of the intensity in the region of the geometrical shadow of a straight edge.

11.10.14. Given two complementary gratings one with its openings one wavelength wide and opaque strips two wavelengths wide, and the other with openings two wavelengths wide and opaque strips one wavelength wide, show that, for the same incident intensity on each grating, the amplitudes of both the first and second orders will be the same for each grating. The amplitude of the zero order will be twice as great for the grating with wider openings. Make use of Eqs. (10.1), (10.2), (10.7), and (10.9). Recall that $\mathbf{u}_0$ is the maximum amplitude of the single-slit diffraction pattern. This problem is a confirmation of Babinet's principle.

chapter XII

Diffraction of Transverse Waves

12.1 Young's Method

The special cases of diffraction which were treated in the previous chapters apply to both longitudinal and transverse waves. These were cases of Fraunhofer diffraction, far-field Fresnel diffraction, and the diffraction pattern along the axis of a circular aperture. For the previous cases which were applicable to all types of wave motion, we have represented the amplitude and phase by the symbol **u**. In this chapter, which applies to transverse electromagnetic waves, we shall express the amplitude of the electric wave by the symbol **E** for electric field strength, and the amplitude of the magnetic wave by the symbol **H** for magnetic field strength. The scalar quantity *I* for intensity of radiation is retained for all types of radiation.

The purpose of this chapter is to unify the treatment of far and near diffraction patterns. The equations which we shall employ are empirical. Common features will be found in the expressions for each type of diffraction. These empirical equations will be found to contain physical ideas which Thomas Young employed to explain diffraction, including his later discovery of polarization. By Young's theory,

a diffraction pattern is the resultant of the unperturbed incident beam and reradiated Huygen's wavelets from points on the edge of the aperture.

300

The ultimate solution of all diffraction problems of electromagnetic waves will be a solution of Maxwell's equations employing the elusive boundary conditions.

12.2 Diffraction Pattern in the Plane of a Circular Aperture

Measurements of plane-polarized microwaves incident normally on the plane of a circular aperture reveal sharp diffraction patterns in the plane of the aperture.[1] As predicted by Fresnel-Kirchhoff methods, the relative intensity at the center of the aperture is a minimum at 0.25 when the aperture is an even number of wavelengths in diameter, and a maximum at 2.25 when the diameter is an odd number of wavelengths. Along the magnetic diameter, the x axis, at right angles to the direction of the incident electric field, the intensity of radiation $|E|^2$ has maximum values separated by about 10% more than 1 wavelength. The intensity along the electric diameter, the y axis, does not show such a sharp pattern except near the center. Sample patterns are indicated in Fig. 219.

A search for a meaningful empirical expression to describe the patterns resulted in

$$\frac{E_y}{E_0} = 1 - \frac{1}{2\pi} \oint e^{-j\beta} \cos\theta \cos\gamma \frac{ds}{r} \qquad (12.1)$$

$$\frac{E_x}{E_0} = -\frac{1}{2\pi} \oint e^{-j\beta} \cos\theta \sin\gamma \frac{ds}{r}, \qquad (12.2)$$

where E is the complex amplitude of the resulting wave at the point P of Fig. 220(a) lying in an aperture of any shape cut in a plane opaque screen, which is thin compared to a wavelength; E_0 is the complex amplitude of the incident plane wave. Subscripts x and y indicate components of E perpendicular and parallel to E_0. The reradiated wavelet is 180° out of phase with the incident wave at the edge, as indicated by the negative sign. The edge element ds is the source of a secondary wavelet which travels the distance r from the edge to P. The phase angle β is $2\pi r/\lambda$. Multiplication by $\cos\theta$ resolves the amplitude E_0 of the incident wave into a component parallel to the edge ds, and $\cos\gamma$ and $\sin\gamma$ resolve the amplitude of the wavelet from ds arriving at P into y and x components. Integration around a closed path is indicated by $\oint$. The factor $1/2\pi$ was inserted to make the equations conform with Kirchhoff's equations for scalar waves at the center of a circular aperture. Anywhere along the axis of a circular aperture Kirchhoff's equation for scalar longitudinal waves also yields the correct relative intensity I/I_0 of polarized waves as noted in Chapter XI. In this case the direction of polarization is the same as that of the incident wave. At any point in the aperture except the

[1] C. L. Andrews, *J. Appl. Phys.*, **28**, 761 (1950).

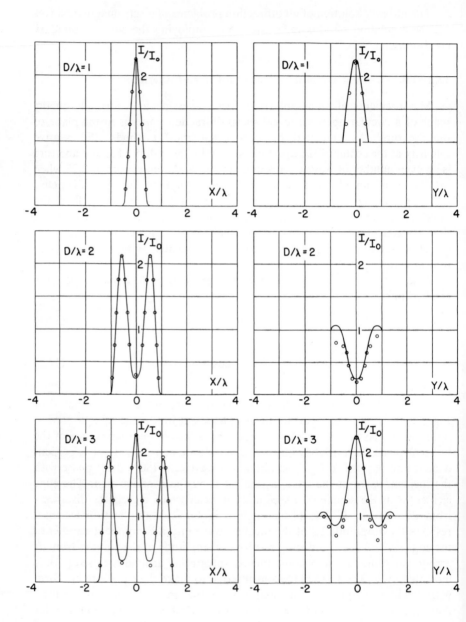

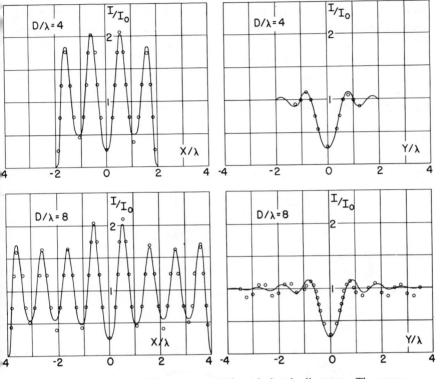

Figure 219. Intensities I/I_0 along magnetic and electric diameters. The curves are computed from Eq. (12.3) and the data measured at a wavelength of 8 cm.

center Kirchhoff's equation for longitudinal waves does not apply to transverse waves.

If the aperture is a circle of radius R, Fig. 220(b), and x and y are the Cartesian coordinates taken along the magnetic and electric diameters from the center to express the position of observation P, we may obtain expressions for $\cos \gamma$ and $\sin \gamma$ by projecting R and r on the x and y axes,

$$\begin{cases} r \cos \gamma = R \cos \theta - x \\ r \sin \gamma = R \sin \theta - y. \end{cases}$$

The element of arc $ds = R \, d\theta$. Substituting for $\cos \gamma$, $\sin \gamma$, and ds in Eqs. (12.1) and (12.2), we obtain

$$\frac{E_y}{E_0} = 1 - \frac{1}{2\pi} \oint e^{-j\beta} \left(\frac{R}{r}\right)^2 \left(\cos^2 \theta - \frac{x}{R} \cos \theta\right) d\theta \qquad (12.3)$$

$$\frac{E_x}{E_0} = -\frac{1}{2\pi} \oint e^{-j\beta} \left(\frac{R}{r}\right)^2 \left(\sin \theta \cos \theta - \frac{y}{R} \cos \theta\right) d\theta. \qquad (12.4)$$

On the electric and magnetic diameters the x components of the electric field from the edges cancel so that the wave is vertically polarized along these axes, and only Eq. (12.3) is employed. All the variables r, θ, γ, and β may be expressed in terms of any one of them.

The positions of maximum intensity along the magnetic diameters are closely the positions that one would predict by a simple treatment of phases. Most of the reradiation from the edge is from the end of the magnetic

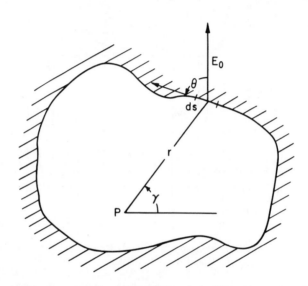

Figure 220(a). Geometry for determination of diffraction pattern in the plane of any aperture of a conducting screen.

diameter where the incident electric field is parallel to the edge. The reradiated wavelets lag the unperturbed wave by the phase change of π upon reradiation plus lag due to the distance traveled along the diameter. If the diameter is an integer number of wavelengths, all three waves, the incident wave and the two reradiated waves from the ends of the magnetic diameter, will be in phase at points which are an odd number of half wavelengths from both ends of the magnetic diameter. By this qualitative prediction the maxima would be one wavelength apart.

The measured peaks were 10% more than one wavelength apart. The first success of Eq. (12.1) was in its check of the positions and values of the maxima in the diffraction pattern along the magnetic diameter. The curves of Fig. 219 for intensities along magnetic and electric diameters are computed from Eq. (12.3), and the points are data taken at a wavelength of 8 cm.

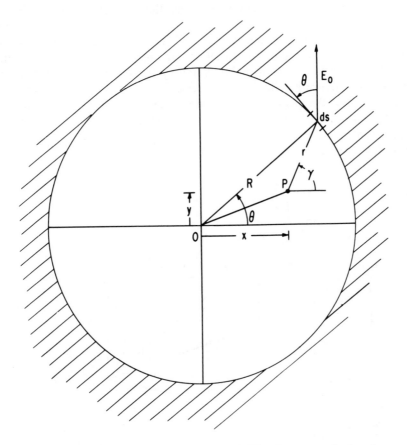

Figure 220(b). Geometry for determination of diffraction pattern in the plane of a circular aperture.

12.3 Diffraction Pattern on the Axis of a Circular Aperture

Our empirical equations for transverse waves and Kirchhoff's integral for longitudinal waves yield identical results for the pattern on the axis of a circular aperture provided we give an obliquity factor $1/\sin \phi$ to the secondary wavelets that are reradiated from the edge. The obliquity angle ϕ is the angle between a ray incident upon a reradiating edge element and a line from that edge element to the point of observation P. Positive ϕ is measured from the edge of the geometrical shadow into the light region and negative ϕ into the dark region. The insertion of the obliquity factor to fit the case at hand will be justified more fully by showing that it yields results that check with experiment for other cases of diffraction that we treat. The obliquity factor becomes unity for wavelets reradiated across the plane of the aperture in the preceding section.

If a plane wave is incident normally on the conducting thin screen containing a circular aperture, as shown in Fig. 221, r is the distance the reradiated wavelet travels to point P, and r_P is the distance of P from the plane of the aperture. The circular aperture lies in the x, y plane, and the electric field of the incident beam is parallel to the y-axis. The unperturbed wave is propagated in the z direction. The edge is divided into elements ds which subtend angle $d\theta$ at the center of the aperture, where θ is measured from the positive x-axis to the element ds.

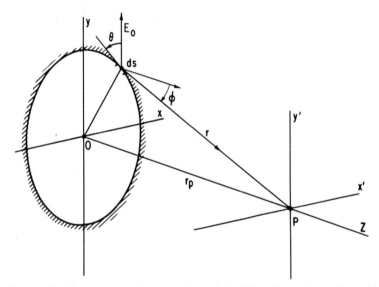

Figure 221. Geometry for determination of the diffraction pattern along the axis of a circular aperture.

We shall divide $\mathbf{E_0}$ into components parallel and perpendicular to the edge of the aperture, and treat the two sets of wavelets reradiated from the edge by the two integrals of the following equation, where $\cos\theta$ and $\sin\theta$ resolve $\mathbf{E_0}$ into components parallel and perpendicular to the edge. The amplitudes of the wavelets reaching P from element ds are proportional to length ds and inversely as the distance r. The component of $\mathbf{E}$ that is parallel to the edge is at right angles to the plane of r and r_P, and the wavelet reaching P will have its electric field in the plane x', y' of Fig. 221. Its y component is obtained by multiplying by $\cos\theta$. The wavelet polarized perpendicular to the edge, in the plane of r and r_P, will not have its field $\mathbf{E}$ in the plane x', y' when it arrives at P. The component in the x', y' plane is obtained by multiplying by $\cos\phi$, as indicated by Fig. 222, which is in the plane of r and r_P. This component is then resolved parallel to the y axis by the factor $\sin \theta$. Thus the y component of the complex amplitude is given by

$$\frac{\mathbf{E}_y}{\mathbf{E}_0} = 1 - \frac{1}{2\pi} \oint e^{-j\beta} \frac{1}{\sin \phi} \cos^2 \theta \frac{ds}{r} - \frac{1}{2\pi} \oint e^{-j\beta} \left(\frac{\cos \phi}{\sin \phi}\right) \sin^2 \theta \frac{ds}{r}. \quad (12.5)$$

From symmetry the x components from the first and fourth quadrants will cancel those from the second and third so that $\mathbf{E}_x/\mathbf{E}_0 = 0$. Because the contributions from each of the four quadrants is the same for the y component, the integrals of Eq. (12.5) may be taken from 0 to $\pi/2$ and multiplied

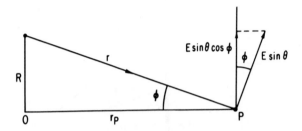

Figure 222. Treatment of component polarized perpendicularly to the edge.

by 4. Here β and ϕ are constants. Since $ds = R\, d\theta$ and $\sin \phi = R/r$, Eq. (12.5) becomes

$$\frac{\mathbf{E}}{\mathbf{E}_0} = 1 - \frac{2}{\pi} e^{-j\beta} \left(\int_0^{\pi/2} \cos^2 \theta\, d\theta + \cos \phi \int_0^{\pi/2} \sin^2 \theta\, d\theta \right) \quad (12.6)$$

Integrating these standard forms, we obtain

$$\frac{\mathbf{E}}{\mathbf{E}_0} = 1 - \frac{1}{2} e^{-j\beta}(1 + \cos \phi), \quad (12.7)$$

which is identical with the results we obtained from Kirchhoff's equation. This equation can be interpreted simply. The amplitude at P is the resultant of interference between two waves, (1) the unperturbed wave and (2) a wave from the whole edge of the circular aperture whose amplitude is $\frac{1}{2}(1 + \cos \phi)$, where $\frac{1}{2}(1 + \cos \phi)$ may be thought of as an obliquity factor of the whole wave from the edge of the aperture reaching any point on the axis.

The relative intensity is

$$\frac{I}{I_0} = 1 + \frac{1}{4} (1 + \cos \phi)^2 - (1 + \cos \phi) \cos \beta. \quad (12.8)$$

12.4 Diffraction Pattern on the Axis of a Ring Opening

If a plane polarized wave is incident normally on a conducting screen with a ring opening as indicated in Fig. 223, the resulting complex amplitude at any point P on the axis of the ring is given by

$$\frac{E}{E_0} = -\frac{1}{2} e^{-j\beta_2}(1 + \cos \phi_2) + \frac{1}{2} e^{-j\beta_1}(1 + \cos \phi_1). \tag{12.9}$$

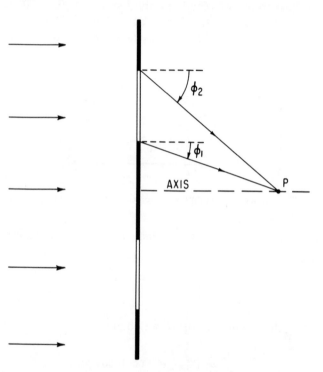

Figure 223. Intensity of radiation along the axis on the shadow side of a disk plotted against the ratio of distance z along the axis to radius R of the disk.

The term unity is missing since the geometrically unperturbed wave does not reach point P. The first term of Eq. (12.9) represents the radiation from the outer boundary of the opening, and the second term the radiation from the inner boundary. Since the wave radiated from the inner edge is entering the shadow, the angle ϕ_1 and the obliquity factor $1/\sin \phi_1$ are negative so that the two integrals of Eq. (12.5), from which the second term of Eq. (12.9) is determined, become positive. The phase angles due to path lengths from the outer and inner edges to point P are β_2 and β_1.

If, as a special case, we let the ring opening uncover the second Fresnel zone, $\beta_2 = 2\pi$ and $\beta_1 = \pi$, and

$$\frac{E}{E_0} = -\frac{(1 + \cos \phi_1) + (1 + \cos \phi_2)}{2},$$ (12.10)

which is the same as Eq. (11.27) obtained by Fresnel-Kirchhoff methods of considering the amplitude at P as the resultant of wavelets reaching P from every point in the aperture.

12.5 Fraunhofer Diffraction by a Single Slit, Young's Method

We shall note the simplicity of Young's method in solving problems of Fraunhofer diffraction. At the large distances of Fraunhofer diffraction by a single slit the unperturbed beam does not contribute. For any direction ϕ of

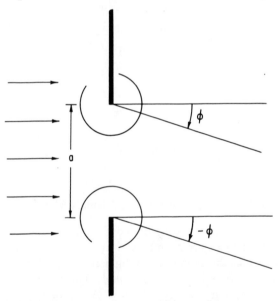

Figure 224. Fraunhofer diffraction by a single slit. Interference between two reradiated cylindrical waves.

Fig. 224 there are but two cylindrical Young's waves reradiated from each edge that contribute to the diffraction pattern. One cylindrical wave reaching P enters the light region making angle ϕ with the incident beam, the other is entering the shadow making angle $-\phi$. We shall define the phase β as in the Fresnel treatment of Fraunhofer diffraction, where β is half the phase difference between wavelets from the two edges.

$$\beta = \frac{\pi a \sin \phi}{\lambda}.$$ (12.11)

Employing the same obliquity factor $1/\sin \phi$ as in the treatment of the circular aperture, we obtain as complex amplitude

$$\mathbf{E} = K\left[\frac{1}{\sin (-\phi)} e^{j\beta} + \frac{1}{\sin \phi} e^{-j\beta}\right], \qquad (12.12)$$

where K is a constant to be evaluated. Expressing Eq. (12.12) in trigonometric form, we obtain

$$\mathbf{E} = -2Kj\frac{\sin \beta}{\sin \phi}. \qquad (12.13)$$

Substituting for $\sin \phi$ from Eq. (12.11) in Eq. (12.13), we obtain

$$\mathbf{E} = -\frac{2\pi Kaj}{\lambda}\frac{\sin \beta}{\beta}. \qquad (12.14)$$

If we let the reference $\mathbf{E}_0$ be the amplitude and phase at $\phi = 0$, $\mathbf{E}_0 = -2K\pi aj/\lambda$,

$$\frac{\mathbf{E}}{\mathbf{E}_0} = \frac{\sin \beta}{\beta} \qquad (12.15)$$

and

$$\frac{I}{I_0} = \frac{\sin^2 \beta}{\beta^2} \qquad (12.16)$$

We note that the results are the same whether the electric field be parallel or perpendicular to the edge, since the same obliquity factor is used for both cases.

12.6 Fraunhofer Diffraction by a Grating, Young's Method

In treating a diffraction grating by Young's method, we obtain a pattern which is the resultant of $2N$ cylindrical wavelets from the edges of N slits. Half the waves enter the geometrically light region as they emerge from the edge and thus have obliquity factors $1/\sin \phi$. The other half enter the dark region and have obliquity factors $-1/\sin \phi$. As in the Fresnel treatment, we shall let β be half the phase difference between wavelets reaching P from two edges of a slit, and γ be half the phase angle between wavelets from corresponding points of adjacent slits.

$$\beta = \frac{\pi a \sin \phi}{\lambda}. \qquad (12.17)$$

$$\gamma = \frac{\pi d \sin \phi}{\lambda}. \qquad (12.18)$$

We shall divide the $2N$ cylindrical wavelets into four sets in the expression for the complex amplitude at the position ϕ on the spectrometer, wavelets from

(1) lower edges of slits above the center of the grating of Fig. 225, (2) lower edges of slits below center, (3) upper edges of slits above center, and (4) upper edges of slits below center. Thus

$$E = K \sum_{n=1}^{n=N/2} \left[\frac{1}{\sin(-\phi)} \left(e^{j[-(2n-1)\gamma+\beta]} + e^{j[(2n-1)\gamma+\beta]}\right) \right.$$
$$\left. + \frac{1}{\sin \phi} \left(e^{j[-(2n-1)\gamma-\beta]} + e^{j[(2n-1)\gamma-\beta]}\right) \right]. \quad (12.19)$$

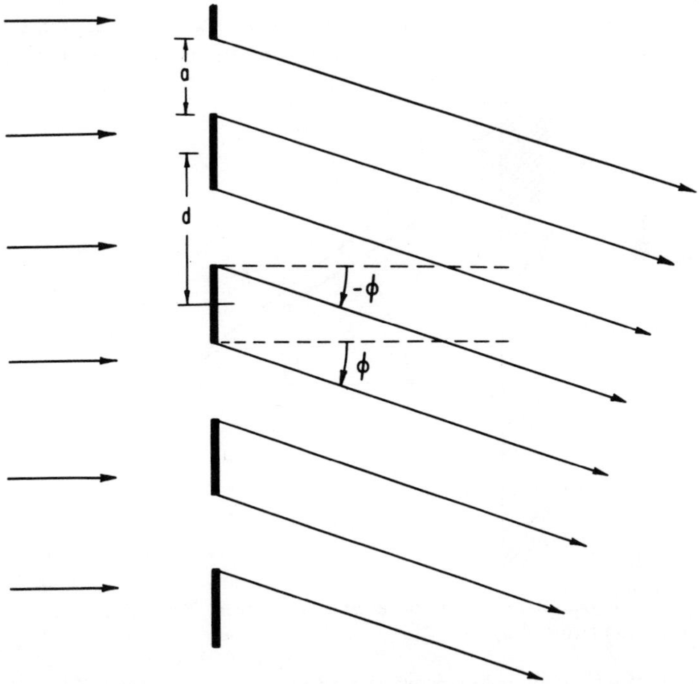

Figure 225. Fraunhofer diffraction by a grating. Interference between $2N$ cylindrical waves.

If we separate the factors of exponent β we obtain

$$E = \frac{K}{\sin \phi} (e^{-j\beta} - e^{j\beta}) \sum_{n=1}^{n=N/2} (e^{j(2n-1)\gamma} + e^{-j(2n-1)\gamma}). \quad (12.20)$$

The summation may be expressed as a fraction

$$\frac{e^{jN\gamma} - e^{-jN\gamma}}{e^{j\gamma} - e^{-j\gamma}},$$

which may be checked by dividing. In turn this fraction may be expressed in trigonometric form $(\sin N\gamma)/\sin \gamma$. If we express the exponential terms in β trigonometrically and substitute the value of $\mathbf{E}_0$ for the center of a single-slit pattern, we obtain

$$\frac{\mathbf{E}}{\mathbf{E}_0} = \frac{\sin \beta}{\beta} \frac{\sin N\gamma}{\sin \gamma}.$$ (12.21)

The polarization is the same as that of the incident beam.

12.7 Diffraction Pattern in the Plane of a Half-Screen

If we apply Young's method to finding the diffraction pattern in the plane of a thin conducting infinite half-screen (straight edge), we shall add the

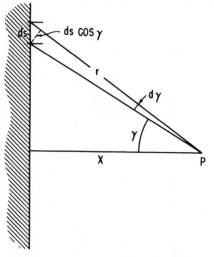

Figure 226. Diffraction in the plane of a half-screen. The element ds may be expressed in terms of $d\gamma$.

elemental spherical wavelets from the edge to the unperturbed wave. If the normally incident plane wave is polarized with its electric field parallel to the edge, we may use Eq. (12.1). From the symmetry, we see that there is no horizontal component of polarization. We may think of an aperture bounded by the straight edge and a semicircle of infinite radius, the contributions from the semicircle being zero. Thus we obtain

$$\frac{\mathbf{E}}{\mathbf{E}_0} = 1 - \frac{1}{\pi} \int_{-\infty}^{\infty} e^{-j\beta} \cos \gamma \frac{ds}{r}.$$ (12.22)

We shall let the angle γ be the independent variable. From Fig. 226 we note that

$$d\gamma = \frac{(\cos \gamma) \, ds}{r}.$$ (12.23)

The phase lag of a wavelet due to distance is

$$\beta = \frac{2\pi r}{\lambda} = \frac{2\pi x}{\lambda \cos \gamma},$$

where x is the distance of P from the edge. Since the contributions from above and below the center to the vertical component of $\mathbf{E}$ are equal, we may multiply by 2 and integrate from $\gamma = 0$ to $\pi/2$.

$$\frac{\mathbf{E}}{\mathbf{E}_0} = 1 - \frac{2}{\pi} \int_0^{\pi/2} e^{-j2\pi x/(\lambda \cos \gamma)} \, d\gamma. \tag{12.24}$$

If we let the constant $y = 2\pi x/\lambda$, the right-hand side of Eq. (12.24) becomes a function of y

$$F(y) = 1 - \frac{2}{\pi} \int_0^{\pi/2} e^{-jy/\cos \gamma} \, d\gamma, \tag{12.25}$$

which may be expressed in terms of Bessel integrals of the first and second kinds for the range 0 to 10 at intervals of 0.01.[2] They may be calculated in terms of other tabulated functions for the range 0 to 16.[3]

$$\frac{\mathbf{E}}{\mathbf{E}_0} = \int_0^y J_0(t) \, dt - j \int_0^y Y_0(t) \, dt, \tag{12.26}$$

and the relative intensity becomes

$$\frac{I}{I_0} = \left[\int_0^y J_0(t) \, dt \right]^2 + \left[\int_0^y Y_0(t) \, dt \right]^2. \tag{12.27}$$

The numerical values of the two integrals

$$v = \int_0^y J_0(t) \, dt \tag{12.28}$$

and

$$w = \int_0^y Y_0(t) \, dt \tag{12.29}$$

are given in Table II for y ranging from 0 to 10 in steps of 0.2. For larger values of y,

$$F(y) = 1 - \sqrt{\frac{2}{\pi y}} \, (e^{-(13/16y^2) + \cdots}) e^{-j(y + \pi/4 - 5/8y + 785/384y^3 + \cdots)}. \tag{12.30}$$

---

[2] *Tables of Functions and Zeros of Functions:* U.S. Department of Commerce, Nat. Bur. Standards, Appl. Math. Ser. 37.

[3] G. N. Watson, *Theory of Bessel Functions*, rev. ed.: New York, Macmillan (1944) p. 752.

Calculations will be as precise as available measurements of microwave intensities in free space if this expression is reduced to

$$F(y) = 1 - \sqrt{\frac{2}{\pi y}}\, e^{-j(y+\pi/4)}, \qquad (12.31)$$

or replacing y by $2\pi x/\lambda$,

$$\frac{E}{E_0} = 1 - \frac{1}{\pi\sqrt{x/\lambda}}\, e^{-j2\pi(x/\lambda+1/8)}. \qquad (12.32)$$

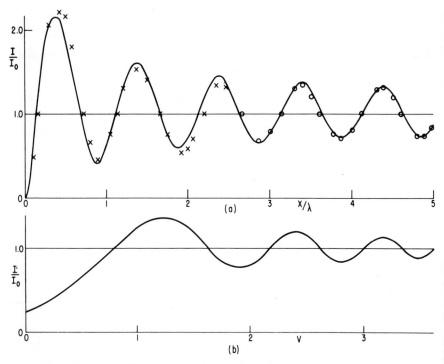

Figure 227. (a) Diffraction pattern in the plane of the half-screen. (b) Classical far-field diffraction pattern of a half-screen.

The expression represents the unperturbed wave and a cylindrical wave from the edge. Outside the very near Gouy region the wavelength of the cylindrical wave is the same as that of a plane wave, the amplitude is inversely as the square root of the radius of the cylinder, and $\pi/4$ in the phase expression is the Gouy phase advance.

In Fig. 227(a) is plotted the experimental data of Lewis[4] together with the curve computed from the empirical Eq. (12.24). For comparison the classical far-field diffraction pattern of the straight edge is shown in Fig. 227(b). We

[4] L. R. Lewis, *J. Appl. Phys.*, **27**, 873 (1956).

note that the fluctuations in intensity are much greater in the plane of the straight edge than in the classical far field.

The portion of Lewis' curve from $x/\lambda = 0$ to 0.1 is still an experimental no man's land. At distances of the dimensions of the probe multiple reradiations between probe and edge cause gross errors. There is need for measurements in the range $x/\lambda = 0$ to 0.1 with wavelengths 100 times the dimension of the probe. The empirical equation gives an electric field of zero at the edge the same as over the surface of the flat screen.

We cannot think of the reradiation as being from the line edge of the screen as in the geometrical point of view. The cylindrical wave from the edge is like that diverging from the focal "line" of a cylindrical mirror or from a straight wire antenna. In physical optics the radiation is not from a focal line but from a Gouy focal region. From the point of view of geometrical optics it is paradoxical that the resultant electric field at the axis of the diverging cylindrical wave is zero.

Beyond the Gouy region of Fig. 227(a) the peaks in the interference pattern are one wavelength apart as nearly as we can measure. The wavelength is that of a plane wave and the electric and magnetic fields are in phase. In the language of transmission lines, the power factor is unity outside the Gouy region.

12.8 Total Diffraction Pattern of a Half-Screen

From the point of view of Young the diffraction pattern of a half-plane conducting thin screen is the resultant of the incident plane wave and the cylindrical wave with axis at the thin edge. In the region between the source and thin conducting screen we must also consider the reflected plane wave.

Outside the Gouy region of about one wavelength in radius, the positions of the maxima and minima in the interference pattern are determined by the path difference $r - z$ indicated in Fig. 228, the π phase change at the edge, and Gouy phase advance $\pi/4$. The condition for maximum intensity is

$$\frac{2\pi(r - z)}{\lambda} - \pi + \frac{\pi}{4} = m2\pi, \tag{12.33}$$

and for minimum intensity is

$$\frac{2\pi(r - z)}{\lambda} - \pi + \frac{\pi}{4} = (2m + 1)\pi, \tag{12.34}$$

where m may be zero or any positive integer. The pattern formed by interference of the plane wave and cylindrical wave is a family of parabolic cylinders of focal lengths

$$f = \frac{r - z}{2}. \tag{12.35}$$

Substituting Eq. (12.35) in Eqs. (12.33) and (12.34), we obtain for the family of parabolic cylinders of *maximum* intensity

$$f = \left(m + \frac{3}{8}\right)\frac{\lambda}{2},$$ (12.36)

and for the family of parabolas of *minimum* intensity

$$f = \left(m + \frac{7}{8}\right)\frac{\lambda}{2}.$$ (12.37)

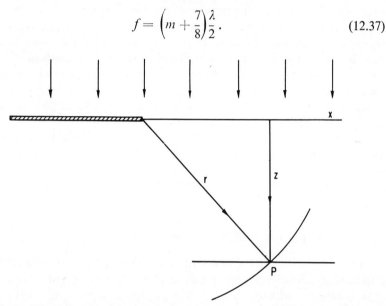

Figure 228. The path difference of the plane wave and reradiated cylindrical wave is $r - z$.

The cross section of the parabolic cylinders in a plane perpendicular to the edge of the screen is a family of parabolas with a common focal point at the edge of the screen. The family of parabolas of maximum intensity is plotted in Fig. 229. These patterns check precisely with the classical diffraction pattern of the far region given by Fig. 227(b) and with the measurements of Lewis in the plane of the screen, Fig. 227(a).

Before attempting to find an equation for the intensity of points in the pattern we shall make an inventory of available data. (1) In the far region the intensity is constant along any of the parabolic cylinders in the family of Fig. 229. For this reason one vibration spiral was sufficient for the treatment of the classical far field. From Young's point of view this constant intensity along the extremes of the parabola can be explained by noting that the product of the distance factor $1/\sqrt{r/\lambda}$, and the obliquity factor for the cylindrical wave is a constant in the far region. (2) In the far Fresnel region inside the geometrical shadow the intensity is due solely to the cylindrical wave and is constant along any one of the family of parabolic cylinders with focal line at the edge of the screen. (3) The measured intensity I/I_0 along the

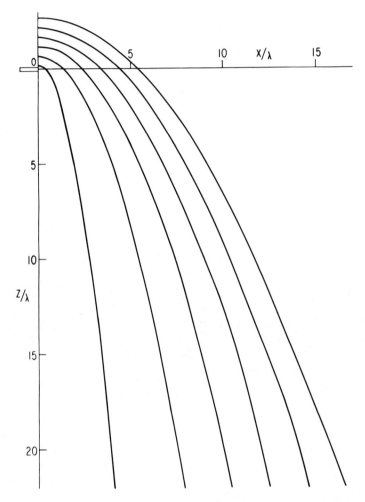

Figure 229. Family of parabolas along which the plane wave and cylindrical wave are in phase.

plane which is the edge of the geometrical shadow is 0.25 up to 0.1 wavelength from the edge, where it drops rapidly toward zero as indicated in the experimental plot of Fig. 230. (4) The amplitude of the cylindrical wave causing the interference pattern measured by Lewis in the plane of the screen is 2.8 times greater than at a point on the same parabola in the far region for parabolas of $f/\lambda > 1$. (5) Harden[5] has measured along the lines $z/\lambda = 0$ and 3 for the electric field of the incident wave both parallel and perpendicular to the edge of the screen.

Although there is scarcity of data for the intermediate region between the plane of the screen and the far Fresnel region, and for the near region between the plane and the source, we shall build an empirical equation to satisfy the existing data in the near and far region.

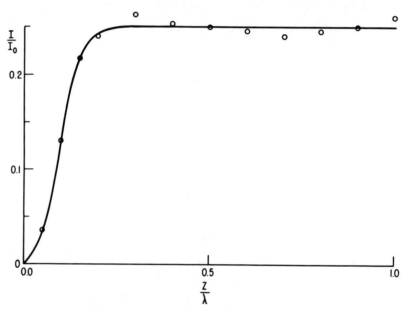

Figure 230. Microwave intensity along the boundary of the geometrical shadow. (Measured by J. J. DeLuisi of the College of Education, State University of New York.)

If we search for a convenient coordinate system, we shall find great simplicity in defining any point P in the plane perpendicular to the straight edge in terms of the focal length of any of the family of parabolas of constant phase and the direction angle ϕ between the direct beam and a ray from the edge to P.

Any of the parabolas of Fig. 229 that fill the plane can be defined by

$$x^2 = 4fz + 4f^2. \tag{12.38}$$

By performing the transformation

$$\begin{cases} r \cos \phi = z \\ r \sin \phi = x, \end{cases}$$

[5] B. N. Harden, *Proc. Inst. Elec. Engrs.*, **99**, 229 (1952).

we obtain the polar form

$$r^2 \sin^2 \phi - 4fr \cos \phi - 4f^2 = 0. \tag{12.39}$$

Solving this quadratic equation for r, we obtain

$$r = \frac{2f(1 + \cos \phi)}{\sin^2 \phi}. \tag{12.40}$$

We shall write and interpret the equation obtained by piecing together the experimental information concerning the parts of the diffraction pattern of the straight edge.

$$\frac{\mathbf{E}}{\mathbf{E}_0} = 1 - \frac{(1 + \sin \phi)e^{-j(\beta + \beta_G)}}{2\pi\sqrt{\dfrac{r}{\lambda} \sin^2 \phi + \dfrac{r_G}{\lambda}}}. \tag{12.41}$$

The term unity is for the unperturbed wave, and is removed in treating the region of the geometrical shadow where x is negative. The second term defines the cylindrical wave from the edge. Its negative sign indicates the reversal of phase at the edge. The second term of the exponent and the second term under the radical are results of the advance in phase and the increased wavelength in the Gouy region. The phase advance due to path difference of the plane and cylindrical waves

$$\beta = \frac{2\pi(r - z)}{\lambda} = \frac{4\pi f}{\lambda}. \tag{12.42}$$

The Gouy phase advance

$$\beta_G = \frac{\pi}{4}\left(1 - \frac{1}{\pi\beta + 1}\right) \tag{12.43}$$

increases from zero at the edge to a constant value of $\pi/4$.

Except for the Gouy effect, the amplitude is inversely as the square root of r/λ. The fourth condition which we must satisfy is that the ratio of amplitudes of the cylindrical wave for any given f/λ greater than unity is 2.8 times as great in the plane of the screen as in the far field. The factors $\sin^2 \phi$ and $(1 + \sin \phi)$ make that ratio $2\sqrt{2} = 2.83$ when $\phi = 0$ and $\phi = \pi/2$ for the same parabola.

The exact value of r_G/λ for the Gouy effect on the amplitude is dependent on the surface resistivity of the straight edge. Faraday was unable to detect any difference between the diffraction pattern of a polished straight edge and a blackened straight edge. Using microwaves, Harden[6] has measured significant differences in the patterns of half-planes of different metals and water in the near field along the line $z/\lambda = 3$. The exact nature of r_G/λ will be determined when measurements have been made for different materials

[6] Harden, *loc. cit.*

within the region $r/\lambda = 0$ to 0.1, using wavelengths of the order of 100 times the dimensions of the probe. If we let

$$\frac{r_G}{\lambda} = \frac{1}{\pi^2},$$ (12.44)

the results fit Lewis' graph of Fig. 227(a) and the tangential electric field will be zero at the edge. Of most significance is the fact that the nature of the surface of the diffracting straight edge affects only the pattern a few wavelengths from the edge.

In the many problems of interference we have found that we could simplify interpretations by letting the independent variable be a phase angle. From Eq. (12.40) for a parabola,

$$\frac{r}{\lambda} \sin^2 \phi = \frac{2f}{\lambda} (1 + \cos \phi).$$

Substituting β from $\beta = 4\pi f/\lambda$, we may rewrite Eq. (12.41)

$$\frac{E}{E_0} = 1 - \frac{(1 + \sin \phi)e^{-j(\beta + \beta_G)}}{2\sqrt{\frac{\pi\beta}{2}(1 + \cos \phi)} + 1}.$$ (12.45)

In the shadow region the term unity for the incident plane wave is omitted. The negative sign before the second term representing π phase change of the reradiated wave into the bright region becomes a positive sign in the dark region. Thus the complex amplitude for the region where x is negative and z positive becomes

$$\frac{E}{E_0} = \frac{(1 + \sin \phi)e^{-j(\beta + \beta_G)}}{2\sqrt{\frac{\pi\beta}{2}(1 + \cos \phi)} + 1}.$$ (12.46)

We are now prepared to examine the special cases.

At the boundary of the geometrical shadow where $\phi = 0$, $\beta = 4\pi f/\lambda = 0$ and Eq. (12.45) becomes $E/E_0 = 1 - \frac{1}{2} = \frac{1}{2}$, and $I/I_0 = \frac{1}{4}$. If we approach this same line from the shadow side we obtain from Eq. (12.46) the same value for the amplitude and intensity. The phase approaches zero as x approaches zero from either side.

In the Fresnel far field, defined in the preceding chapter, $\phi \approx 0$ and Eqs. (12.45) and (12.46) become

$$\frac{E}{E_0} = 1 - \frac{e^{-j(\beta + \beta_G)}}{2\sqrt{\pi\beta + 1}},$$ (12.47)

and

$$\frac{E}{E_0} = \frac{e^{-j(\beta + \beta_G)}}{2\sqrt{\pi\beta + 1}}$$ (12.48)

for the regions of x positive and negative, respectively. We note the simplicity gained in the algebra by letting the independent variable be a phase angle.

The intensities in the two parts of the far field become

$$\frac{I}{I_0} = \left|\frac{\mathbf{E}}{\mathbf{E}_0}\right|^2 = 1 + \frac{1}{4(\pi\beta + 1)} - \frac{\cos(\beta + \beta_G)}{\sqrt{\pi\beta + 1}}, \qquad (12.49)$$

and

$$\frac{I}{I_0} = \left|\frac{\mathbf{E}}{\mathbf{E}_0}\right|^2 = \frac{1}{4(\pi\beta + 1)}. \qquad (12.50)$$

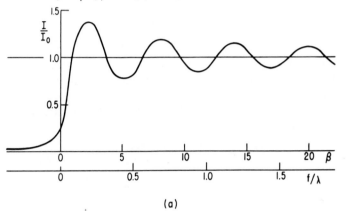

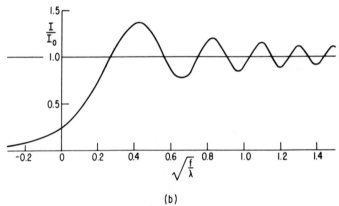

Figure 231. (a) Plot of I/I_0 against β and f/λ for the far-field diffraction pattern. (b) Plot of I/I_0 against $\sqrt{f/\lambda}$ for the far-field diffraction pattern.

Figure 231(a) is a plot of I/I_0 against β. The values f/λ of the constant phase parabolas are also indicated along the axis of ordinates. Figure 231(b) is a plot of I/I_0 against $\sqrt{f/\lambda}$. In this far region Eq. (12.38) for a parabola becomes $x^2 = 4fz$, and

$$\sqrt{\frac{f}{\lambda}} = \frac{1}{2}\frac{x}{\lambda}\sqrt{\frac{\lambda}{z}}. \qquad (12.51)$$

Thus the plot of Fig. 231(b) has the shape of a graph of I/I_0 against x/λ for a fixed value of z/λ in the Fresnel far field, and I/I_0 can be determined for any value of x/λ and z/λ. We note that the graph as well as the algebra is simpler when the intensity is expressed as a function of a phase angle. Beyond the first maximum the values of the maxima and minima occur when $\cos(\beta + \beta_G)$ has the values $+1$ and -1. Since the right-hand side of Eq. (12.49) becomes a perfect square,

$$\frac{I}{I_0} = \left(1 \pm \frac{1}{2\sqrt{\pi\beta + 1}}\right)^2,$$ (12.52)

the positive sign being for maximum and negative for minimum values. The maxima and minima lie on the parabolas numbered in order by Eqs. (12.36) and (12.37).

In the plane of the half-screen, $\phi = \pi/2$ when x is positive and

$$\frac{E}{E_0} = 1 - \frac{e^{-j(\beta + \beta_G)}}{\sqrt{\dfrac{\pi\beta}{2} + 1}}.$$ (12.53)

On the shadow side of the surface of the metal, where $\phi = -\pi/2$,

$$\frac{E}{E_0} = 0.$$ (12.54)

The corresponding intensities for x positive become

$$\frac{I}{I_0} = 1 + \frac{1}{\dfrac{\pi\beta}{2} + 1} - \frac{2\cos(\beta + \beta_G)}{\sqrt{\dfrac{\pi\beta}{2} + 1}}.$$ (12.55)

Expressing I/I_0 in terms of distance x/λ, we obtain

$$\frac{I}{I_0} = 1 + \frac{1}{\dfrac{\pi^2 x}{\lambda} + 1} - \frac{2\cos 2\pi\left[\dfrac{x}{\lambda} + \dfrac{1}{8}\left(1 - \dfrac{1}{2\pi^2 \dfrac{x}{\lambda} + 1}\right)\right]}{\sqrt{\dfrac{\pi^2 x}{\lambda} + 1}}.$$ (12.56)

Figure 232 is a plot of the computed intensities from Eq. (12.56). The results agree with the measurements of Lewis shown in Fig. 227(a), and with the calculations from Eq. (12.22) which is a special case of the empirical Eq. (12.1).

The resultant of the incident beam and reradiated cylindrical wave along the line $\phi = \pi$ is

$$\frac{E}{E_0} = 1 - \frac{e^{-j(\beta + \beta_G)}}{2},$$ (12.57)

and the intensity is

$$\frac{I}{I_0} = 1 + \frac{1}{4} - \cos(\beta + \beta_G).$$ (12.58)

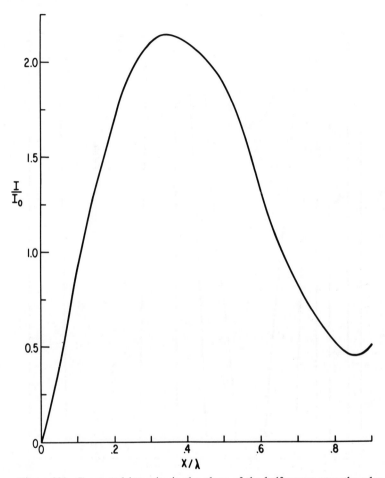

Figure 232. Computed intensity in the plane of the half-screen near the edge.

Along this line $f = r = -z$. By using the perfectly absorbing thin interference absorber, Sec. 8.9, which reradiates only from the edges and eliminates the reflected plane wave, we should be able to check Eq. (12.58). *Data are lacking in this region.*

Figure 233 is a contour plot of the relative intensity I/I_0 on coordinates of β and z in the range from $z = 0$ to 5. By plotting the phase angle β instead of distance x we obtain positions of maxima and minima which are parallel to the z axis. We note that within the short distance of 5 wavelengths from the plane of the screen the maxima in intensity have dropped by 50% to within 5% of their classical far-field value. Although the changes in the intermediate region are slow, they are important for both light and microwaves. We may

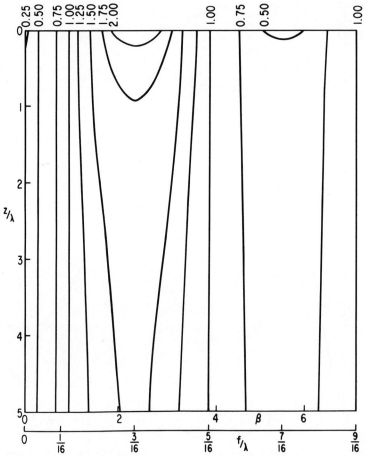

Figure 233. Contour of relative intensity on coordinates of phase angle β and distance z/λ from the half-plane. $\beta = 4\pi f/\lambda$.

pass through this region rapidly by plotting the values of maxima and minima in relative intensity I/I_0 corresponding to parabolas of constant phase β against z/λ on a logarithmic scale in Fig. 234. This family of curves tells us how far from the edge the simple Fresnel far field is in terms of the error we wish to tolerate.

If the normally incident wave has its *electric field perpendicular to the edge of the screen* as indicated in Fig. 235, the electric field of the cylindrical wave arriving at P may be resolved into components parallel and perpendicular to the unperturbed electric field so that the resultant wave is elliptically polarized. This slight elliptical polarization may be detected in the region $\phi = 45°$ for

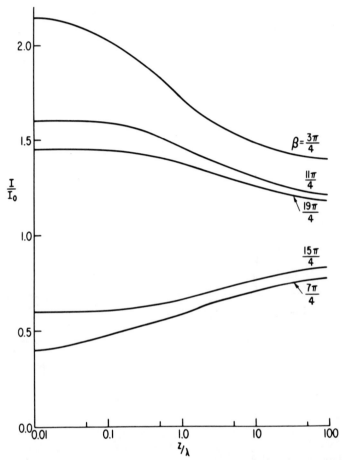

Figure 234. Family of curves of maximum and minimum intensities plotted against the logarithm of z. As indicated, the intensities approach the constant far-field value.

several wavelengths from the edge. The ellipse lies in the plane perpendicular to the edge as indicated in Fig. 235.

In the shadow region the measured intensity of the polarized wave is maximum when the axis of the dipole detector is perpendicular to a ray from the edge and in the plane perpendicular to the straight edge. This is evidence of a cylindrical wave from the edge. The intensity I/I_0 is identical with that when the electric field of the incident wave is parallel to the edge. If we scan along line AB of Fig. 235 with the axis of the dipole detector parallel to the unperturbed E field, the terms of Eqs. (12.45) and (12.46) which represent the cylindrical wave must be multiplied by $\cos \phi$ to resolve the component parallel to AB.

In the Fresnel far field where ϕ is so small that $\cos \phi = 1$ we can not detect polarization effects upon the diffraction pattern. The diffracted wave

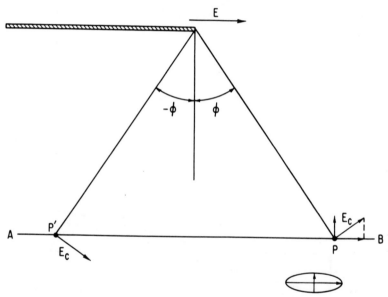

Figure 235. Electric field perpendicular to the edge of the screen.

is plane polarized in the direction of polarization of the unperturbed incident wave.

In the plane of the screen, where the $\cos \phi$ factor is zero and x is positive, the intensity I/I_0 is unity except for one or two wavelengths in the Gouy region. The cylindrical wave does not radiate in that direction. Figure 236 is a plot of measured intensity against x/λ taken by Harden.[7] The high intensity within 0.1 wavelength of the edge is like that of an electrostatic field affected by the insertion of a conducting straight edge. The intensity this close to the edge rises with decreasing thickness of screen.

Figure 237 is a set of graphs of the values of maxima and minima in intensity I/I_0 measured along the parabolas of constant phase against z/λ.

[7] Harden, *loc. cit.*

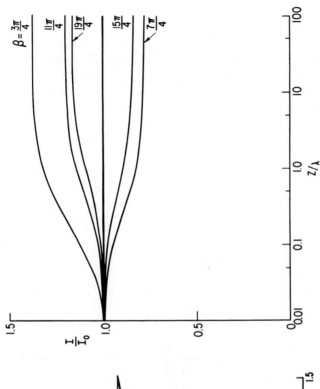

Figure 237. Family of curves of maximum and minimum intensities plotted against the logarithm of z for the case in which the incident wave is polarized perpendicularly to the edge.

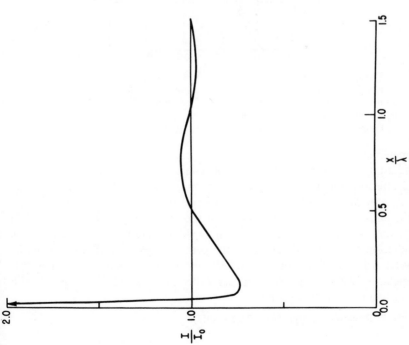

Figure 236. Diffraction pattern in the plane of the screen when the electric field of the incident wave is perpendicular to the edge.

12.9 Small Apertures

The measurements of diffraction patterns in the planes of circular apertures less than 1 wavelength in diameter require probes small compared to the size of aperture and thus small compared to a wavelength. Using wavelengths of 16 and 32 cm, Robinson[8] measured the intensities in the planes of circular apertures ranging from 0.2 to 1.0 wavelength in diameter. Figure 238 is a plot of intensity of radiation at the center of the aperture against diameter of the aperture showing a surprising peak of intensity corresponding to a

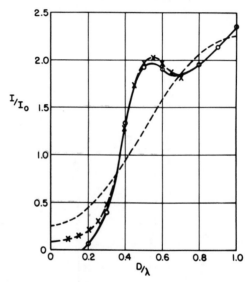

Figure 238. Intensity of radiation at the center of circular aperture plotted against the diameter. The broken line is computed from Eq. (12.8). The circled data points are experimental for a wavelength of 16 cm. The crosses are experimental data points for a wavelength of 32 cm.

diameter of $\frac{1}{2}$ wavelength, which was not predicted by Eq. (12.8) based on reradiation of Young wavelets from the edge.

Robinson noted that this secondary maximum might be explained by treating *multiple* reflections between the edges of the aperture. If A and B are at the ends of the magnetic diameter of the circular aperture of Fig. 239, a secondary wavelet from edge A passing O will undergo π phase change upon reradiation from B and return to the center in phase with the oncoming wavelet from A. Thus multiple reflections from the ends of the magnetic diameter would be in phase with each other even though not in phase with the incident unperturbed wave.

[8] H. L. Robinson, *J. Appl. Phys.*, **24**, 35 (1953).

Following Robinson's suggestion, Hadlock[9] studied the intensity in narrow slits of widths 0.2 to 2.5 wavelengths to see if he could detect effects of multiple reradiation of cylindrical waves from the straight edges. Hadlock discovered not a small secondary maximum as that for a circular aperture, but the highest intensity to be observed in the plane of any aperture. He found an intensity $I/I_0 = 6$ at the center of a slit $\frac{1}{2}$ wave wide, as compared to $I/I_0 = 2$ at the center of a circular aperture $\frac{1}{2}$ wavelength in diameter.

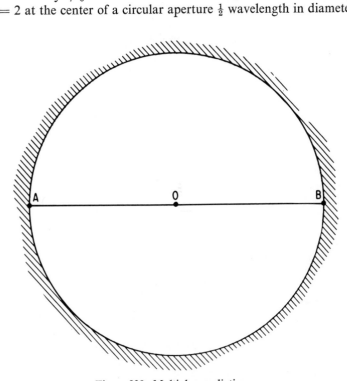

Figure 239. Multiple reradiation.

Using Lewis' expression for the interference pattern between a normally incident wave polarized with electric field parallel to the edge and the reradiated cylindrical wave from the edge,

$$F(y) = 1 - \frac{2}{\pi} \int_0^{\pi/2} e^{-jy/\cos \gamma} \, d\gamma,$$

where $y = 2\pi x/\lambda$, Hadlock computed the intensity at the center of slits for one, two, three, and finally an infinite number of reradiations. Roe's[10] discovery that $F(y)$ could be expressed in terms of the Bessel integrals of the

[9] R. K. Hadlock, *J. Appl. Phys.*, **29**, 918 (1958).
[10] C. L. Andrews, *J. Appl. Phys.*, **28**, 1070 (1957).

first and second kinds given by Eq. (12.26) simplified the calculations. If we assume that the resultant complex amplitude at the center of the slit is made up of the direct wave, plus two reradiated cylindrical waves, one from each edge, plus the infinite number of reradiated cylindrical waves between the edges,

$$\frac{E}{E_0} = 1 + 2\frac{E_1}{E_0}\left[1 + \frac{E_2}{E_0} + \left(\frac{E_2}{E_0}\right)^2 + \left(\frac{E_2}{E_0}\right)^3 + \cdots\right], \qquad (12.59)$$

where E_1/E_0 and E_2/E_0 are defined as follows: E_1/E_0 is the ratio of the complex amplitude of a reradiated cylindrical wave reaching the center of the slit from the edge to the amplitude of the particular incident wave that excited it at the edge; S is the width of the slit.

$$\frac{E_1}{E_0} = \left[\int_0^{\pi S/\lambda} J_0(t)\, dt - 1\right] + j\left[-\int_0^{\pi S/\lambda} Y_0(t)\, dt\right], \qquad (12.60)$$

where E/E_0 is the ratio of the complex amplitude of a reradiated cylindrical wave reaching the opposite side of the slit to the amplitude of the particular incident wave that excited it at the edge.

$$\frac{E_2}{E_0} = \left[\int_0^{2\pi S/\lambda} J_0(t)\, dt - 1\right] + j\left[-\int_0^{2\pi S/\lambda} Y_0(t)\, dt\right]. \qquad (12.61)$$

Since Eq. (12.59) reduces to

$$\frac{E}{E_0} = 1 + \frac{2E_1/E_0}{1 - (E_2/E_0)}, \qquad (12.62)$$

the resultant pattern from an infinite number of reradiations was computed more easily than from two reradiations. Figure 240 shows by a broken line the computed intensity I/I_0 caused by the incident wave and one reradiated cylindrical wave from each side. The solid line indicates the computed intensities for an infinite number of reradiations. The indicated experimental data follow the same shape with the peak corresponding to slits one-half wave wide and a plateau for slits one wavelength wide. The possibility of loss to heat at the edge of the screen has not been treated.

Derwin[11] has compared the intensities in and near slits in highly absorbing thin screens and highly conducting thin screens. The absorbing thin screen was of the *interference absorber type* described in Sec. 8.9. His screen was one-eighth wavelength thick and absorbed over 99% of the incident micro-wave intensity. Figure 241 shows Derwin's comparison of the diffraction patterns in the slits of the two screens. The diffraction patterns in the slits of the reflecting and absorbing screens were identical within the limits of

[11] C. C. Derwin, *J. Appl. Phys.*, **29**, 921 (1958).

experimental error for slit widths greater than 1 wavelength. Derwin's thin absorbing screens permit the study of the diffraction patterns of apertures on the side of the screen toward the source without inclusion of specular reflection from the surface. Figure 242, from Derwin's measurements, indicates the close equivalence of patterns of the absorbing and reflecting screens on the side opposite the source, and the great reduction in the standing wave behind the screen when the reradiation is only from the edge and not from the flat surface.

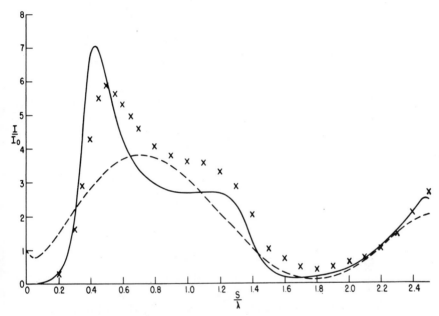

Figure 240. Diffraction pattern at the center of the plane of a slit. The broken line is computed for the incident wave and one reradiation. The solid line indicates computed intensity for an infinite number of reradiations. The experimental data are indicated by crosses.

12.10 Trends in Diffraction Studies

The study of diffraction of electromagnetic waves is approaching an exciting stage. Bits of the puzzle are fitting together with surprises. We shall not be bold enough to say which pieces of the puzzle should be tried next, though we have suggested that the region between the aperture and source and the region within 0.1 wavelength from the edge are untouched. Silver[12] and Ehrlich have measured very constant tangential *magnetic* fields over

[12] S. Silver, *Supplimento del Nuovo Cimento*, **9**, Serie 9, 401 (1952).

circular apertures ranging from D/λ equal to 1.0 to 10. Although the electric field alone has been frequently sufficient in solving problems in physical optics, in those regions near the aperture where the phase relations between

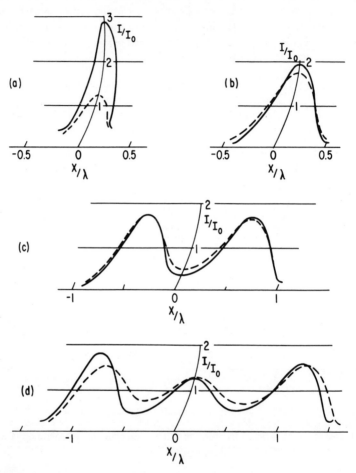

Figure 241. Comparison of diffraction patterns in the planes of reflecting and absorbing thin screens.

electric and magnetic fields are changing we must know the direction, amplitude, and phase of both fields if we are to determine the direction and rate of energy flow.

No experimental arrangement has been found to provide a microwave beam of amplitude and phase which are constant to 2% over a cube ten wavelengths on a side, and near enough to the earth to be usable. This constancy is needed to resolve conflicting theories.

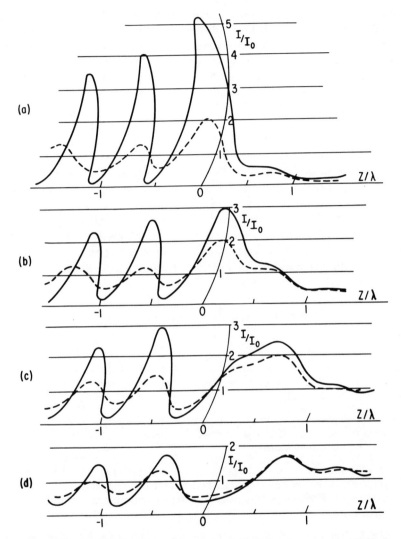

Figure 242. Comparison of the intensities of the diffraction patterns of slits in reflecting and absorbing screens along a line perpendicular to the plane of the screen through the centers of the slits.

A fruitful study has been made of the theory and measurement of the diffraction pattern in the plane of an elliptical aperture, special cases of which are a circle and an approach to a slit.[13] Measurements have been made at wavelengths of 1.25 cm in the neighborhood of lenses 30 wavelengths in

[13] S. J. Bushbaum, A. R. Milne, D. C. Hogg, G. Bekefi, and G. A. Woonton, *J. Appl. Phys.*, **26**, 706 (1955).

diameter showing the features of the diffraction pattern of a circular aperture.[14] The most widely applied of all microwave diffraction studies are the Bethe holes of microwave engineering used to couple cavities with feed-through of the desired amplitude and phase. Bethe's[15] theory of diffraction by a small hole is a complete solution for all angles of incidence, satisfying Maxwell's equations and the boundary conditions everywhere. His solution yields the electric and magnetic fields in and near the aperture, Poynting's vector of the diffracted field, and total radiation through the aperture. The experimental question remains of how large a "small hole" may be and still satisfy Bethe's results. Noting Robinson's measurements of Fig. 238, we may ask about the measurements of $|E/E_0|^2$ at the center of the aperture. For diameters of aperture D/λ below 0.3 the curve was higher for the longer wavelength. If the probe were still smaller compared to a wavelength, would the curve lie closer to the value given for Bethe's small holes?

In the following chapters we shall introduce Maxwell's wave equations and solve some boundary value problems anticipating the simplicity and generality with which diffraction problems may ultimately be treated.

PROBLEMS FOR CHAPTER XII

12.2.1. For a circular aperture 7 wavelengths in diameter, plot the intensity of radiation I/I_0 along the magnetic diameter from the center to a distance of 1.2 wavelengths. Determine the distance between maxima to two significant figures. (Requires about ten hours of computations.)

12.3.2. Express the direction angle ϕ and the phase angle β of Eq. (12.8) in terms of the radius R of the aperture, the distance r_P from the center of the aperture, and the wavelength.

12.8.3. Compare the distance between first and second minimum in the plane of the half-screen with the distance between the first and second minimum at a distance z of 10^6 wavelengths, a distance used in optical studies of diffraction by a half-plane.

12.8.4. From Eq. (12.49) determine the relative intensities I/I_0 of the first two maxima and minima of the far field of a straight edge. Compare with the results obtained from the Fresnel integrals or Cornu spiral.

12.8.5. Plot the spiral for the classical far-field diffraction pattern of a straight edge as given by Eqs. (12.47) and (12.48). Equation (12.48) is represented by the left-hand half of the spiral and Eq. (12.49) by the right-hand half. The two spirals are joined at 0.5 on the real axis. (Requires three hours of computations.)

[14] D. C. Hogg, *J. Appl. Phys.*, **25**, 542 (1954).
[15] H. A. Bethe, *Phys. Rev.*, **66**, 163 (1944).

chapter XIII

Electromagnetic Theory

13.1 Light as a Branch of Electricity and Magnetism

As we have used man-made electrical oscillators to produce hand-sized wavelengths for the study of the near-field diffraction patterns, we have become aware that the waves of the spectrum should be treated as a branch of the study of electricity and magnetism. We have been content to measure $|E/E_0|^2$, the E's representing either maximum or root-mean-square values of sinusoidal transverse electric waves. We have ignored the magnetic field.

In this chapter we shall deduce from the laws of electricity of elementary physics a differential equation of wave motion for the interdependent changing electric and magnetic fields.

Faraday was not a mathematician. Coulomb's inverse square law to describe forces between electric charges did not appeal to his imagination. Faraday devised the pictorial electric and magnetic lines of force to explain force at a distance. His field pictures suggested many of his experiments. Faraday speculated whether changing electric and magnetic fields moved outward with infinite or finite velocity. He even distinguished the tangential and radial components of changing fields and showed pictorially that only the tangential component of the moving lines of force would be significant at large distances.

The genius of James Clerk Maxwell was of two kinds. (1) He was a mathematician at home with differential equations, particularly differential equations of wave motion. (2) He was an experimentalist in his ability to appreciate Faraday's field pictures and understand all that Faraday had published in experimental electricity and magnetism. Under Maxwell's mathematical treatment, Faraday lines of force, which had been a substitute for mathematics, became the unifying basis of electricity and magnetism including electromagnetic waves.

The elementary laws which we shall express in differential form are (1) *Gauss' law for the electric field* of a charge which may be derived from Coulomb's law, and *Gauss' law for magnetic fields*; (2) *Ampere's law in circuital form* for the magnetic field accompanying a current of electricity; and (3) *Faraday's law* in circuital form for the induced emf caused by a rate of change of magnetic flux linkage with the path.

The differential equations which we shall derive will be expressed in Cartesian form and the wave equations will be for plane waves. Other coordinate systems suitable to particular problems are found in advanced textbooks in electromagnetic theory.[1,2]

13.2 Gauss' Law

By Gauss' law,

the total normal outward flux of electric lines of force through a closed surface is proportional to the electric charge enclosed by the surface.

In the meter-kilogram-second-ampere rationalized system the proportionality constant will be the reciprocal of ϵ known as the *permittivity of the medium*; ϵ_0 is the *permittivity of empty space* and has the value $\epsilon_0 = 8.85 \times 10^{-12}$ farad/m. The *dielectric constant* $K = \epsilon/\epsilon_0$, and is the same for all systems of units. Gauss' law may be expressed

$$\int_s E_n \, ds = \frac{q}{\epsilon}. \tag{13.1}$$

Positive E_n is the outward normal component of the electric field strength, and $E_n \, ds$ is the outward flux through an element ds. The integral is taken over the closed surface, and q is the charge enclosed by the surface.

We shall place the origin of the Cartesian coordinates at point P at which we wish finally to express Gauss' law in differential form. We may so orient the coordinates that the direction of increasing field strength through P is toward the octant of positive x, y, and z. We may enclose a region in this octant by an imaginary box of infinitesimal dimensions dx, dy, and dz. Figure 243 indicates the components of electric field normal to the six surfaces.

[1] J. A. Stratton, *Electromagnetic Theory:* New York, McGraw-Hill (1941).
[2] S. A. Schelkunoff, *Electromagnetic Waves:* New York, Van Nostrand (1943).

If there is positive charge in the box, there are more lines of force out of than into the box. We shall add the total outward flux. The flux into the box through the surface in plane $x = 0$ is $E_x \, dy \, dz$. The outward flux through the opposite side is

$$\left(E_x + \frac{\partial E_x}{\partial x} \, dx\right) dy \, dz.$$

The net outward flux through these two surfaces is

$$\frac{\partial E_x}{\partial x} \, dx \, dy \, dz.$$

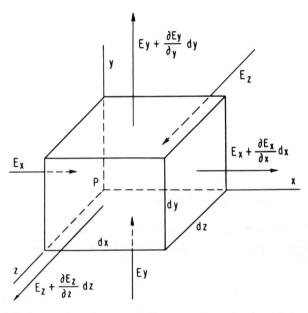

Figure 243. Summation of outward flux through a closed cubical surface.

Treating the y and z components of $\mathbf{E}$ in the same manner, we obtain the net outward flux through the six surfaces,

$$\int_s E_n \, ds = \left(\frac{\partial E_x}{\partial x} + \frac{\partial E_y}{\partial y} + \frac{\partial E_z}{\partial z}\right) dx \, dy \, dz. \qquad (13.2)$$

If ρ is the charge density (coulombs per cubic meter) inside the box, we may express the total charge

$$q = \rho \, dx \, dy \, dz. \qquad (13.3)$$

In the limit as dx, dy, and dz approach zero, the charge density becomes that at point P and the space rates of change of the components of field strength are those at point P. Substituting from Eqs. (13.2) and (13.3) in Eq. (13.1), we obtain

$$\left(\frac{\partial E_x}{\partial x} + \frac{\partial E_y}{\partial y} + \frac{\partial E_z}{\partial z}\right) dx\, dy\, dz = \frac{\rho}{\epsilon} dx\, dy\, dz.$$

Thus Gauss' law is expressed in differential form at point P,

$$\frac{\partial E_x}{\partial x} + \frac{\partial E_y}{\partial y} + \frac{\partial E_z}{\partial z} = \frac{\rho}{\epsilon}. \tag{13.4}$$

In vector analysis the left-hand side of the equation is called the *divergence of the vector* **E**, and abbreviated div **E**. Thus in vector shorthand,

$$\text{div } \mathbf{E} = \frac{\rho}{\epsilon}.$$

We may treat the magnetic field strength **H** in the same manner. However, since there is no isolated magnetic pole as a counterpart of electric charge, the right-hand side of the equation becomes zero and

$$\frac{\partial H_x}{\partial x} + \frac{\partial H_y}{\partial y} + \frac{\partial H_z}{\partial z} = 0. \tag{13.5}$$

In vector shorthand,

$$\text{div } \mathbf{H} = 0. \tag{13.6}$$

13.3 Ampere's Law in Circuital Form

By Ampere's law,

the magnetomotive force around any complete path is proportional to the current linked with the path.

The magnetomotive force is the line integral $\oint H \cos\theta\, dl$ around the complete path, and θ is the angle between the element of path dl and the magnetic field strength **H** at dl. The total current linking the path may be expressed as a surface integral $\int_s j_n\, ds$. The surface is bounded by the path, and j_n is the component of current density (amperes per square meter) normal to the surface element ds. If the fingers of the right hand are wrapped around the closed path in the direction of the magnetomotive force, the thumb points in the direction of the current. In the mksa rationalized system of units, Ampere's law is expressed

$$\frac{1}{\mu_0} \oint B \cos\theta\, dl = \int_s j_n\, ds, \tag{13.7}$$

where μ_0 is the permeability of free space and has the value $4\pi 10^{-7}$ henry/m. In all except magnetic materials the permeability is closely that of free space, and $\mathbf{B} = \mu_0 \mathbf{H}$, where $\mathbf{B}$ is the flux density of lines of induction. The general expression of Ampere's law for all media is

$$\oint H \cos \theta \, dl = \int_s j_n \, ds. \tag{13.8}$$

If we wish to express the conditions at some point P in differential form, we may place the origin of coordinates at point P of Fig. 244. If the surface

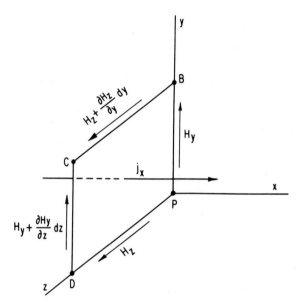

Figure 244. Determination of magnetomotive force around a complete path.

is chosen to be a rectangle with a corner at the origin and sides of infinitesimal length dy and dz, the magnetomotive force becomes around the path $PBCDP$

$$H_y \, dy + \left(H_z + \frac{\partial H_z}{\partial y} \, dy \right) dz - \left(H_y + \frac{\partial H_y}{\partial z} \, dz \right) dy - H_z \, dz$$

$$= \frac{\partial H_z}{\partial y} \, dy \, dz - \frac{\partial H_y}{\partial z} \, dy \, dz.$$

In the limit as dy and dz approach zero, the current density is that at point P and the space rates of change of magnetic field strength are those at P. Substituting the magnetomotive force and current in Eq. (13.8), we obtain at point P

$$j_x = \frac{\partial H_z}{\partial y} - \frac{\partial H_y}{\partial z} \tag{13.9}$$

The coordinates of Fig. 244 are a right-hand system. When the fingers of the right hand swing from the positive x to the positive y direction the thumb points in the positive z direction. If in this system we treat rectangular paths linking with j_y and j_z in the same manner that we treated that linking with the x component of current density, we obtain the following symmetrical set of simultaneous differential equations:

$$\left\{ \begin{array}{l} j_x = \dfrac{\partial H_z}{\partial y} - \dfrac{\partial H_y}{\partial z} \\[2mm] j_y = \dfrac{\partial H_x}{\partial z} - \dfrac{\partial H_z}{\partial x} \quad (13.10) \\[2mm] j_z = \dfrac{\partial H_y}{\partial x} - \dfrac{\partial H_x}{\partial y}. \end{array} \right.$$

Although this is the form that we shall employ, we may note that in vector analysis this relation between the two vectors $\mathbf{j}$ and $\mathbf{H}$ is expressed curl $\mathbf{H} = \mathbf{j}$.

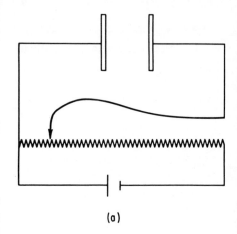

(a)

13.4 Displacement Current

Maxwell noted that, if the time rate of change of electric field were equivalent to an electric current in producing a magnetic field, symmetry would be given to the total set of field equations that express the elementary laws of electricity and magnetism. Although it had not been discovered at that time that a changing electric field produces a

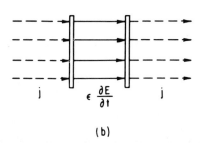

(b)

Figure 245. (a) Arrangement for producing an electric field which changes at a constant rate. (b) Equivalence of current density and rate of change of electric field.

magnetic field, Maxwell proceeded with faith in the symmetry of nature to equate the time rate of change of an electric field to a current density. The time rate of change of electric field he called *displacement current*, as distinguished from a flow of electric charge.

We shall illustrate by treating the special case of the electric circuit of Fig. 245(a) containing a parallel plate capacitor. If the slider of the potentiometer is moved at a slow rate to the right in a time large compared to the time constant of the circuit, the electric field strength $\mathbf{E}$ between the plates of the capacitor will increase at a constant rate. The current to the plate of the capacitor equals the rate of increase of charge on the plate. Algebraically,

$i = dq/dt$. If the plates were being charged by a uniformly distributed current in space as indicated in Fig. 245(b),

$$j = \frac{d\sigma}{dt},$$ (13.11)

where σ is the charge per surface area of the plate. From electrostatics,

$$\epsilon E = \sigma,$$ (13.12)

where ϵ is the permittivity of the dielectric. Thus

$$j = \epsilon \frac{\partial E}{\partial t}.$$ (13.13)

If we consider the displacement current as well as the current of electricity, the current is the same at every point in a series circuit including the capacitor.

If in the neighborhood of point P of Fig. 244 there is both current of electricity and an electric field that is changing with time, Eq. (13.9) should be written to include both current of charge and displacement current so that

$$j_x + \epsilon \frac{\partial E_x}{\partial t} = \frac{\partial H_z}{\partial y} - \frac{\partial H_y}{\partial z}.$$ (13.14)

We shall not be concerned with charges moving in space, so that the set of equations derived from Ampere's law and Maxwell's concept of displacement current become an expression of the space rate of change of magnetic field as dependent on the time rate of change of electric field. Thus,

$$\begin{cases} \epsilon \dfrac{\partial E_x}{\partial t} = \dfrac{\partial H_z}{\partial y} - \dfrac{\partial H_y}{\partial z} \\[2mm] \epsilon \dfrac{\partial E_y}{\partial t} = \dfrac{\partial H_x}{\partial z} - \dfrac{\partial H_z}{\partial x} \\[2mm] \epsilon \dfrac{\partial E_z}{\partial t} = \dfrac{\partial H_y}{\partial x} - \dfrac{\partial H_x}{\partial y}. \end{cases}$$ (13.15)

13.5 Faraday's Law of Induced Electromotive Force

By Faraday's law,

the electromotive force around any complete path is proportional to the rate of decrease of magnetic flux linked with that path.

The emf is the line integral $\oint E \cos \theta \, dl$ around the complete path, where θ is the angle between the element of path dl and the electric field strength $\mathbf{E}$ at dl. The rate of decrease of flux linkage of magnetic lines of induction may be expressed

$$-\frac{d\phi}{dt} = -\int_s \frac{\partial B_n}{\partial t} \, ds,$$ (13.16)

where B_n is the component of the magnetic induction B normal to the element ds. If the fingers of the right hand are wrapped around the circuit in the direction of the induced emf, the thumb points in the direction of the decreasing magnetic flux or opposite to the direction of an increasing magnetic flux. In all except magnetic materials the permeability is nearly equal to that

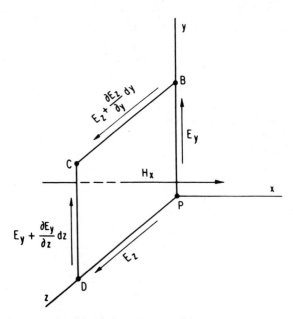

Figure 246. Determination of electromotive force around a complete path.

of free space and $\mathbf{B} = \mu_0\mathbf{H}$. Thus for regions outside magnetic materials Faraday's law becomes

$$\oint E \cos \theta \, dl = \mu_0 \int_s \frac{\partial H_n}{\partial t} \, ds. \tag{13.17}$$

If we wish to express the field conditions at some point P in differential form, we may place the origin of coordinates at P of Fig. 246. If the surface is chosen to be a rectangle with a corner at the origin and sides of infinitesimal lengths dy and dz, the emf around the complete path $PBCDP$ becomes

$$E_y \, dy + \left(E_z + \frac{\partial E_z}{\partial y} \, dy\right) dz - \left(E_y + \frac{\partial E_y}{\partial z} \, dz\right) dy - E_z \, dz$$

$$= \frac{\partial E_z}{\partial y} \, dy \, dz - \frac{\partial E_y}{\partial z} \, dy \, dz. \tag{13.18}$$

In the limit as dy and dz approach zero, the time rate of change of the magnetic field strength **H** and the space rate of change of the electric field strength **E** are those at point P. If the area of the rectangle is sufficiently small that the flux may be considered uniform over the surface,

$$\frac{\partial \phi_x}{\partial t} = \mu_0 \frac{\partial H_x}{\partial t} \, dy \, dz. \tag{13.19}$$

Substituting the expressions for the emf and the rate of change of flux linkage from Eqs. (13.18) and (13.19) in Eq. (13.17), we obtain

$$-\mu_0 \frac{\partial H_x}{\partial t} = \frac{\partial E_z}{\partial y} - \frac{\partial E_y}{\partial z}. \tag{13.20}$$

Noting the right-hand system of coordinates, we may, from the conditions of symmetry, write the set of three simultaneous equations to express the time rate of change of magnetic field in terms of the space rate of change of electric field

$$\left\{ \begin{array}{l} -\mu_0 \dfrac{\partial H_x}{\partial t} = \dfrac{\partial E_z}{\partial y} - \dfrac{\partial E_y}{\partial z} \\[2ex] -\mu_0 \dfrac{\partial H_y}{\partial t} = \dfrac{\partial E_x}{\partial z} - \dfrac{\partial E_z}{\partial x} \\[2ex] -\mu_0 \dfrac{\partial H_z}{\partial t} = \dfrac{\partial E_y}{\partial x} - \dfrac{\partial E_x}{\partial y}. \end{array} \right. \tag{13.21}$$

13.6 The Wave Equations

We shall collect the differential equations which express the laws of electricity and magnetism for a space containing no magnetic material, no free charges, and no current of electricity.

$$\frac{\partial E_x}{\partial x} + \frac{\partial E_y}{\partial y} + \frac{\partial E_z}{\partial z} = 0. \tag{13.22}$$

$$\frac{\partial H_x}{\partial x} + \frac{\partial H_y}{\partial y} + \frac{\partial H_z}{\partial z} = 0. \tag{13.23}$$

$$\left\{ \begin{array}{l} \epsilon \dfrac{\partial E_x}{\partial t} = \dfrac{\partial H_z}{\partial y} - \dfrac{\partial H_y}{\partial z} \\[2ex] \epsilon \dfrac{\partial E_y}{\partial t} = \dfrac{\partial H_x}{\partial z} - \dfrac{\partial H_z}{\partial x} \\[2ex] \epsilon \dfrac{\partial E_z}{\partial t} = \dfrac{\partial H_y}{\partial x} - \dfrac{\partial H_x}{\partial y} \end{array} \right. \tag{13.24}$$

$$\begin{cases} -\mu_0 \dfrac{\partial H_x}{\partial t} = \dfrac{\partial E_z}{\partial y} - \dfrac{\partial E_y}{\partial z} \\[2mm] -\mu_0 \dfrac{\partial H_y}{\partial t} = \dfrac{\partial E_x}{\partial z} - \dfrac{\partial E_z}{\partial x} \\[2mm] -\mu_0 \dfrac{\partial H_z}{\partial t} = \dfrac{\partial E_y}{\partial x} - \dfrac{\partial E_x}{\partial y} \, . \end{cases} \tag{13.25}$$

Recalling Eq. (2.9), the differential equation of wave motion, we shall separate the components of **E** and **H** and express their second derivatives with respect to time and distance. We shall attempt to find a wave equation for the electric field component E_x. If we take the second partial respect to time of the first of the set of Eqs. (13.24), we obtain

$$\epsilon \frac{\partial^2 E_x}{\partial t^2} = \frac{\partial^2 H_z}{\partial y \, \partial t} - \frac{\partial^2 H_y}{\partial z \, \partial t} \, . \tag{13.26}$$

By taking partials with respect to z and y of the last two Eqs. (13.25) and substituting in Eq. (13.26), we may eliminate terms in **H**.

$$\epsilon \frac{\partial^2 E_x}{\partial t^2} = - \frac{1}{\mu_0}\left(\frac{\partial^2 E_y}{\partial x \, \partial y} - \frac{\partial^2 E_x}{\partial y^2} - \frac{\partial^2 E_x}{\partial z^2} + \frac{\partial^2 E_z}{\partial x \, \partial z} \right),$$

which may be written

$$\mu_0 \epsilon \frac{\partial^2 E_x}{\partial t^2} = - \frac{\partial}{\partial x}\left(\frac{\partial E_y}{\partial y} + \frac{\partial E_z}{\partial z} \right) + \frac{\partial^2 E_x}{\partial y^2} + \frac{\partial^2 E_x}{\partial z^2} \, .$$

Substituting for $\partial E_y/\partial y + \partial E_z/\partial z$ from Eq. (13.22), we obtain an equation in which E_x is the only field component. From the symmetry, we may write similar equations in E_y and E_z. In like manner, we may eliminate the electric fields and obtain equations in H_x, H_y, and H_z.

$$\begin{cases} \mu_0\epsilon \dfrac{\partial^2 E_x}{\partial t^2} = \dfrac{\partial^2 E_x}{\partial x^2} + \dfrac{\partial^2 E_x}{\partial y^2} + \dfrac{\partial^2 E_x}{\partial z^2} \\[2mm] \mu_0\epsilon \dfrac{\partial^2 E_y}{\partial t^2} = \dfrac{\partial^2 E_y}{\partial x^2} + \dfrac{\partial^2 E_y}{\partial y^2} + \dfrac{\partial^2 E_y}{\partial z^2} \\[2mm] \mu_0\epsilon \dfrac{\partial^2 E_z}{\partial t^2} = \dfrac{\partial^2 E_z}{\partial x^2} + \dfrac{\partial^2 E_z}{\partial y^2} + \dfrac{\partial^2 E_z}{\partial z^2} \end{cases} \tag{13.27}$$

$$\begin{cases} \mu_0\epsilon \dfrac{\partial^2 H_x}{\partial t^2} = \dfrac{\partial^2 H_x}{\partial x^2} + \dfrac{\partial^2 H_x}{\partial y^2} + \dfrac{\partial^2 H_x}{\partial z^2} \\[2mm] \mu_0\epsilon \dfrac{\partial^2 H_y}{\partial t^2} = \dfrac{\partial^2 H_y}{\partial x^2} + \dfrac{\partial^2 H_y}{\partial y^2} + \dfrac{\partial^2 H_y}{\partial z^2} \\[2mm] \mu_0\epsilon \dfrac{\partial^2 H_z}{\partial t^2} = \dfrac{\partial^2 H_z}{\partial x^2} + \dfrac{\partial^2 H_z}{\partial y^2} + \dfrac{\partial^2 H_z}{\partial z^2} \, . \end{cases} \tag{13.28}$$

These are differential equations of wave motion of the electric and magnetic field strengths, provided $\mu_0\epsilon = 1/v^2$ where v is the velocity of the wave.

In free space,

$$\mu_0\epsilon_0 = 4\pi 10^{-7}\,\frac{\text{henry}}{\text{meter}} \times 8.85 \times 10^{-12}\,\frac{\text{farad}}{\text{meter}},$$

so that approximately

$$\frac{1}{\mu_0\epsilon_0} = 9.0 \times 10^{16}\,\frac{\text{meters}^2}{\text{sec}^2}$$

and

$$\frac{1}{\sqrt{\mu_0\epsilon_0}} = 3.0 \times 10^8\,\frac{\text{meters}}{\text{sec}},$$

which is the measured velocity of light and microwaves in empty space. The measurement of c, the number of electrostatic units of charge in an electromagnetic unit of charge, by Rosa and Dorsey may be considered as a measurement of the quantity $\mu_0\epsilon_0$ in the mksa rationalized system of units.

In a dielectric, $v = 1/\sqrt{\mu_0\epsilon}$. By definition, the index of refraction of the dielectric is $n = c/v$. Substituting the values for the velocity from the wave equation, we obtain

$$n = \sqrt{\frac{\epsilon}{\epsilon_0}} = \sqrt{K}$$

The dielectric constant K, as well as the index of refraction, varies widely with frequency at the frequencies of the strong emission lines of the atoms of the dielectric. At microwave frequencies the index of refraction is very nearly equal to the square root of dielectric constant measured at direct current. For instance the d-c dielectric constant of water is 81.07, and the index of refraction of water for microwaves at the frequency of 3000 megacycles/sec is 9.03 which is the square root of the dielectric constant within the limits of experimental error. In the infrared the squares of the indices of refraction are still closely equal to the d-c dielectric constant. For instance, the dielectric constant of dry air is 1.000586 and the square of its index of refraction is 1.000585.

13.7 The Interdependence of the Electric and Magnetic Waves

The sets of differential equations Eqs. (13.24) and (13.25) derived from Ampere's and Faraday's laws show that an electric field which is changing with time is accompanied by a magnetic field that varies in space, and that a magnetic field that varies with time is accompanied by an electric field that varies in space. By treating the special case of a plane wave moving in the positive x direction, we shall show the interdependence of the electric and magnetic waves.

For a plane wave moving in the x direction the fields can vary only with x and time and not with y or z. Thus the last two terms of Eqs. (13.27) and (13.28) become zero. Since

$$\frac{\partial E_y}{\partial y} = \frac{\partial E_z}{\partial z} = 0,$$

Eq. (13.22) becomes $\partial E_x/\partial x = 0$. Similarly $\partial H_x/\partial x = 0$. Thus there can be no longitudinal wave of electric or magnetic field. Maxwell's electromagnetic waves are *transverse* precisely as found experimentally for all waves of the spectrum.

We have remaining only the last two of each of the sets of Eqs. (13.27) and (13.28), and of these equations the last two terms of each is zero, so that

$$\mu_0\epsilon \frac{\partial^2 E_y}{\partial t^2} = \frac{\partial^2 E_y}{\partial x^2}, \tag{13.29a}$$

$$\mu_0\epsilon \frac{\partial^2 E_z}{\partial t^2} = \frac{\partial^2 E_z}{\partial x^2}, \tag{13.29b}$$

$$\mu_0\epsilon \frac{\partial^2 H_y}{\partial t^2} = \frac{\partial^2 H_y}{\partial x^2}, \tag{13.29c}$$

$$\mu_0\epsilon \frac{\partial^2 H_z}{\partial t^2} = \frac{\partial^2 H_z}{\partial x^2}. \tag{13.29d}$$

We now ask, can each of these four transverse waves traveling in the positive x direction exist independently? We return to Eqs. (13.24) and (13.25) which state the interdependence of fields that vary in time and space. Since from the definition of a plane wave $\partial H_x/\partial z = 0$, the second of Eqs. (13.24) becomes

$$\epsilon \frac{\partial E_y}{\partial t} = -\frac{\partial H_z}{\partial x}. \tag{13.30}$$

This equation tells us that, if E_y varies with time, H_z must vary with x. Since Eq. (13.29a) contains a term in which E_y varies with time, and Eq. (13.29d) contains a term in which H_z varies with x, the two waves must exist simultaneously. We shall collect this interdependent pair.

$$\left[\begin{array}{l} \mu_0\epsilon \dfrac{\partial^2 E_y}{\partial t^2} = \dfrac{\partial^2 E_y}{\partial x^2} \\[3mm] \mu_0\epsilon \dfrac{\partial^2 H_z}{\partial t^2} = \dfrac{\partial^2 H_z}{\partial x^2}. \end{array} \right.$$

Similarly, the second of Eqs. (13.25) makes wave Eqs. (13.29b) and (13.29c) interdependent. Either of these pairs of equations represents a plane-polarized wave. Their electric and magnetic parts are polarized at right angles to each other.

Any equation of the form $E_y = f(x - vt)$ is a solution of differential equation (13.29a). The form of this solution with which we have been concerned is

$$E_y = E_{y0}e^{j(2\pi/\lambda)(x-vt)}, \tag{13.31}$$

which describes a sinusoidal wave of amplitude E_{y0} traveling in the x direction. We arbitrarily picked the phase as zero when $x = t = 0$. Similarly,

$$H_z = H_{z0}e^{j[(2\pi/\lambda)(x-vt)+\alpha]} \tag{13.32}$$

is a solution of Eq. (13.29e), where H_{z0} is the amplitude and α is the phase of this magnetic wave relative to the electric wave of Eq. (13.31). We wish to find the phase angle α between the two waves. If we take the partial of Eq. (13.31) with respect to time and the partial of Eq. (13.32) with respect to x, we obtain

$$\frac{\partial E_y}{\partial t} = \frac{-jE_{y0}2\pi v}{\lambda}e^{j(2\pi/\lambda)(x-vt)}, \tag{13.33}$$

$$\frac{\partial H_z}{\partial x} = \frac{jH_{z0}2\pi}{\lambda}e^{j[(2\pi/\lambda)(x-vt)+\alpha]}. \tag{13.34}$$

Substituting from these two equations in Eq. (13.30), we obtain

$$\epsilon E_{y0}v = H_{z0}e^{j\alpha}, \tag{13.35}$$

or in trigonometric form,

$$\epsilon E_{y0}v = H_{z0}(\cos \alpha + j \sin \alpha). \tag{13.36}$$

Since the imaginary terms of the two sides of the equation must be equal, $\sin \alpha = 0$ and $\alpha = 0$, or $180°$. Equation (13.30) dictates that the rate of change of E_y with t must be opposite in sign to the rate of change of H_z with x. As seen from Fig. 247(a), Eq. (13.30) is satisfied if the waves are in phase and traveling in the positive x direction. At the point x, H_z is increasing with x while E_y is decreasing with time as the wave moves forward to the dotted position. If α is $180°$, Eq. (13.30) dictates that the wave be moving in a negative x direction. For the wave moving in the positive x direction Eq. (13.36) reduces to

$$\epsilon E_{y0}v = H_{z0}. \tag{13.37}$$

Since $v = 1/\sqrt{\mu_0\epsilon}$, we may relate the amplitudes of the electric and magnetic waves of Eq. (13.37) by

$$\mu_0 H_{z0}^2 = \epsilon E_{y0}^2. \tag{13.38}$$

Similarly, we may treat the waves of Eqs. (13.29b) and (13.29c) to show that, if the wave is traveling in the positive x direction, E_z has a positive maximum when H_y has a negative maximum. Actually Eqs. (13.29b) and (13.29c) yield no new information. If we merely rotate the coordinate system about the x axis through $90°$ in a direction from positive y toward positive z, the equations that described the first pair of waves now describe the second pair.

The interdependence of the electric and magnetic waves has been noted in three ways. (1) Their amplitudes are related by Eq. (13.38). (2) Their absolute values are in phase. (3) They are polarized at right angles to each

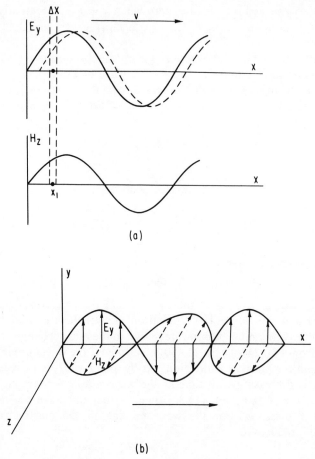

(a)

(b)

Figure 247. (a) Comparison of signs of $\delta E_y/\delta t$ and $\delta H_z/\delta x$ in a wave traveling in the positive x direction. (b) Interdependent electric and magnetic waves traveling in the positive x direction.

other such that, if the fingers of the right hand swing from the direction of the electric field to the direction of the magnetic field, the thumb points in the direction of propagation of the wave as indicated in Fig. 247(b). When waves are polarized at right angles to each other they are often said to be in phase if the absolute values go through zero and maximum values together.

13.8 The Flux of Energy

We wish to determine the intensity of radiation, or the rate of flow of energy per area, in the direction x of propagation of the wave. First we shall calculate the energy density at a point in an electric field by treating the special case of the field in a parallel-plate capacitor. The total energy stored in the field of the capacitor is $\frac{1}{2}Vq$, where V is the potential difference between the plates and q the charge on a plate. The surface charge density is

$$\frac{q}{H} = \epsilon E, \tag{13.39}$$

where A is the cross-sectional area perpendicular to the field. The potential $V = Ed$, where d is the distance between plates. Thus the energy stored in the capacitor is

$$U = \tfrac{1}{2}\epsilon E^2 Ad. \tag{13.40}$$

Dividing by Ad, we obtain the

$$\text{energy density} = \tfrac{1}{2}\epsilon E^2 \tag{13.41}$$

expressed in joules per cubic meter. Since the field is uniform, this energy density is that at any point in the field.

Likewise, using the special case of a toroidal coil inductance with its uniform field, we may show[3] that in the magnetic field

$$\text{energy density} = \tfrac{1}{2}\mu_0 H^2 \tag{13.42}$$

expressed in joules per cubic meter. The total instantaneous energy density at a point in the electromagnetic wave is

$$\frac{\mu_0 H^2 + \epsilon E^2}{2}.$$

Since μ_0 and ϵ are constants in Eq. (13.38) for the relation between amplitudes of the sinusoidal magnetic and electric waves in phase with each other, we may relate the instantaneous values of the fields at any point in the wave by

$$\mu_0 H^2 = \epsilon E^2. \tag{13.43}$$

Thus the instantaneous

$$\text{energy density} = \frac{\mu_0 H^2 + \epsilon E^2}{2}$$

$$= \mu_0 H^2 = \epsilon E^2. \tag{13.44}$$

[3] R. P. Winch, *Electricity and Magnetism:* Englewood Cliffs, N.J., Prentice-Hall (1955), Sec. 16–8.

We note that the Eq. (13.38) relating the amplitudes of the two waves states that the energy is equally divided between the waves.

The rate of flow of energy per area taken at right angles to the flow is the product of the energy density and the wave velocity v. Thus

$$I = v\mu_0 H^2. \tag{13.45}$$

Replacing one H in Eq. (13.45) by its equivalent from Eq. (13.43), we obtain $I = vEH\sqrt{\epsilon\mu_0}$. Since $v = 1/\sqrt{\epsilon\mu_0}$,

$$I = EH \tag{13.46}$$

expressed in watts per square meter. A vector notation of the magnitude and direction of the intensity is treated in the problems.

13.9 Applications and Limitations

Our treatment of Maxwell's equations for plane waves serves to indicate methods of treating electromagnetic waves in a continuous isotropic medium. Applications of Maxwell's wave equations combined with equations of electric and magnetic boundary conditions will be made for reflections from plane metal surfaces and for reflection and refraction at plane surfaces between dielectrics in the chapter on polarization. A recent application of Maxwell's equations and the boundary conditions has been made in the study of wave guides.[4,5]

We have not treated the wave equations of spherical and cylindrical waves. In modern literature on the diffraction of waves we find cylindrical, spherical, ellipsoidal, and parabolic systems in use.

If we were to treat electromagnetic waves in magnetic media such as modern ferrites, we would recall that the complete relation between magnetic induction B and field strength H is

$$\mathbf{H} = \frac{\mathbf{B}}{\mu_0} - \mathbf{I},$$

where $\mathbf{I}$ is the magnetic moment per unit volume.

When we restricted our treatment to media that did not contain currents of electric charge we excluded the new science of electromagnetic waves in a plasma.

The formalism of this chapter should not suggest a completed work. Although we may have faith that the behavior of electromagnetic waves can be completely described by Maxwell's equations and the boundary conditions, we recognize that the task is just begun.

---

[4] L. Page and N. I. Adams, *Principles of Electricity*, 2nd ed.: New York, Van Nostrand (1948), Sec. 136.

[5] S. Ramo and J. Whinnery, *Fields and Waves in Modern Radio*, 2nd ed.: New York, Wiley (1953).

PROBLEMS FOR CHAPTER XIII

13.2.1. From Gauss' law, derive Coulomb's law for the direction and magnitude of the electric field strength E due to a point charge q.

13.3.2. From Ampere's circuital law, derive Biot and Savart's experimental law for the magnetic field strength H in the neighborhood of a long straight current bearing wire.

13.3.3. Find, by summation over four infinitesimal elements of path, the magnetomotive force around a small rectangle with sides dx and dz in terms of space rates of change of magnetic field strength H and the area enclosed by the path.

13.5.4. Find, by summation over four infinitesimal elements of path, the emf around a small rectangle with sides dx and dz in terms of space rates of change of electric field strength E and the area enclosed by the path.

13.6.5. From the set of eight partial differential equations expressing the laws of electricity and magnetism at a point in a Cartesian coordinate system, derive the wave equation for the y component of the magnetic field strength H.

13.6.6. What is the velocity of microwaves in pure water? The dielectric constant K of water is 81.

13.7.7. Prove the interdependence of waves of the z component of electric field and y component of magnetic field, each traveling in the positive x direction.

13.8.8. If Eq. (13.46) expresses the relation between the values I, E, and H in a sinusoidal wave,

$$\bar{I} = \overline{EH},$$

where $\bar{I}$ is the average intensity over a cycle and $\overline{EH}$ is the average of the products of the instantaneous values of the fields. Show that the product of the root-mean-square values of E and H equals the average of the products $\overline{EH}$, taken over a cycle. Only magnitudes of the vectors E and H are treated in this problem.

13.8.9. By vector methods we may express the direction as well as the magnitude of the rate of flow of energy per area. If C is a product of the vectors A and B which are at right angles to each other, and the direction of C is the direction of the thumb of the right hand when the fingers are swung from the direction of A to the direction of B, the vector product is expressed by the symbolism

$$C = A \times B.$$

Poynting's vector S is the rate of flow of energy per unit of area, where I is the magnitude of S. Express S as a vector product of the interdependent electric and magnetic field strengths in a plane-polarized wave.

13.9.10. Express Ampere's law in differential form to include both current densities and displacement currents at a point.

chapter XIV

Absorption of
Electromagnetic Waves

14.1 Bougier's Law

Up to this time we have considered only wave energy that was conserved. In our treatment of interference and diffraction the total wave energy remained a constant. All materials absorb the waves that pass through them to some extent.

Measurements of absorption are made of parallel beams of radiation with blocks or cells of absorber set with plane surfaces perpendicular to the beam. The fractional loss of intensity in a continuous medium is given by Bougier's law. The fractional loss of intensity of the wave passing through the absorbing medium is proportional to the element of thickness.

$$\frac{\Delta I}{I} = -\mu \, \Delta x, \tag{14.1}$$

where ΔI is the loss in intensity of the wave in passing through element of thickness Δx shown in Fig. 248(a), and μ is the linear absorption coefficient. For many practical problems in absorption the wave will not be plane. In empty space the power is conserved for all shapes of waves, while the intensity

352

is conserved only for a plane wave. Thus the absorption law for the spherical wave indicated in Fig. 248(b) is

$$\frac{\Delta P}{P} = -\mu \, \Delta x, \tag{14.2}$$

where $\Delta P/P$ is the fractional loss of power of the wave as it passes through the shell of thickness Δx.

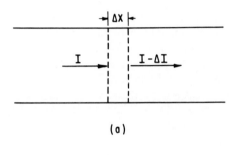

(a)

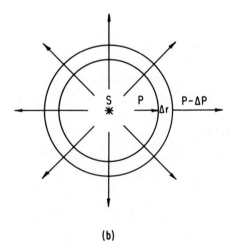

(b)

Figure 248. (a) Absorption of a plane wave. (b) Absorption of a spherical wave.

If we integrate Eq. (14.1) over the total thickness, we obtain the resultant intensity transmitted by the absorber.

$$\int_{I_0}^{I_x} \frac{dI}{I} = -\mu \int_0^x dx, \tag{14.3}$$

where I_0 is the incident intensity and I_x the transmitted intensity through thickness x. Integrating Eq. (14.3) we obtain

$$\ln \frac{I_x}{I_0} = -\mu x. \tag{14.4}$$

If Eq. (14.4) is expressed in exponential form,

$$\frac{I_x}{I_0} = e^{-\mu x}. \tag{14.5}$$

If we measure the linear absorption coefficient μ by placing a block of absorber in a parallel beam, intensity may be extracted from the beam in several ways: (a) transformation of wave energy to thermal energy; (b) scattering of the wave out of the beam by particles without change in wavelength, a form of diffraction observed at large distance from the diffracting particles; (c) Compton scattering with decrease in frequency when some of the energy is given to a recoil electron; (d) fluorescence absorption by atoms which are excited by the incident radiation and reradiate a lower frequency; (e) resonance absorption in low-pressure gases and vapors; (f) Raman scattering, in which the scattered waves extract from or lose to the scattering molecules some vibrational or rotational energy with corresponding gain or loss of frequency; (g) photoelectric absorption, in which a photon is absorbed by an atom and its energy is used to extract an electron from the atom, the remaining energy becoming kinetic energy of the electron; and (h) pair production, in which a photon collides with the field of a nucleus and is annihilated with the creation of a positron and electron.

14.2 True Absorption

All waves of the spectrum from x-rays to radio waves undergo conversion to thermal energy, a process of *true absorption* of wave energy. Absolute wattmeters are devised to measure the power in electromagnetic waves at all wavelengths by converting all the wave energy, the primary wave, fluorescence, and scattered waves, to thermal energy in a calorimeter. Conversion to thermal energy is the final fate of all wave energy. The heating of the earth by the sun involves true absorption. Recent applications of true absorption are solar cookers, microwave ovens, and microwave heat therapy.

Selective absorption of bands of the spectrum is primarily responsible for the colors of dielectric materials observed by visible light. Colored glass filters convert certain ranges of frequency to thermal energy. Red glass[1] transmits red and orange, and almost completely absorbs the remainder.

---

[1] *Handbook of Chemistry and Physics:* Cleveland, Ohio, Chemical Rubber Publishing Company (see Transmission of Wratten Filters).

The colors of dielectric objects such as pigments of flowers and paints are caused likewise by selective absorption within the pigment as the light undergoes multiple reflections between particles of the material. These substances are the same color by reflection and transmission, since both cases involve transmission through the medium.

Coats of metal thin enough to transmit light affect light quite differently. If we evaporate gold onto a glass plate in a bell jar, we may see the gold film become yellow by reflected light, but blue-green by transmission, before the layer of gold is 1 wavelength thick. Later, when we study resonance absorption in metal vapors at increasing pressures, we shall note this same metallic reflection taking place within 1 wavelength from the surface.

High percentage of transmission by certain glasses and crystals, such as quartz and rock salt of the visible, the near-ultraviolet, and the near-infrared portions of the spectrum, is important to the optical industry and was essential to the early development of spectroscopy. One reason why the two portions of the electromagnetic spectrum between 10 A and 1000 A, and between 0.001 cm and 0.1 cm are the last to be developed is that these are regions of high absorption by all materials.

14.3 Scattering

In Sec. 6.3 we studied the interference pattern between a microwave beam and the reradiated wave from a resonant dipole, a metal rod $\frac{1}{2}$ wavelength long. As the length of the rod is diminished below this resonant value, reradiated or scattered power diminishes rapidly so that the diffraction pattern of a rod one-tenth wavelength long can scarcely be detected at the distance of two wavelengths. Nevertheless, the blue sky light on a clear day is primarily the result of reradiation from molecules of nitrogen and oxygen which have linear dimensions 1/1000 that of the light wavelengths they scatter. The effect is that of a large number of scatters in a depth of atmosphere. At a height of 20 miles the sky above appears black.

The atoms and molecules themselves are electric dipoles. Using this analogy between molecular dipoles and insulated metal rods in an oscillating electric field as dipoles, we are able to design model crystals for Bragg diffraction with metal rods or balls. Artificial dielectrics for microwave lenses and prisms are designed on the basis of the analogue between the molecular dipole and metal rods or disks. When the molecules are closer together than one wavelength the reradiation from neighboring molecules is coherent, giving rise to interference and thus to refraction which is treated in the next chapter.

Scattering by gases and vapors is from molecules that are far apart compared to a wavelength and randomly oriented so that the reradiation is incoherent. The intensities and not the amplitudes are added. The intensity lost from a cell of gas by scattering as the beam passes through is proportional to the number of scatterers N, provided the density is so low that one scatterer does not block radiation to another.

From classical electromagnetic theory it is shown[2] that the rate of scattered radiation in all directions from a unit volume is

$$F_s = \frac{2Ne^2I}{3\epsilon_0 m^2 c^4 \left(\frac{\nu_0^2}{\nu^2} - 1\right)^2},$$ (14.6)

where N is the number of scattering dipoles per volume, e the charge on the electron, m the mass of the electron, c the velocity of light, and I the incident intensity. Here F_s/I is called the *scattering power*, ν_0 the natural frequency of the dipole oscillator, and ν the frequency of the incident radiation. Equation (14.6) has found confirmation except when ν is near ν_0, for which the expression becomes infinite. If the natural frequencies of the scattering particles are large compared to the frequency of the wave, the scattering power becomes

$$\frac{F_s}{I} = \frac{2Ne^2}{3\epsilon_0 m^2 \nu_0^4 \lambda^4}.$$ (14.7)

This expression of the inverse fourth power of the wavelength is Rayleigh's scattering law. It explains why the sunlight scattered by molecules, which are small compared to a wavelength, is blue. If the natural frequencies of the scattering particles are small compared to the frequency of the wave, the scattering power becomes

$$\frac{F_s}{I} = \frac{2Ne^2}{3\epsilon_0 m^2 c^4},$$ (14.8)

which is independent of wavelength. Particles of chalk dust much larger than a wavelength scatter all wavelengths equally from a beam of white light. The natural frequencies ν_0 of the atomic and molecular dipoles lie in the far ultraviolet and soft x-ray region, so that their natural frequencies are less than x-ray frequencies. Equation (14.8) is Thomson's classical equation for scattering of x-rays. The polarization of the scattered waves will be treated in a later chapter.

The derivation of Thomson's equation, Eq. (14.8), is performed[3] by integrating over all angles of scattering. The intensity of the scattered beam is proportional to $(1 + \cos \phi)$, where ϕ is the angle of deviation of the scattered beam from the direction of the incident beam. Using sheets of carbon and

[2] Joseph Valasek, *Introduction to Theoretical and Experimental Optics:* New York, Wiley (1949) Chap. 21.

[3] A. H. Compton and S. K. Allison, *X-Rays in Theory and Experiment*, 2nd ed.: New York, Van Nostrand (1934) Chap. III.

paper which were made thin to avoid multiple scattering, and wavelengths in the range 0.1 to 1.0 A, Compton and Hagenow[4] obtained results in accord with Thomson's electromagnetic theory of x-ray scattering.

The very experiments that confirmed classical electromagnetic theory of scattering so well served at shorter wavelengths to confirm the quantum nature of radiation. At the shorter wavelengths the scattered radiation was more intense than predicted. More surprising, the wavelength of the scattered radiation was measurably greater than that of the incident wave. The observation and explanation won A. H. Compton the Nobel Prize in 1927.

14.4 Compton Scattering

Compton solved the problem by treating an incident photon of x-rays hitting an outer electron of an atom in a collision. An outer electron requires very little energy to remove it from the atom compared to the energy of the photon, so the collision is that of two perfectly elastic bodies. By applying conservation of momentum and conservation of energy to a photon of known energy and momentum colliding with an electron at rest to give the electron momentum in a known direction, he could determine the resulting momenta and energies of the recoiling electron and the photon after collision.

By Planck's quantum theory, the energy of the incident photon is $h\nu$ and that of the scattered photon $h\nu'$, where h is Planck's constant and ν and ν' are the frequencies of the incident and scattered photons. The momenta p and p' of the two photons may be expressed $p = h\nu/c$ and $p' = h\nu'/c$. Einstein has shown that the mass m of the electron is equivalent to energy as expressed by

$$E = mc^2. \tag{14.9}$$

The dependence of the mass m of the electron on velocity is expressed by

$$m = m_0 \bigg/ \sqrt{1 - \left(\frac{v}{c}\right)^2}, \tag{14.10}$$

where v is the velocity of the recoiling electron after collision. Thus the momentum of the electron

$$p_e = \frac{m_0 v}{\sqrt{1 - (v/c)^2}} \tag{14.11}$$

and the kinetic energy of the electron

$$E_k = mc^2 - m_0 c^2 = m_0 c^2 \left(\frac{1}{\sqrt{1 - (v/c)^2}} - 1\right). \tag{14.12}$$

[4] A. H. Compton and C. F. Hagenow, *J. Opt. Soc. Am.*, **8**, 487 (1924).

Figure 249 indicates the momenta p, p', and p_e, where α and β are the angles of deviation of the paths of the photon and electron after collision from the direction of the path of the photon before collision. The solution is the classical problem in mechanics of applying the laws of conservation of momentum and energy. The following three simultaneous equations express (1) equality of momentum parallel to the direction of incidence before and

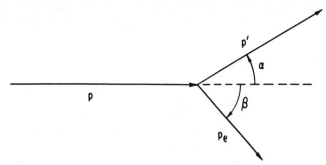

Figure 249. Momenta of photon before collision and of photon and electron after collision.

after collision (2) the equality of the momentum perpendicular to the direction of incidence before and after collision, (3) the equality of kinetic energy before and after collision.

$$p = p' \cos \alpha + p_e \cos \beta \qquad (14.13)$$

$$0 = p' \sin \alpha + p_e \sin \beta \qquad (14.14)$$

$$pc = p'c + E_k. \qquad (14.15)$$

If we solve Eqs. (14.13) and (14.14) for the right-hand terms and add, we obtain an expression for p_e^2. Solving for E_k^2, we obtain the following simultaneous equations

$$p_e^2 = p^2 - 2pp' \cos \alpha + p'^2 \qquad (14.16)$$

$$\left(\frac{E_k}{c}\right)^2 = p^2 - 2pp' + p'^2. \qquad (14.17)$$

Subtracting Eq. (14.17) from Eq. (14.16), we obtain

$$p_e^2 - \left(\frac{E_k}{c}\right)^2 = 2pp'(1 - \cos \alpha). \qquad (14.18)$$

Squaring Eqs. (14.11) and (14.12) and subtracting, we obtain

$$p_e^2 - \left(\frac{E_k}{c}\right)^2 = \frac{m_0^2 v^2}{1 - (v/c)^2} - m_0^2 c^2 \left[\frac{1}{1 - (v/c)^2} - \frac{2}{\sqrt{1 - (v/c)^2}} + 1\right]. \qquad (14.19)$$

Simplifying, we find

$$p_e^2 - \left(\frac{E_k}{c}\right)^2 = 2m_0^2c^2\left(\frac{1}{\sqrt{1 - (v/c)^2}} - 1\right) = 2m_0E_k. \quad (14.20)$$

Substituting in Eq. (14.20) from Eq. (14.15), we obtain

$$p_e^2 - \left(\frac{E_k}{c}\right)^2 = 2m_0c(p - p'). \quad (14.21)$$

Thus Eq. (14.18) becomes

$$m_0c(p - p') = pp'(1 - \cos \alpha), \quad (14.22)$$

and

$$\frac{1}{p'} - \frac{1}{p} = \frac{1 - \cos \alpha}{m_0c}. \quad (14.23)$$

Since $p = h\nu/c = h/\lambda$, and $p' = h\nu'/c = h/\lambda'$, Eq. (14.23) becomes

$$\lambda' - \lambda = \frac{h}{m_0c}(1 - \cos \alpha), \quad (14.24)$$

where λ and λ' are the wavelengths of the incident and scattered photons. Their difference is the *Compton shift*. Here h, m_0, and c are constants, so the Compton shift is expressed in terms of α as the only variable. Since the shift is independent of the wavelength, this quantum effect is observed more easily at shorter wavelengths. The chromatic resolving power $\lambda/(\lambda' - \lambda)$ required for observation of the shift is proportional to the wavelength of x-rays. Originally Compton observed the average effects due to many collisions. In later work individual collisions were observed in a Wilson cloud chamber. The paths of recoil electrons are readily distinguished from the paths of higher energy photoelectrons ejected in fluorescence absorption of x-rays which will be treated in Sec. 14.6. Photographs are shown in textbooks on x-rays.[5] By counting the electrons ejected by the two processes, we may compare quantitatively the fluorescence absorption and the absorption by scattering.

The Compton shift can not be observed for light. Since a light photon has not enough energy to remove the electron from the atom, the recoil is that of the atom instead of the electron. The substitution of atomic mass in Eq. (14.24) yields a Compton shift in wavelength too small to be detected with optical instruments.

14.5 Resonance

By analogy with sound we might expect atomic oscillators to resonate to their natural frequencies, just as a tuning fork resonates to another of the

[5] Compton and Allison, *op. cit.*, p. 213.

same natural frequency. In 1904 R. W. Wood discovered and pursued[6] the study of *resonance radiation*. The lateness of the discovery was due to the masking of resonance absorption by true absorption. Wood made the discovery with sodium vapor. If the pressure of the vapor in an evacuated tube is less than 1 mm of mercury, most of the excited atoms will reradiate before they have time to collide with other atoms so that very little intensity is lost from the beam by conversion to heat. Unlike scattering, resonance reradiation is in all directions.

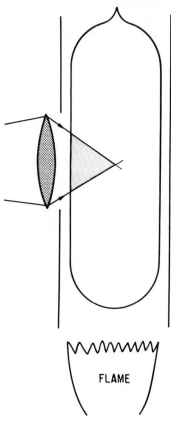

Wood designed sodium vapor tubes which are available from supply companies for scientific apparatus. If the evacuated tube containing sodium metal is heated while a converging cone of light from a sodium lamp is focused in the middle of the tube as indicated in Fig. 250, we may observe increasing reradiation from the cone as the temperature rises. If we study the direct beam with a spectrometer of sufficient resolving power, we observe a black absorption line in the middle of each of the sodium *D* lines. The absorption lines are narrower than the emission lines of the primary source since the absorbing sodium is at lower temperature. Indeed, the width of the absorption lines is that predicted from the Doppler effect at the temperature of the reradiating vapor.

As the pressure of the vapor increases, we observe reradiation only from the side of the tube toward the source. Finally we see only reradiation from the inner surface of the tube toward the source, which looks precisely like reflection from a metal mirror

FLAME

Figure 250. Wood's tube for demonstration of resonance radiation of sodium vapor.

even though there could be no sodium vapor condensed on the wall at this temperature. Most of the reradiation is now from a region less than 1 wavelength thick. The reradiated wavelets from the small range of depth are coherent and in phase. No other wavelengths are reflected from this surface. The fact that the reradiated sodium light is coherent is evidence that resonance reradiation from an atom takes place in a time short compared to the period of the wave, less than 10^{-14} sec for light.

[6] R. W. Wood, *Physical Optics*, 3rd ed.: New York, Macmillan (1934).

Resonance reradiation may be explained as classical wave resonance. However, Wood also observed other characteristic lines of lower frequency than that of the incident radiation. This *fluorescent radiation* could be explained only by quantum theory. In fluorescence the excited atom may retain its energy and reradiate as much as 10^{-7} sec later. If the pressure of the vapor or gas is so low that the mean time between collisions is 10^{-6} sec, the excited atoms will reradiate before colliding with other atoms. If atoms collide before reradiating, the stored energy becomes kinetic energy of random motion of the molecules.

14.6 Fluorescence

Intensity is extracted from a beam of electromagnetic waves when a photon excites an atom which in turn radiates a photon of lower energy and frequency than the incident photon. Before Planck's discovery of the quantum nature of radiation, Stokes had noted that the fluorescent radiation was always of lower frequency than the waves which excite it. The reradiated frequencies are characteristic frequencies of the atoms of the absorber. Under quantum theory, Stoke's law becomes a consequence of conservation of energy. The reradiated quantum hv' can not be greater than the incident quantum hv.

Fluorescence of vapors is beautifully illustrated by evacuating a glass bulb containing a few crystals of iodine. If light from a carbon arc is focused to a cone within the bulb, a complex fluorescence spectrum of many lines may be observed by examining the reradiation with a spectrometer at right angles to the incident beam.

Wood describes in detail apparatus and methods for observing the fluorescence spectrum of iodine vapor when it is illuminated by the green line of mercury,[7] $\lambda = 5460.74$ A.

Demonstrations of the fluorescence of liquids and solids are effectively performed with a mercury lamp with a quartz envelope to transmit the ultraviolet, and a filter to transmit only invisible ultraviolet in a dark room. Oils, many organic dies, detergents, and minerals emit a fluorescent radiation of visible light in colors characteristic of the substances.

14.7 Fluorescence Absorption of X-Rays

All substances absorb x-rays by fluorescence. When a photon of x-rays strikes an atom the most common mode of excitation is to knock an electron completely out of the atom. An electron from an outer level then drops to the empty level and the energy difference is emitted in a fluorescence photon. Although this type of absorption is usually called *fluorescence absorption*, it may also be called *photoelectric absorption*, since the energy of the absorbed

---

[7] Wood, *op. cit.*, p. 623.

photon becomes both energy of the fluorescence photon and kinetic energy of the electron. That is,

$$hv = hv_f + E_k, \tag{14.25}$$

where v is the frequency of the incident x-rays, v_f the frequency of the fluorescence x-rays, and E_k the kinetic energy of the photoelectron.

In the x-ray region of the spectrum we more commonly treat the *mass absorption coefficient* μ/ρ than the *linear absorption coefficient* μ.

$$\mu x = \left(\frac{\mu}{\rho}\right)(\rho x) = \left(\frac{\mu}{\rho}\right)\frac{\text{mass}}{\text{area}}, \tag{14.26}$$

where ρ is the density of the material. The area is taken at right angles to the thickness x. In the soft x-ray region, when the absorbers are thin enough to transmit measurable intensities, the thickness x is too small to be measured directly. The masses of the thin foil absorbers are measured on microbalances. Equation (14.5) becomes

$$\frac{I}{I_0} = e^{-(\mu/\rho)(\text{mass/area})}. \tag{14.27}$$

Still more fundamental is the *atomic absorption coefficient*

$$\mu_a = \frac{\mu/\rho}{N_0/A}, \tag{14.28}$$

where N_0 is Avogadro's number and A the atomic weight. An approximate empirical expression for the atomic mass absorption coefficient which includes all wavelengths and all elements is

$$\mu_a = C_a Z^4 \lambda^3 + b_a, \tag{14.29}$$

where Z is the atomic number of the element, C_a is a constant, and b_a is a constant for a portion of the curve between two absorption limits of Fig. 251.

We may distinguish the two kinds of absorption by

$$\mu_a = \tau_a + \sigma_a, \tag{14.30}$$

where τ_a is the atomic fluorescence absorption coefficient and σ_a is the atomic scattering absorption coefficient.

Figure 251 is a plot of the mass absorption coefficient μ/ρ against wavelength of x-rays for the element gold as absorber. The discontinuities in the absorption curve correspond to energy levels in the atom. X-ray spectral lines correspond to differences in energy levels but they do not give the absolute energy levels. The discontinuities in the absorption curve correspond to the energy levels hv. Proceeding from shorter to longer wavelengths or toward lower frequencies, we note that as the frequency and corresponding energy of the incident photons is decreased the absorption increases until at the K

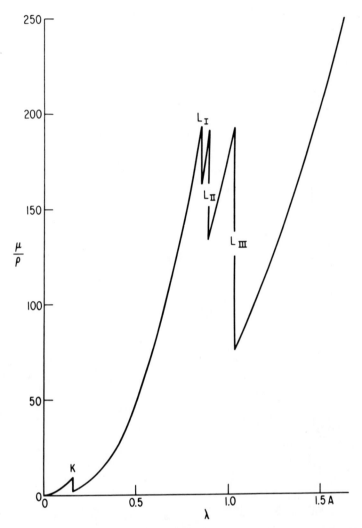

Figure 251. Plot of mass absorption coefficient of gold against wavelength of x-rays showing the K and L absorption limits.

discontinuity the absorption suddenly decreases when the photon does not have sufficient energy to remove the K electron from the deepest level known as the K *shell of the atom*. Again as the frequency is decreased the absorption rises, the absorption coefficient increasing approximately as the cube of the wavelength. When the frequency passes the L_I limit the photon does not have sufficient energy to remove an electron from the L_I shell. For heavy elements such as gold there are three L absorption limits corresponding to three energy levels. At absorption coefficients many times higher appear five M absorption limits, still farther seven N limits, and so on.

Popularly x-rays are thought to be the most penetrating of electromagnetic waves. However, as we consider the λ^3 law we are not surprised to find that

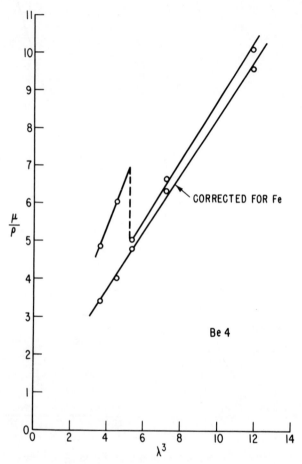

Figure 252. Plot for quantitative analysis of iron in beryllium.

soft x-rays are among the most highly absorbed radiations. For instance, as the wavelength increases from 0.7 to 7.0 A the mass absorption coefficient μ/ρ of aluminum increases from 5 to 3000.

In the soft x-ray region above wavelengths of 10 A the absorption is nearly all fluorescence absorption. The absorption by scattering is negligible so that $\mu_a = \tau_a$, making this region excellent for the study of the laws of fluorescence absorption. One reason why the study of absorption is so incomplete in this region is the lack of sources of x-radiation continuous with wavelength. This region of the spectrum obtained by conventional x-ray or ultraviolet techniques consists of characteristic line radiation plus a faint continuous radiation. Tomboulian and Hartman[8] have studied the radiation emitted by the centripetally accelerated electrons in a 300 mev synchrotron, and found it to be a good source of radiation for continuous absorption measurements in soft x-ray and ultraviolet regions.

The dependence of the absorption coefficient on the fourth power of the atomic number accounts for the much greater absorption by bones than by flesh of animals. Calcium has atomic number 20 as compared to oxygen 8, carbon 6, and hydrogen 1. It also provides a means of quantitative chemical analysis of small amounts of high atomic number impurities mixed with low atomic number elements.[9] Figure 252 is a plot of the mass absorption coefficient of a sample of beryllium against the third power of the wavelength which reveals a ratio of mass of iron to mass of beryllium of 0.0044.

From the early studies of x-ray spectra and x-ray absorption measurements we would conclude that x-rays are characteristic only of the atoms. The emission and absorption by an atom was independent of the compound it was in and whether that compound were in gas, liquid, or solid phase. However, absorption measurements with instruments of higher resolving power and measurements taken in the soft x-ray region are revealing energy levels of outer electrons that belong to the whole solid.[10] Much as absorption measurements in the range 0.01 A to 10 A have contributed to our understanding of atomic structure, we may expect absorption measurements in the range 10 A to 1000 A to contribute to our knowledge of the solid state.

14.8 Raman Scattering

Using the techniques of studying scattering and fluorescence of light, Raman[11] discovered a series of faint lines near the line of unaltered frequency due to Rayleigh scattering. These lines were unique in absorption spectroscopy. (1) Their change in frequency from that of the incident radiation was greater than in any other scattering including Compton scattering. (2) When the frequency of the incident radiation was continuously changed the lines of the scattered radiation kept a constant spacing from the parent line. (3) The *difference* in frequencies of the lines, but not the frequencies themselves, was characteristic of the scattering substance. (4) If the molecules of the scatterer were already excited by temperature, anti-Stokes lines of higher frequency

[8] D. H. Tomboulian and P. L. Hartman, *Phys. Rev.*, **102**, 1423 (1956).
[9] C. L. Andrews, *Phys. Rev.*, **54**, 994 (1938).
[10] C. Kittel, *Introduction to Solid State Physics*, 2nd ed.: New York, Wiley (1957) p. 310.
[11] C. V. Raman and K. S. Krishnan, *Nature*, **121**, 501 (1928), also C. V. Raman, *Indian J. Phys.*, **2**, 387 (1928).

than the parent line were observed. If the temperature was increased these faint anti-Stokes lines became brighter.

The apparatus used for the study of the Raman effect is an adaptation of the equipment used in the original resonance studies by Wood. The cell of Fig. 253 is radiated by light from the annular ring discharge tube. The scattered light is received axially to the spectrograph. The internally blackened horn is a good black body background opposite the spectrometer slits.

Raman lines can be predicted from quantum theory by considering a new kind of interaction between quanta and matter. If as the quantum is scattered it gives up a portion of its energy to raise the molecule to a higher energy state, it is scattered at a lesser frequency corresponding to lesser energy. No time will be required for the process as in fluorescence. If the scattering molecules are excited previously by other means, the incident quantum may, upon being scattered, take on energy from the excited molecule, thus having anti-Stokes frequencies.

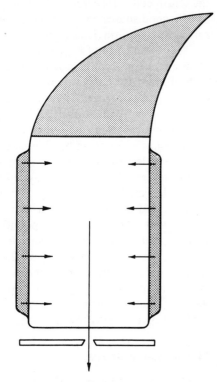

Figure 253. Arrangement for study of Raman scattering.

The importance of the Raman spectra lies in the following facts: (1) It demonstrates an entirely different kind of interaction between quanta and matter than previously observed. The effect had been predicted five years earlier by Smekal. Raman's observation gives more complete confirmation of the theory of interaction between quanta and matter. (2) The frequency difference between Raman lines and the direct radiation corresponds to energy level differences of the scattering molecules which do not always give rise to lines in the emission spectrum. Thus the Raman effect is a tool for measuring the molecular structure of matter.

PROBLEMS FOR CHAPTER XIV

14.3.1. Compare the scattering power of an oxygen molecule for blue light of 4500 A with that of red light of 6500 A.

14.4.2. Find the Compton shift in wavelength when the angle of scattering of the photon is $90°$. Planck's constant $h = 6.62 \times 10^{-27}$ erg-sec. The mass of the electron $m_0 = 0.911 \times 10^{-27}$ g. The velocity of light $c = 3.00 \times 10^{10}$ cm/sec.

14.4.3. What must be the resolving power of an x-ray spectrometer which will separate the wavelength of the scattered wave in $90°$ Compton scattering from the incident radiation which is the $K_{\alpha 1}$ line of tungsten of 0.209 A?

14.7.4. Find the thickness of aluminum foil of density 2.70 g/cm^3 that will transmit half the intensity of the K line of silicon of 7.111 A. The mass absorption coefficient of aluminum for this wavelength is 3170 cm^2/g.

chapter XV

Dispersion

15.1 Newton's Treatment of Color Aberration

Newton[1] discovered that chromatic aberration, as well as spherical aberration, was responsible for the deficiency in the resolution of a refracting telescope. Blue light was focused closer to the objective lens than red. In a study of chromatic aberration, Newton built a glass prism and a water prism with such vertex angles that the angles of dispersion between the red and blue light were the same for both prisms. Newton concluded on the basis of too few measurements that for any two prisms of different media the angles of dispersion δ were proportional to the mean deviation D of the spectrum, Fig. 254(a). He concluded that it would be impossible to build pairs of lenses that would reduce chromatic aberration of a refracting telescope and therefore he designed and built with his own hands the first reflecting telescope. So great was the authority of Newton that no attempts were made to improve refracting telescopes for over 100 years.

The incorrectness of Newton's conclusion is illustrated by the elementary classroom demonstrations with achromatic combinations of prisms, Fig. 254(b), of crown and flint glass which deviate white light without angular dispersion, and the direct vision spectroscope, Fig. 254(c), which disperses the light but gives zero deviation for the middle of the spectrum.

[1] Isaac Newton, *Opticks, Book I*, Prop. V.

368

15.2 Normal Dispersion by Transparent Dielectrics

Figure 255 is a graph of the indices of refraction of crown and light flint glass as measured on a spectrometer with a prism, and employing the method of minimum deviation. If we multiply the values of the index of refraction of

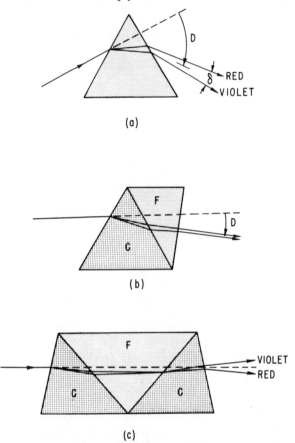

Figure 254. (a) Illustration of angles of deviation and dispersion for a prism. (b) Combination of crown and flint glass prisms to produce deviation without angular dispersion. (c) Combination of crown and flint glass prisms to produce dispersion without deviation of the middle of the spectrum.

the flint glass by a constant which is the ratio of the index of refraction of the crown glass to that of the flint glass at 8000 A, and plot the results as a broken line in Fig. 255, we note that the change of scale does not cause the curves to overlap. The *dispersion* for a given dielectric at any wavelength, defined in Sec. 9.6, is the slope of the curve $dn/d\lambda$.

The first substances studied were the glasses and liquids that are transparent over the whole visible spectrum. The graphical plots of index of refraction against wavelength for all glass used in optical instruments have negative values of dispersion, $dn/d\lambda$, over the whole visible range. The index of refraction changes most rapidly in the violet and appears to approach a constant at the red end. If we compare the spectrum of a glass prism with the normal spectrum of a grating, we note that the prism spectrum has its greatest dispersion in the ultraviolet while the orange and red are crowded together.

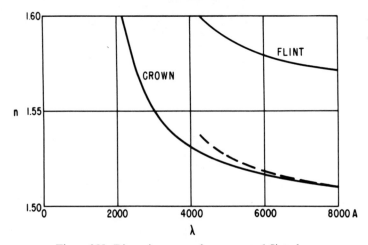

Figure 255. Dispersion curves for crown and flint glass.

In 1836 Cauchy found an empirical equation for the dependence of the index of refraction on wavelength for the few substances that are transparent over the visible portion of the spectrum. The index of refraction

$$n = A + \frac{B}{\lambda^2}.$$ (15.1)

A closer approximation was given by a power series

$$n = A + \frac{B}{\lambda^2} + \frac{C}{\lambda^4} + \cdots,$$ (15.2)

where A, B, and C are different constants for each material; A is the asymptotic value which the index of refraction seems to approach at the red end of the spectrum.

15.3 Anomalous Dispersion

A more complete understanding of the nature of refraction and dispersion resulted from the measurement of indices of refraction in the spectral region of their absorption lines. It is difficult to measure indices of refraction in an absorption band, but measurements taken near the absorption band give indices of refraction that decrease rapidly as the absorption wavelength is approached from the short wavelength side, and jump to large values on the long wavelength side. The dispersion in the neighborhood of the absorption line is called *anomalous dispersion*, since historically this was the first observation of the index of refraction increasing with wavelength. Since all substances possess many resonant frequencies over the range of the whole electromagnetic spectrum, this behavior is normal.

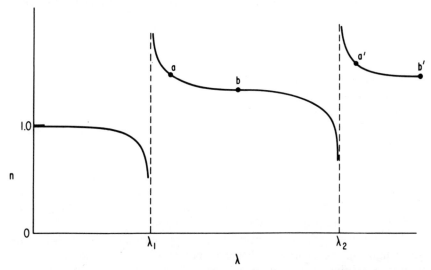

Figure 256. Typical dispersion curve in the region of two absorption lines.

Figure 256 is a typical plot of index of refraction against wavelength including two absorption wavelengths. In practice there are many such absorption lines. The regions ab and $a'b'$ are each closely approximated by the Cauchy Eq. (15.1) with a different set of constants A and B for each of the two regions. In the x-ray and far ultraviolet regions the indices of refraction are all near unity, except near resonant frequencies. This is one reason for the difficulty we are having in building an x-ray microscope. The value of A increases with each successive Cauchy region up to the far infrared and microwave wavelengths, where for instance the index of refraction of water approaches a value of 9 as compared to 1.3 in the visible.

Anomalous dispersion of visible light may be demonstrated with fuchsine dye in a hollow prism. The reversal and overlapping of portions of the spectrum are surprising. Wood[2] describes a beautiful and ingenious experiment by which a prism of sodium vapor makes its own graph of the index of

[2] R. W. Wood, *Physical Optics*, 3rd ed.: New York, Macmillan (1934) p. 492 and colored pictures in the frontispiece.

refraction against wavelength in the region of the sodium D lines. The sodium vapor cell so heated as to have decreasing vapor density from bottom to top has the effect of a prism. This "prism" is set to give vertical dispersion superposed upon the horizontal dispersion by a glass prism or grating in the spectroscope.

By consideration of frictionless vibrators with natural frequencies in an elastic solid, Sellmeier (1871) found a semiempirical equation which not only fitted the experimental data near the absorption lines but also agreed with the "normal" portions of the experimental curve better than Cauchy's equation. By Sellmeier's derivation,

$$n^2 = 1 + \sum_{j=1}^{N} \frac{A_j \lambda^2}{\lambda^2 - \lambda_j^2},$$ (15.3)

where λ is the wavelength of the incident wave; λ_j is the resonant wavelength and A_j a constant, both of which correspond to one of the N natural frequencies of the medium.

These natural absorption wavelengths are never much shorter than 1000 A. Thus in the x-ray region λ_j is large compared to λ for all values of λ_j. In the limit as $\lambda \ll \lambda_j$, $A_j \lambda^2/(\lambda^2 - \lambda_j^2)$ becomes a small negative number approaching zero. Thus in the x-ray region n is slightly less than unity. That is, the phase velocity of x-rays is greater in the medium than in a vacuum. In Sec. 10.7 we treated the total external reflection and glancing angle x-ray gratings made possible by an index of refraction less than unity.

As the wavelength of the incident wave approaches a natural absorption wavelength λ_j, the expression becomes negatively infinite and then jumps positively infinite on the other side of the absorption line. Between two resonances the curve passes through an inflection point, and the index of refraction becomes less than unity again.

In the microwave region on the long wavelength side of the resonances, λ becomes much greater than any of the λ_j values, so that $A_j \lambda^2/(\lambda^2 - \lambda_j^2)$ approaches A_j, and

$$n^2 = 1 + A_1 + A_2 + A_3.$$ (15.4)

Measurements of indices of refraction near the absorption frequencies are difficult because of the weak transmission. However, using sensitive detectors and making measurements of indices of refraction of solids which have broader absorption lines, we can show that there is no discontinuity in the curve. Because of friction in the natural oscillator the resonance term does not become negatively infinite but drops to a value between one and zero, Fig. 257, where it turns upward to cross the absorption line and has values large compared to unity, and then drops down again as n approaches the Cauchy region.

The next step in perfecting the equation for the dependence of the index of refraction on wavelength must include the effect of damping of the particles of the medium that vibrate with natural frequencies.

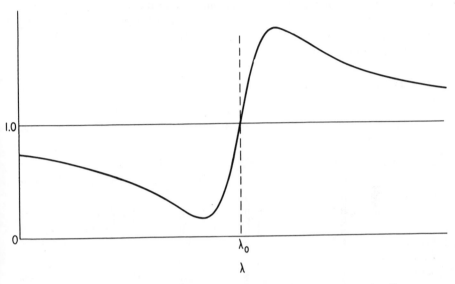

Figure 257. Continuous dispersion curve in the region of an absorption line.

15.4 The Developing Theory of Dispersion

The development of the theory of dispersion has been by a series of successively more general treatments satisfying the experimental data of the time. (1) Cauchy's empirical formula was satisfied by the data taken for optical glass in the visible region. (2) Sellmeier's equation for scattering by frictionless vibrators embedded in an elastic solid agreed with the experimental measurements of the index of refraction at wavelengths approaching absorption lines. (3) Helmholtz added friction to the mechanical oscillators in the elastic medium to fit the measurements of index of refraction at wavelengths continuing all the way through the absorption band. (4) With the development of electromagnetic theory the mechanical vibrator was replaced by an atomic dipole which was made to undergo forced vibrations by the passing electromagnetic waves. (5) With the advent of quantum theory and photons, the forced vibrations were replaced by induced transitions between energy states of the atom. The final equations involve the frequencies in the same manner as the equations for electromagnetic waves. Only the constants take on a new meaning. (6) In the x-ray region where absorption bands replace the absorption lines, the wave mechanics of matter yields a more general solution to the theory of dispersion of which the classical treatments are but special cases applicable in the low-frequency range. The wave mechanics treatment will be found in textbooks on x-rays.[3] We note that each succeeding generation is adding to the theory of dispersion, satisfying the experimental data available at that time.

In an introduction to the study of dispersion we may begin in the newly developed low-frequency region of microwaves for which the electric dipole is a spike driven in the top of a fence post.

15.5 Dispersion of Microwaves

The lenses of artificial dielectrics used in point-to-point communications systems of the telephone, telegraph, and television industries are sometimes

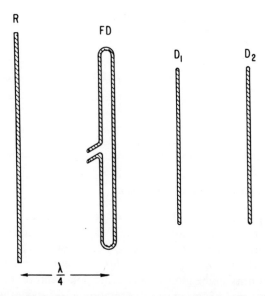

Figure 258. Folded microwave dipole with a reflector and two directors.

made of arrays of metal rods. The metal rods are analogous to the molecular dipoles in a real dielectric. The developers[4,5] of artificial dielectrics have drawn ingeniously upon knowledge of real dielectrics. In turn they have provided a concrete picture for the study of real dielectrics.

If we place a metal rod in a microwave beam parallel to the direction of the electric field as in the interference studies of Sec. 6.3, the reradiation by the rod will be a maximum when the rod is one-half wave long and resonant.

[3] A. H. Compton and S. K. Allison, *X-Rays in Theory and Experiment*, 2nd ed.: New York, Van Nostrand (1936) Chap. IV.

[4] J. Brown, *Microwave Lenses:* New York, Wiley (1953).

[5] W. E. Kock, *Proc. I.R.E.*, **34**, 828 (1946), and **37**, 852 (1949).

If the length of the rod is slightly less than one-half wavelength, the wave is reradiated with no change in phase. If the length is a little greater than one-half wavelength, the reradiated wave undergoes a π phase change upon reradiation.

These two facts are used in the design of the television antenna of Fig. 258. The folded dipole FD is one-half wavelength long and fed from the source with a matched line of twin lead. A rod R 10% more than one-half wave long is placed parallel to the source antenna FD and approximately one-quarter wave away. Since the reradiation from the longer rod undergoes π phase change, the waves from R and FD cancel on the left of R. The portion of the wave reflected back to FD will have traveled one-half wave plus undergoing the π phase change, and arrive in phase with the wave emerging from the source antenna FD, giving a maximum of radiation to the right. The rods D_1 and D_2 are less than one-half wave long, and reradiate the wave with no change in phase. Thus the reradiated waves are in phase with the waves from the source on the right of the system. Rods D_1 and D_2 are called *directors*, and R a *reflector*. A long array of directors may be used to give high angular resolving power. In microwave techniques the reflector rod is often replaced by a disk which is 10% more than one-half wave in diameter. We note the rod or disk is a reflector by virtue of its position with respect to the source.

If we build a prism of artificial dielectric as an array of metal rods or disks supported by Polyfoam, we may make an experimental plot of the anomalous dispersion curve of Fig. 256. As the wavelength is increased to approach resonance with the dipoles, the index of refraction becomes increasingly less than 1.0. The refraction of the beam is as in Fig. 259(a), indicating that the phase velocity in the prism is greater than in air. As the wavelength passes resonance with rods, the prism no longer transmits a beam but reradiates in all directions. As the wavelength is increased beyond resonance, the index of refraction jumps to a value greater than 1.0, and the beam is bent as in Fig. 259(b).

If the dipole rods of an artificial dielectric lens are longer than the resonant length, a converging lens is thinner in the middle than the out edges as in Fig. 260(a). If the dipole rods are shorter than the resonant length, a convergent lens is thicker in the middle as in Fig. 260(b).

In summary we note that as the increasing wavelength passes the natural frequency of the dipoles in the dielectric, the phase of reradiation changes from zero to π and the index of refraction changes from less than 1.0 to greater than 1.0. We may anticipate that the change in phase is a cause of the change in the index of refraction.

15.6 Mechanical Analogue of the Forced Electric Oscillation

The same phase effects may be demonstrated in forced oscillations of mechanical systems which have natural frequencies. The pendulum of

Fig. 261(a) with the more massive ball corresponds to the driving wave from the external source. The slightly shorter pendulum of higher frequency and the longer pendulum of lower frequency are coupled loosely to the larger pendulum through the elastic support above. A metal pendulum clamp is sufficient, although closer coupling is obtained with a horizontal string

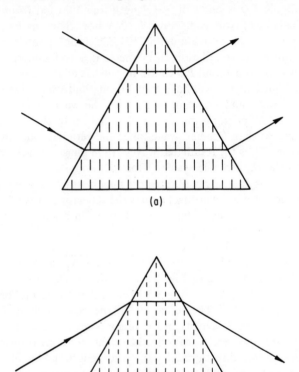

(a)

(b)

Figure 259. Refraction of microwaves by prisms of artificial dielectric. (a) The phase velocity is greater than in air. (b) The phase velocity is less than in air.

support. If the driver pendulum is set swinging perpendicularly to the plane of the figure, we note, after a transient period of a few vibrations is past, that the longer pendulum is π out of phase with the driver, while the higher-frequency pendulum is in phase with the driver.

Another method is to let the massive pendulum be the oscillator driven by the hand through a rubber band as in Fig. 261(b). If the frequency of the hand is much higher than the natural frequency of the pendulum, the pendulum does not respond. This corresponds to the higher frequency case in which the wave is scarcely affected by the dipoles and the index of refraction is near 1.0. As the frequency of the hand is decreased and approaches the natural period of the pendulum, the pendulum vibrates with increasing

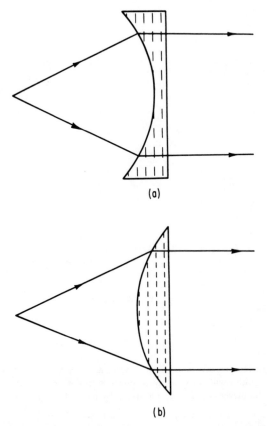

(a)

(b)

Figure 260. Two converging lenses for microwaves made of artificial dielectric. (a) Index of refraction less than one. (b) Index of refraction greater than one.

amplitude and in phase with the hand. This corresponds to the case in which the dipoles give the phase velocity a boost and the index of refraction is less than 1.0. As the frequency of the hand slowly passes the natural frequency of the pendulum, the amplitude of the pendulum passes through a maximum and the phase increases to 180° ahead of that of the hand. The rubber band is under high tension at the instant the pendulum and hand are farthest apart. This corresponds to the phase condition in which the dipoles react most strongly on the wave. The phase velocity is less than in air, and the index of refraction greater than 1.0.

A more quantitative analogue may be made to include damping of the oscillators of the dielectric if we use a variable frequency oscillator to drive the pendulum. If we let an aluminum disk of the pendulum swing between the poles of an electromagnet with variable current, the frictional damping factor will be adjustable and the frictional force proportional to the velocity.

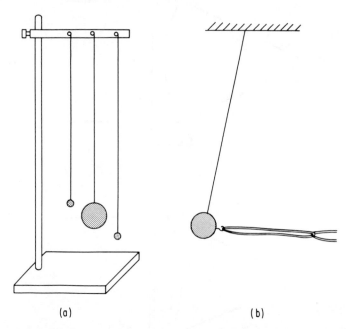

(a)   (b)

Figure 261. (a) The massive pendulum drives the two smaller pendulum balls. The longer pendulum will swing π out of phase with the driver and the shorter in phase with the driver. (b) Pendulum driven by hand through a rubber band.

A torsion pendulum with a disk oscillating between the pole pieces is still more satisfactory. If the relative phases of the driver and pendulum are to be measured visually, the torsion pendulum should have a period of several seconds. An electric contactor to flash a light near the pendulum may be used to indicate when the source is passing through maximum displacement.

The measured values of the amplitude of the mechanical oscillator plotted against frequency of the driving wave may be compared with that of the electric dipole as computed and plotted in Fig. 262(a) of the following section for two values of the damping constant. Fig. 262(b) shows corresponding plots of phase of the oscillator against frequency of the driving wave.

15.7 Forced Oscillation of a Dipole

We shall express and solve the differential equation for a forced oscillation of an ion in a dielectric.

$$m\frac{d^2\mathbf{s}}{dt^2} + R\frac{d\mathbf{s}}{dt} + k\mathbf{s} = eE_0\epsilon^{j\omega t}, \tag{15.5}$$

where m is the mass of the oscillating electron or ion, and $\mathbf{s}$ is its displacement at any instant. The direction of $\mathbf{s}$ is from the positive toward the negative charge. The dipole moment at any instant due to the separation of charges e by the electromagnetic wave is $\mathbf{p} = s e$. The frictional force is proportional to the velocity ds/dt, R is the proportionality constant, k is the spring constant or force of restitution per unit of displacement, $eE_0\epsilon^{j\omega t}$ is the sinusoidally varying force by the wave on charge e, and $\mathbf{E}_0$ is the maximum value of the electric field. We shall let the Naperian base be ϵ in this case to distinguish it from charge e. Letting the varying dipole moment be the dependent variable, we obtain

$$\frac{d^2\mathbf{p}}{dt^2} + \frac{R}{m}\frac{d\mathbf{p}}{dt} + \frac{k}{m}\mathbf{p} = \frac{e^2}{m}\mathbf{E}_0\epsilon^{j\omega t}. \tag{15.6}$$

The resonant frequency of the system is $\nu_0 = (1/2\pi)\sqrt{k/m}$ and the angular frequency is

$$\omega_0 = 2\pi\nu_0 = \sqrt{\frac{k}{m}}$$

for the cases of low damping that we shall treat. If we define a unitless *friction constant* g by the expression $g\omega_0 = R/m$, we obtain a standard form of the differential equation of the forced oscillation of a dipole.

$$\frac{d^2\mathbf{p}}{dt^2} + g\omega_0\frac{d\mathbf{p}}{dt} + \omega_0^2\mathbf{p} = \frac{e^2}{m}\mathbf{E}_0\epsilon^{j\omega t}. \tag{15.7}$$

We shall assume that the steady-state value of $\mathbf{p}$ is varying with the same frequency as the electric field of the wave. We are neglecting transient effects. Thus

$$\mathbf{p} = \mathbf{p}_0\epsilon^{j(\omega t + \phi)}.$$

The magnitude $\mathbf{p}_0$ and the phase ϕ of $\mathbf{p}$ with respect to $\mathbf{E}$ are to be found. If we take the first and second derivatives of $\mathbf{p}$ with respect to time and substitute in Eq. (15.7), we obtain

$$(-\omega^2 + jg\omega_0\omega + \omega_0^2)\mathbf{p}_0\epsilon^{j\phi} = \frac{e^2}{m}\mathbf{E}_0. \tag{15.8}$$

Solving for $\mathbf{p}_0$, we obtain

$$\mathbf{p}_0 = \frac{e^2\mathbf{E}_0}{m}\frac{\epsilon^{-j\phi}}{(\omega_0^2 - \omega^2) - jg\omega_0\omega}. \tag{15.9}$$

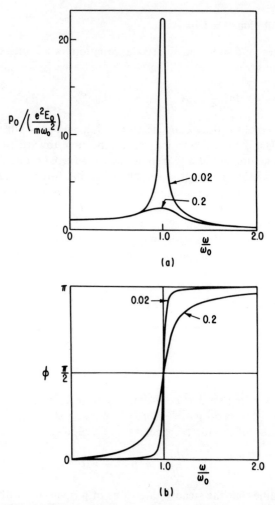

Figure 262. (a) Plots of amplitude of the dipole moment against ω/ω_0 for the cases of $g = 0.2$ and 0.02. (b) Plots of the phase of the oscillator against ω/ω_0 for the cases $g = 0.2$ and 0.02.

The magnitude of $\mathbf{p}_0$ is

$$|\mathbf{p}_0| = \frac{e^2 \mathbf{E}_0}{m} \frac{1}{\sqrt{(\omega_0^2 - \omega^2)^2 + g^2 \omega_0^2 \omega^2}}, \tag{15.10}$$

and the phase relative to that of the rotating vector $\mathbf{E}_0$ is ϕ given by

$$\tan \phi = -\frac{g\omega_0\omega}{\omega_0^2 - \omega^2}. \tag{15.11}$$

Figure 262(a) is a plot of the amplitude of the sinusoidally varying dipole moment divided by the constant $(e^2E_0)/(m\omega_0^2)$ against ω/ω_0 for two values of the friction constant g. The calculations were made for $g = 0.2$ and 0.02. As g decreases from unity toward zero, the resonance peak increases from unity toward infinity. We note that the ratio $\Delta\omega/\omega_0$, the frequency width at half maximum to the resonant frequency, when $g = 0.02$, Fig. 262(a), is wide compared to an absorption line of a gas or vapor. We have chosen a very high friction constant g for our illustration. For a vapor or gas the friction constant g is of the order of 10^{-10}. The suppression of the resonance peak with increase in g is caused by reradiation from the dipole as well by Joule heating. Figure 262(b) is a plot of the phase ϕ of the oscillating dipole against ω/ω_0. Whatever the value of g, the phase increases from zero toward π passing through $\pi/2$ at resonance. In the limit as g approaches zero, ϕ has the value zero for frequencies of the wave below resonance, and π for frequencies of the wave above resonance, with a discontinuity at resonance.

Using our knowledge of forced oscillation of dipoles and electromagnetic theory, we are now prepared to show the effect of the oscillating dipoles on the waves that pass through the medium.

15.8 The Index of Refraction of a Dielectric

In our derivation of Maxwell's equation for electromagnetic waves, we found a surprising relation between the index of refraction n and the dielectric constant K.

$$n = \sqrt{K}. \tag{15.12}$$

We noted the dependence of n and K upon the frequency of the wave. All the molecules of a dielectric become electric dipoles in the presence of an electric field. If there are N molecules per unit volume, we may define the polarization per unit volume $\mathbf{P}$ by the equation

$$\mathbf{P} = N\mathbf{p}. \tag{15.13}$$

For the treatment of dielectrics in the study of electricity[6] a vector quantity $\mathbf{D}$, called the *electric displacement*, is defined such that its normal component is continuous across the boundaries of dielectrics. The electric displacement

$$\mathbf{D} = \epsilon\mathbf{E}, \tag{15.14}$$

where ϵ is the permittivity of the dielectric. Here $\mathbf{D}$ is related to the polarization by

$$\mathbf{D} = \epsilon_0\mathbf{E} + \mathbf{P}, \tag{15.15}$$

[6] R. P. Winch, *Electricity and Magnetism:* Englewood Cliffs, N. J., Prentice-Hall (1955) Chap. XI.

ϵ_0 being the permittivity of empty space. The dielectric constant

$$K = \frac{\epsilon}{\epsilon_0}. \qquad (15.16)$$

Thus

$$n^2 = \frac{\epsilon}{\epsilon_0} = \frac{D}{\epsilon_0 E}. \qquad (15.17)$$

Substituting for **D** from Eq. (15.15), we obtain

$$n^2 = \frac{\epsilon_0 E + P}{\epsilon_0 E}$$

and

$$n^2 - 1 = \frac{P}{\epsilon_0 E}. \qquad (15.18)$$

If we consider for the present a dielectric with dipoles of but one natural frequency, the index of refraction may be expressed by substitution from Eqs. (15.9) and (15.13) in Eq. (15.18),

$$\mathbf{n}^2 - 1 = \frac{Ne^2}{\epsilon_0 m} \frac{1}{(\omega_0^2 - \omega^2) + jg\omega_0\omega}. \qquad (15.19)$$

We note from this equation that **n** is complex. We shall express this complex index of refraction by

$$\mathbf{n} = n(1 - j\kappa). \qquad (15.20)$$

Since κ will be found to have a sharp peak at resonance frequency, we may call it the *index of absorption*. Equating the real and imaginary parts of Eqs. (15.19) and (15.20), we obtain the simultaneous equations

$$n^2(1 - \kappa^2) = 1 + \frac{Ne^2}{\epsilon_0 m} \frac{\omega_0^2 - \omega^2}{(\omega_0^2 - \omega^2)^2 + g^2\omega_0^2\omega^2} \qquad (15.21)$$

$$2n^2\kappa = \frac{Ne^2}{\epsilon_0 m} \frac{g\omega_0\omega}{(\omega_0^2 - \omega^2)^2 + g^2\omega_0^2\omega^2}. \qquad (15.22)$$

We note that explicit algebraic solutions for n and κ would yield complicated expressions. If we wish to plot graphs of n and κ against ω/ω_0 for fixed values of g, we shall find it simpler to solve numerically for a series of values of $n^2(1 - \kappa^2)$ and $2n^2\kappa$ in columns, after which each numerical value n and κ may be calculated from the values of $2n^2\kappa$ and $n^2(1 - \kappa^2)$. Equations (15.21) and (15.22) are called *implicit solutions* for n and κ.

At resonance when $\omega = \omega_0$

$$n^2(1 - \kappa^2) = 1 \qquad (15.23)$$

and

$$2n^2\kappa = \left(\frac{Ne^2}{\epsilon_0 m\omega_0^2}\right)\frac{1}{g}. \qquad (15.24)$$

Since $2n^2\kappa$ and g are unitless, $Ne/(\epsilon_0 m\omega_0^2)$ must also be unitless. We shall let

$$A_0 = \frac{Ne^2}{\epsilon_0 m\omega_0^2}. \tag{15.25}$$

If ω_0 corresponds to the frequency of a yellow line and N is the number of molecules per cubic meter of an ideal gas at atmospheric pressure and room temperature, $A_0 = 10^{-2}$. The solution is retained for the problems.

In the following sections we shall solve for the index of refraction for special frequency ranges.

15.9 Indices of Refraction in Spectral Regions of Low Absorption

If the dielectric has M natural frequencies, we may express the index of refraction at any frequency sufficiently far from a resonant frequency by neglecting the imaginary term in the denominator of Eq. (15.19). Thus we obtain

$$n^2 - 1 = \sum_{j=1}^{M} \frac{A_j \omega_j^2}{\omega_j^2 - \omega^2}, \tag{15.26}$$

where

$$A_j = \frac{N_j e^2}{\epsilon_0 m_j \omega_j^2}. \tag{15.27}$$

Here ω_j is the natural frequency of the set of N_j oscillators per unit volume. The masses m_j are distinguished by a subscript since they are not always electrons. As the frequency of the wave is decreased, ions of larger mass within the same dielectric are made to oscillate. An ionized molecule may resonate to frequencies in the infrared and microwave regions. Since $\omega = 2\pi c/\lambda$, Eq. (15.26) may be expressed

$$n^2 - 1 = \sum_{j=1}^{M} A_j \frac{\lambda^2}{\lambda^2 - \lambda_j^2}, \tag{15.28}$$

which is Sellmeier's Eq. (15.3).

15.10 Index of Refraction in the Region of an Absorption Line

In a very narrow spectral region of an absorption line like a D line of sodium vapor, the effect of the other sufficiently different absorption frequencies on the index of refraction is essentially constant over the short range. The only variable is the term corresponding to one natural frequency of the oscillator. Thus the effect of all terms except the 0th, together with the term unity, may be lumped in a constant n_0^2. In this narrow range of ω we may replace $\omega_0 + \omega$ by $2\omega_0$ so that Eqs. (15.21) and (15.22) become

$$n^2(1 - \kappa^2) = n_0^2 + A_0 \frac{2\omega_0(\omega_0 - \omega)}{4(\omega_0 - \omega)^2 + g^2\omega^2} \tag{15.29}$$

$$2n^2\kappa = A_0 \frac{g\omega_0\omega}{4(\omega_0 - \omega)^2 + g^2\omega^2}. \tag{15.30}$$

Vapors and gases even at very low pressures exhibit surprisingly high absorption at resonant frequencies. For instance, if an ultraviolet germicidal lamp, 90% of the radiation of which is the 2537 A line, is directed upon a 2 ft square fluorescent screen in front of which is placed a dish of mercury at room temperature, the mercury vapor rising from the dish casts a wavy black shadow on the screen. At this temperature the vapor pressure of saturated mercury vapor is 10^{-6} of atmospheric pressure. If this rising vapor is less than 0.1% saturated, the pressure of mercury vapor is 10^{-9} atm and A_0 of Eq. (15.25) is 10^{-11}.

For vapors and gases of sufficiently low pressure $\kappa \ll 1$, so that we may neglect the term $n^2\kappa^2$ in Eq. (15.29). The refractive index n is so near n_0 that we may replace $n^2 - n_0^2$ by $2n_0(n - n_0)$, and Eq. (15.29) becomes

$$n = n_0 + \frac{A_0}{n_0} \frac{\omega_0(\omega_0 - \omega)}{4(\omega_0 - \omega)^2 + g^2\omega^2}. \tag{15.31}$$

Equating the derivative of n with respect to ω to zero, we obtain the conditions for the extremes in the values of the index of refraction.

$$g^2\omega\omega_0 = 4(\omega_0 - \omega)^2. \tag{15.32}$$

To a good approximation $\omega\omega_0$ may be replaced by ω^2. The maximum in the index of refraction lies at

$$\frac{\omega}{\omega_0} = 1 - \frac{g}{2}, \tag{15.33}$$

and the minimum at

$$\frac{\omega}{\omega_0} = 1 + \frac{g}{2}. \tag{15.34}$$

The separation of the extreme values of n on the scale of ω/ω_0 is g. At these extremes in the index of refraction

$$n - n_0 = \pm \frac{A_0}{n_0 4g}.$$

At these same positions on the scale of ω/ω_0,

$$2n^2\kappa = \frac{A_0}{2g}. \tag{15.35}$$

From Eqs. (15.24) and (15.25) we note that $A_0/2g = \frac{1}{2}(2n^2\kappa)_{\max}$.

The width of the resonance plot of $2n^2\kappa$ at half maximum is equal to the separation of the extremes in index of refraction on the frequency scale.

Figure 263 is of superposed plots of the index of refraction n and the product $2n^2\kappa$ against ω/ω_0 for the case in which $n_0 = 1$, $g = 0.001$, and $A_0 = 0.0001$. For similar plots of n and $2n^2\kappa$ against λ/λ_0, the scale of λ/λ_0 would be in reverse direction from that of ω/ω_0.

We may relate the index of absorption κ which was defined from a molecular point of view, to the coefficient of absorption μ which was defined from a macroscopic point of view. From Bougier's law we obtained the relative intensity

$$\frac{I}{I_0} = \epsilon^{-\mu x}. \tag{15.36}$$

The ratio of the corresponding amplitudes of electric field is

$$\frac{A}{A_0} = \epsilon^{-(\mu/2)x}. \tag{15.37}$$

A plane wave in an absorbing dielectric is not sinusoidal, but damped, the wave equation being

$$\frac{E}{E_0} = \epsilon^{-(\mu/2)x}\epsilon^{j\omega(t-x/v)}. \tag{15.38}$$

The first factor expresses the damping of the amplitude with distance x. The second factor is complex and expresses the phase. If we combine the exponents in x, we obtain

$$\frac{E}{E_0} = \epsilon^{-j(\omega/v)[1-j(\mu v/2\omega)]x}\epsilon^{j\omega t}. \tag{15.39}$$

The velocity of the wave in the dielectric may be expressed in terms of the velocity in vacuum and the index of refraction by $v = c/n$. The ratio

$$\frac{v}{\omega} = \frac{\lambda}{2\pi}.$$

The wavelength in the dielectric is indicated by λ. By substitution in Eq. (15.39) we obtain

$$\frac{E}{E_0} = \epsilon^{-j(\omega n/c)[1-j(\mu\lambda/4\pi)]x}\epsilon^{j\omega t}. \tag{15.40}$$

For simplicity we define a *complex index of refraction*

$$\mathbf{n} = n\left(1 - j\frac{\mu\lambda}{4\pi}\right).$$

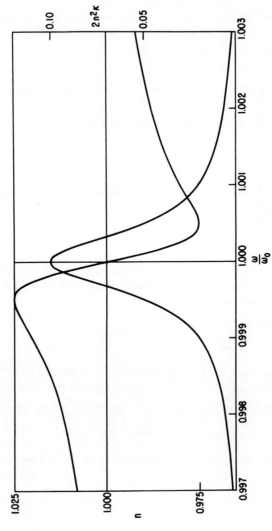

Figure 263. Plots of the index of refraction n and of the product $2n^2\kappa$ against ω/ω_0. The scale of $2n^2\kappa$ is on the right-hand side.

We note that the imaginary term is the index of absorption defined by Eq. (15.20). Thus

$$\kappa = \frac{\mu\lambda}{4\pi}. \tag{15.41}$$

We may examine the physical meanings of the two constants μ and κ. The absorption coefficient $\mu/2$ expresses the fractional rate of decrease of amplitude with distance x, in the limit as Δx approaches zero,

$$\frac{\Delta A}{A} = -\frac{\mu}{2}\,\Delta x, \tag{15.42}$$

where μ is dependent on the system of units used and expressed in reciprocal meters or reciprocal centimeters. The index of absorption expresses the fractional decrease of amplitude with phase angle $\Delta\beta = 2\pi\,\Delta x/\lambda$, so that in the limit as $\Delta\beta$ approaches zero

$$\frac{\Delta A}{A} = -\kappa\,\Delta\beta, \tag{15.43}$$

where κ is unitless.

PROBLEMS FOR CHAPTER XV

15.2.1. Plot a graph of index of refraction against wavelength in the range 4000 A to 8000 A for the Cauchy Eq. (15.1). The constant A for a particular dielectric is 1.1, and B is $1.0 \times 10^7 A^2$.

15.2.2. For the dielectric of problem 15.2.1, compare the dispersion at 5000 A and 7000 A.

15.3.3. In the neighborhood of an absorption line all terms in Sellmeier's Eq. (15.3) except the j term corresponding to the resonant wavelength λ_j may be treated as a constant. Plot a graph of $A_j\lambda^2/(\lambda^2 - \lambda_j^2)$ against λ in the region 5900 A to 6100 A near an absorption line of wavelength 6000 A, where $A_j = 3.0 \times 10^{-3}$.

15.7.4. Make a graphical plot of the phase angle ϕ of the oscillating dipole against ω/ω_0 for the range ω/ω_0 equals zero to 2.0, and the case of $g = 0.05$.

15.8.5. Find the value of the unitless constant A_0 in Eq. (15.25) for an ideal gas under standard conditions of pressure and temperature, in which case $N = 2.7 \times 10^{25}$ molecules/m^3. For yellow light $\omega_0 = 3.1 \times 10^{15}$ sec^{-1}.

15.10.6. Derive Eq. (15.32) for the conditions for extremes in the values of the index of refraction in the neighborhood of a resonant frequency.

chapter XVI

Polarization

16.1 Sources of Polarized Electromagnetic Waves

A source consisting of many atoms emits randomly polarized radiation. Some of the most promising tools for the study of matter by reflection and transmission of electromagnetic waves are the sources of polarized light currently being developed. (1) The centripetally accelerated electrons moving in circular paths in a synchrotron or betatron[1] emit polarized electromagnetic waves in a continuous spectrum extending from x-rays to the infrared. (2) The waves from a dipole antenna of a microwave source are polarized with the electric field parallel to the antenna. The spectral ranges of these two sources are indicated in Fig. 264.

Older methods of producing polarized sources are those of placing the source in strong magnetic fields and strong electric fields to produce what are known as the *Zeeman* and *Stark effects*, respectively. The splitting and polarization of spectral lines in both the Zeeman and Stark effects are explained by quantum theory. However, the first observations by Zeeman[2] were predicted with simple classical theory by Lorentz.

The oscillations of electrons in the source S of Fig. 265 may be divided into components parallel and perpendicular to the magnetic field. We may think of a vibration perpendicular to the field as made up of two circular

[1] Elder, Gurewitsch, Langmuir, and Pollock, *Phys. Rev.*, **71**, 829 (1947).
[2] P. Zeeman, *Researches in Magneto-Optics:* London, Macmillan and Co., Ltd. (1913).

motions in opposite directions lying in a plane perpendicular to the magnetic field. As seen in Fig. 266, the horizontal components of v_0, the velocities of the particles moving in circles, cancel. Their vertical components add to give the velocity of the electron undergoing simple harmonic motion. The electrons

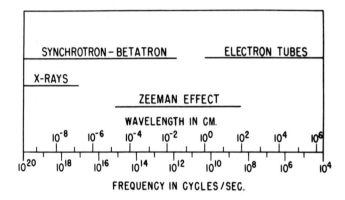

Figure 264. Spectral ranges of polarized sources.

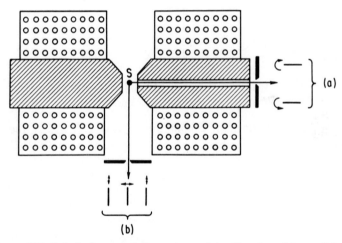

Figure 265. Polarized spectral lines observed in directions (a) parallel and (b) perpendicular to the magnetic field.

vibrating parallel to the magnetic field are unaffected by the field. Electrons moving in a counter-clockwise direction relative to an observer looking into the magnetic field will experience a radially inward force Bev_1 by the field of magnetic induction B. Those rotating in a clockwise direction will experience an outward force Bev_2.

By Newton's second law of motion, the centripetal force in the absence of a magnetic field is

$$f = \frac{mv_0^2}{r} = m\omega_0^2 r, \tag{16.1}$$

where ω_0 is the angular velocity in zero magnetic field. If the motion is circular or simple harmonic the central electrostatic force is

$$f = kr, \tag{16.2}$$

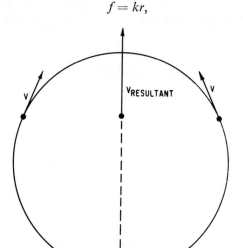

Figure 266. Simple harmonic motion in a straight line may be thought of as the resultant of two oppositely directed circular motions.

where k is the force constant. Eliminating f from Eqs. (16.1) and (16.2), we obtain

$$\omega_0^2 = \frac{k}{m}.$$

When the magnetic induction is increased from zero to B, the frequency of the counter-clockwise moving electron is increased to ω_1 given by

$$m\omega_1^2 r_1 = kr_1 + Bev_1.$$

But $kr_1 = m\omega_0^2 r_1$, so that

$$m\omega_1^2 r_1 = m\omega_0^2 r_1 + Bev_1,$$

and

$$\omega_1^2 = \omega_0^2 + \frac{Bev_1}{mr_1}.$$

But $v_1/r_1 = \omega_1$ by definition, so that

$$\omega_1^2 = \omega_0^2 + \frac{Be\omega_1}{m}.$$

Since ω_1 differs only slightly from ω_0,

$$2\omega_1(\omega_1 - \omega_0) = \frac{Be\omega_1}{m},$$

and

$$\omega_1 - \omega_0 = \frac{Be}{2m}.$$

Hence

$$\nu_1 = \nu_0 + \frac{Be}{4\pi m}. \qquad (16.3)$$

For the clockwise motion,

$$\nu_2 = \nu_0 - \frac{Be}{4\pi m}. \qquad (16.4)$$

If we set the spectrometer to receive light traveling through the hole parallel to the field as in Fig. 265, we observe two frequencies of circularly polarized light, one of higher and one of lower frequency than that received when the field is zero. If we observe at right angles to the field, we note three lines; the above two frequencies, and one polarized parallel to the magnetic field with its frequency unaffected by the magnetic field. This is radiation from the electron oscillating parallel to the field. The electrons moving in the circular paths are radiating to the spectrometer in a direction within their planes. From the spectrometer the circles are "seen" as straight lines. The waves from these electrons moving in planes perpendicular to the magnetic field are plane polarized with their electric field perpendicular to the direction of the field of the magnet, and have frequencies differing from the center line by $Be/4\pi m$. The experimental value of charge to mass computed from the measured field strength and the frequencies is the value of e/m for the electron, indicating that the radiating charge is an electron. For the quantum treatment of the Zeeman effect we may turn to books in atomic physics and spectroscopy. The Zeeman and Stark effects are used in the modulation of the microwave frequencies[3,4,5] in microwave spectroscopy of molecules. The gases or vapors are subject to a magnetic field in a rectangular wave guide. The field is parallel to the length of the guide.

The continuous spectrum of x-rays at wavelengths much shorter than the highest energy characteristic lines is polarized. The continuous radiation is emitted by the electrons as they are stopped by the target. The radiation is perpendicular to the deceleration as shown in Sec. 2.1. Characteristic line radiation is emitted in all directions by excited atoms. Continuous radiation from an aluminum foil target bombarded by 30 kv electrons is over 99% plane polarized. The continuous x-ray spectrum, like the continuous spectrum

[3] G. Herzberg, *Atomic Spectra and Atomic Structure:* Englewood Cliffs, N.J., Prentice-Hall (1937).
[4] H. E. White, *Introduction to Atomic Spectra:* New York, McGraw-Hill (1934).
[5] C. H. Townes and A. L. Shawlow, *Microwave Spectroscopy:* New York, McGraw-Hill (1955).

from centripetally accelerated electrons in the betatron, is emitted by electrons and not by excited atoms. Figure 267 indicates the distribution of intensity in an x-ray spectrum. At the longer wavelengths the characteristic lines of the atoms are superposed on the continuous spectrum from the decelerated electrons.

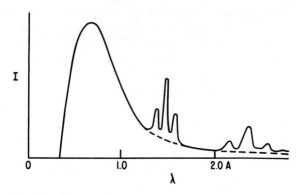

Figure 267. Distribution of intensity in an x-ray spectrum showing the continuous spectrum with characteristic lines of an element superposed.

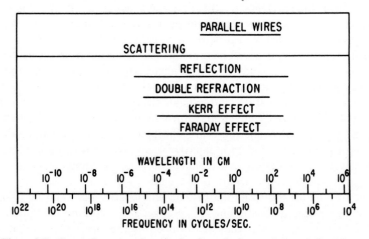

Figure 268. Spectral ranges of methods of producing a plane-polarized beam.

16.2 Polarizing Devices

Our most common sources of electromagnetic waves in the range from x-rays to infrared are atoms and molecules in large numbers emitting random polarization. They may be used with polarizing devices which will be treated in this and the following chapter. Figure 268 indicates the spectral range of producing plane-polarized waves from an unpolarized beam.

(1) The most convenient polarizer for an introduction to the subject of polarization is the parallel-wire screen for use with wavelengths from 1.0 to 200 cm. (2) Polarization by scattering can be obtained throughout the electromagnetic spectrum. (3) Polarization by reflection is produced with all wavelengths that can be reflected from a mirror. Mirrors can be found for all wavelengths from 2000 A in the ultraviolet through radio waves. Total external reflection is obtained for soft x-rays and for ultraviolet only at very small glancing angles. No mirrors have been found for hard x-rays. (4) Crystals divide the randomly polarized waves into two components polarized perpendicularly to each other. The crystals have different indices of refraction for these two polarized components. By ingenious cutting and combining certain crystals in such forms as the Nicol prism, we are able to separate the two beams and eliminate one of them. (5) Certain crystals such as tourmaline, called *dichroic crystals*, absorb or partially reflect one of the components, and are thus natural polarizers. Land[6] has developed large sheet polarizers made up of microscopic dichroic crystals aligned in a plastic film. They transmit one component throughout the visible spectrum. The other component is completely absorbed in the visible spectrum except for a trace in the red and violet. These polarizing sheets, known by the trade name of Polaroid, are widely used in optical instruments, and are convenient in elementary demonstrations of polarization of the visible spectrum. (6) Certain dielectrics become doubly refracting in magnetic and electric fields. These include the historic magnetic Faraday effect and the electric Kerr effect. Since electric fields can be changed in a very short time, Kerr cells serve as optical shutters which are faster than mechanical shutters.

16.3 Polarization of Microwaves

When the study of polarization is begun with light we must rely upon theory or analogy to give the direction of polarization. If the study is begun

Figure 269. Observation of the cosine squared law.

with microwaves, the electric field is parallel to the antenna of the transmitter. The intensity meter with its antenna serves as analyzer. If the transmitter and intensity meter are aligned as in Fig. 269, and the intensity meter rotated

[6] E. H. Land, *J. Opt. Soc. Amer.*, **41**, 957 (1951).

about axis AB, the intensity will be found to be proportional to the square of the cosine of the angle through which the antenna is rotated.

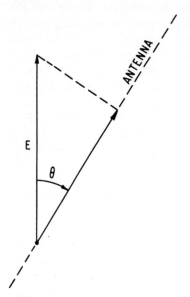

The cosine square law is readily explained. If the amplitude of the incident electric field is E_0, its component parallel to the antenna of the intensity meter is

$$E = E_0 \cos \theta,$$

as indicated in Fig. 270. The intensity is as the square of the amplitude of the electric field, so that

$$I = I_0 \cos^2 \theta. \qquad (16.5)$$

16.4 Polarization by Parallel Wires

If a parallel wire plane screen is inserted between the transmitter and intensity meter of Fig. 269 so that its plane is perpendicular to line AB and its wires parallel to the antenna of the transmitter, the oscillating electric field produces currents in the wires. The electric field undergoes $180°$ phase change while the magnetic field undergoes no phase change, so that

Figure 270. Component of the electric field received by the intensity meter.

Poynting's vector is reversed. The wave is reflected. If the parallel screen is rotated about axis AB, the transmitted intensity

$$I_t = I_0 \cos^2 \theta. \qquad (16.6)$$

When the wires are perpendicular to the field there is no component of field parallel to the wires and the wave is completely transmitted.

We must conclude that the wires do not sift the waves as they might sift corpuscles or straws in Fig. 271. The $\cos^2 \theta$ law reveals that polarization by the parallel wires is not a sifting process, but one of resolution into components. The components parallel to the wires are reflected, while those perpendicular to the wires are transmitted.

The reflected component is studied by the arrangement of Fig. 272. The screen may be rotated about axis CD. The intensity of the reflected wave

$$I_r = I_0 \sin^2 \theta. \qquad (16.7)$$

Adding Eqs. (16.6) and (16.7), we obtain

$$I_t + I_r = I_0$$

for all values of θ, which is an expression of conservation of energy.

If the screen is to transmit zero intensity when the wires are parallel to the incident electric field, the wires should not be more than 0.1 wavelength apart and not less than 0.01 wavelength in diameter. A finer wire presents too high

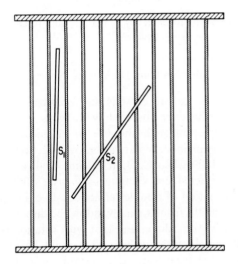

Figure 271. Polarization by a wire screen is not a sifting process but a division into components.

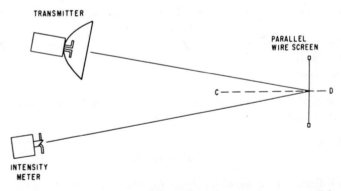

Figure 272. Arrangement for studying reflected waves from a parallel wire screen.

surface resistance. Strips of metal foil $\frac{1}{4}$ in. wide, separated by $\frac{1}{2}$ in. and fastened to a manila folder with a Scotch tape, provide an excellent polarizing screen. To avoid effects of Fresnel diffraction around the edges of the polarizing screen, we may mount it over a circular aperture in a metal screen such as the first zone aperture of the screen in Fig. 195.

If we examine plane-polarized light by rotating a sheet of Polaroid in the same manner as the parallel wire screen for microwaves, we find again that

$$I_t = I_{max} \cos^2 \theta.$$

The maximum value of the intensity I_{max} is not equal to the incident intensity I_0, since part of the intensity is absorbed.

16.5 Polarization by Reflection from Dielectrics

Double refraction by calcite crystals and polarization of the two rays transmitted by the crystals were observed by Huygens and Newton. Huygens explained double refraction with the use of elliptical wavelets, but the polarization was not explained. Polarization by reflection by dielectrics was not discovered until 1809 when Captain Etienne Malus, an engineer in the French army, was attracted one evening by a prize offered by the French Institute for an explanation of double refraction. Looking through a calcite crystal at reflected sunlight from a glass window, he discovered that only one ray was transmitted by the calcite, and that with rotation of the crystal the two rays were alternately extinguished. That night he observed the same effect with light reflected from water at a certain angle. The cosine squared law which we have treated is known as *Malus' law*.

After Malus' discovery Thomas Young pondered for eight years how light waves could be polarized. Polarization was being used as evidence for the corpuscular theory of light. Suddenly the idea occurred to Young that if light waves were transverse they could be polarized.

Sir David Brewster discovered a simple law to define Malus' certain angle of incidence for which the light reflected from the dielectric surface is totally plane polarized.

The reflected light is plane polarized when the angle between the reflected ray and refracted ray is $\pi/2$.

In this case,

$$\sin \bar{\phi}' = \cos \bar{\phi}, \tag{16.8}$$

where $\bar{\phi}$ is Brewster's angle of incidence for which the reflected beam is totally polarized, and $\bar{\phi}'$ is the corresponding angle of refraction indicated in Fig. 273. If we combine Eq. (16.8) with the definition of index of refraction

$$n = \frac{\sin \phi}{\sin \phi'}, \tag{16.9}$$

we obtain

$$n = \frac{\sin \bar{\phi}}{\cos \bar{\phi}} = \tan \bar{\phi}. \tag{16.10}$$

The refracted beam is never completely polarized, but contains both components.

The direction of polarization of the reflected beam, that is, the direction of the electric field, can not be determined for light except from electromagnetic theory.

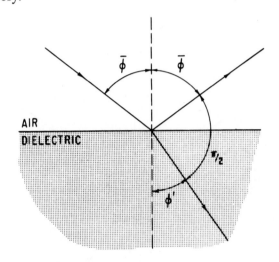

Figure 273. Totally polarized reflection.

We shall turn therefore to microwaves to find the direction of the electric field in the reflected polarized wave. In describing the directions of polarization of the reflected and refracted waves, we shall use the *plane of incidence* as reference plane. The plane of incidence is the plane including the incident ray and the normal to the surface at the point of incidence. Figure 274 is a

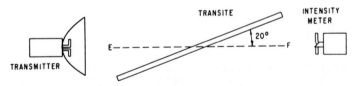

Figure 274. Polarization of microwaves by reflection from a dielectric.

diagram of an arrangement for studying polarization by reflection of microwaves. If either glass or transite is used as the dielectric, the dielectric constant is approximately 2.5, Brewster's angle is 70°, and the glancing angle is 20°. For such a high index of refraction the transmitted beam is as completely polarized as is light by a stack of glass plates. If we rotate the dielectric sheet about axis *EF* of Fig. 274 with the angle of incidence maintained at 70°, we may discover the direction of polarization of the reflected ray. When the incident electric field is in the plane of incidence, the wave is completely transmitted. When the incident electric field is perpendicular to the plane of incidence, the transmission is small, most of the wave being reflected.

Figure 275 indicates the direction of polarization of the reflected and refracted waves when randomly polarized light is incident upon the surface of the dielectric. The dots indicate polarization perpendicular to the plane of incidence. The refracted wave contains both the parallel and perpendicular components of **E**.

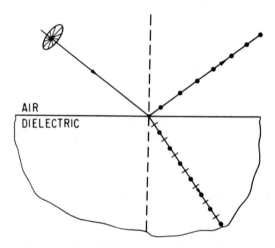

Figure 275. Indication of directions of polarization of the reflected and refracted beams.

Knowing the direction of polarization of the wave reflected from glass at Brewster's angle, we may use this reflected ray to determine the direction of the electric field that is transmitted by Polaroid and mark the Polaroid to indicate that direction.

16.6 Theory of Reflection and Refraction

From electromagnetic theory we wish to derive the known laws of the behavior of the waves at a boundary and obtain new information concerning the amplitudes and phases of the reflected and refracted waves. The known experimental laws which are to be derived as further confirmation of electromagnetic theory are: (1) the reflected and refracted rays lie in the plane of incidence; (2) the angle of reflection equals the angle of incidence; (3) Snell's law to the effect that $\sin \phi / \sin \phi'$ is a constant; and (4) Brewster's law for the conditions of complete polarization of the reflected ray.

We have at hand Maxwell's wave equations plus four boundary conditions the proofs of which are standard theorems in textbooks of electricity and magnetism.[7,8] (1) From Faraday's law of induced emf's is derived the continuity of the tangential component of **E** across the bounding surface between the dielectrics. (2) From Ampere's circuital law is derived the continuity of the tangential component of **H** across the bounding surface. From Gauss' law is derived the continuity of the normal components of (3) the electric displacement **D** and (4) the magnetic induction **B** across the bounding surface. Since the permeability of transparent substances is unity

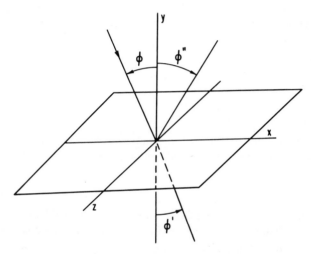

Figure 276. Geometry used in application of Maxwell's equations to derive the laws of reflection and refraction.

at high frequencies, the magnetic induction **B** may be replaced by μ_0 times the magnetic field strength **H**.

We shall let the plane $y = 0$ of Fig. 276 be the surface between the dielectrics of permittivities ϵ_1 and ϵ_2. The plane of incidence is the x, y plane. Angles ϕ, ϕ'', and ϕ' are the angles by the incident, reflected, and refracted rays with the normal to the surface at the point of incidence. The normal is the y axis. We do not assume that the reflected and refracted rays lie in the plane of incidence. We shall find it convenient to divide the directions of the electric and magnetic fields into components perpendicular and parallel to the plane of incidence.

Case I. Electric field of incident wave normal to the plane of incidence,

[7] R. P. Winch, *Electricity and Magnetism:* Englewood Cliffs, N.J., Prentice-Hall (1955).

[8] L. Page and N. I. Adams, *Principles of Electricity:* New York, Van Nostrand (1949).

where E_z is in the positive z direction. The incident, reflected, and refracted waves of the z component of electric field may be written

$$E_z = A_z e^{j[\omega t - (2\pi/\lambda)(lx + my + pz)]} \tag{16.11}$$

$$E_z'' = A_z'' e^{j[\omega t - (2\pi/\lambda)(l''x + m''y + p''z)]} \tag{16.12}$$

$$E_z' = A_z' e^{j[\omega' t - (2\pi/\lambda')(l'x + m'y + p'z)]} \tag{16.13}$$

For the incident, reflected, and refracted waves, respectively, the complex field E, the amplitude A, the angular frequencies ω, and the direction cosines l, m, and p with respect to x, y, and z are unprimed, double primed, and primed. The wavelengths and frequencies of the incident and reflected waves are the same since they are in the same medium. For the incident ray the direction cosines are $l = \cos(\pi/2 - \phi) = \sin\phi$, $m = \cos\phi$, and $p = 0$. From the first boundary condition,

$$E_z + E_z'' = E_z' \tag{16.14}$$

when $y = 0$, so that

$$A_z e^{j[\omega t - (2\pi/\lambda)(lx + pz)]} + A_z'' e^{j[\omega'' t - (2\pi/\lambda)(l''x + p''z)]} = A_z' e^{j[\omega' t - (2\pi/\lambda')(l'x + p'z)]}. \tag{16.15}$$

Since this equality is true for all times and for all values of x and z on the boundary, the coefficients of t, x, and z must be the same in each of the three terms. Thus

$$\omega = \omega'' = \omega'.$$

The frequency of each of the rays is the same. Since the incident ray lies in the x, y plane, $p = 0$ and thus $p'' = p' = 0$. *The reflected and refracted waves lie in the plane of incidence.*

$$\frac{l}{\lambda} = \frac{l''}{\lambda}.$$

Thus $l = l''$, and *the angle of reflection equals the angle of incidence.* Also

$$\frac{l}{\lambda} = \frac{l'}{\lambda'},$$

and

$$\frac{\sin\phi}{\sin\phi'} = \frac{l}{l'} = \frac{\lambda}{\lambda'}.$$

Since the frequencies are the same in both media the ratio of velocities in the two media

$$\frac{v_1}{v_2} = \frac{\lambda}{\lambda'},$$

where v_1 and v_2 are the velocities in the media of permittivities ϵ_1 and ϵ_2, respectively, of Fig. 276. Since the velocities are constant for each medium, *the ratio of the sines of the angles of incidence and reflection is a constant.*

Inserting the values of the direction cosines, we simplify Eq. (16.15) to obtain

$$A_z e^{-j(2\pi/\lambda)(x\sin\phi - y\cos\phi)} + A_z'' e^{-j(2\pi/\lambda)(x\sin\phi + y\cos\phi)} = A_z' e^{-j(2\pi/\lambda')(x\sin\phi' - y\cos\phi')}.$$

$$(16.16)$$

Thus far we have derived from electromagnetic theory some *known* laws of optics. Next we shall use electromagnetic theory to obtain two new bits of information, (1) the ratio of A_z''/A_z which we shall call the coefficient of amplitude reflection r_N, and (2) the ratio A_z'/A_z which we shall call the coefficient of amplitude transmission t_N. The subscripts N indicate the electric field normal to the plane of incidence treated in this case.

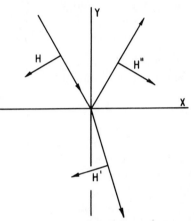

Since the electric field is taken perpendicular to the plane of incidence and directed outward in the positive z direction, the magnetic field must be parallel to the plane of incidence. If our assumption for the directions of $\mathbf{E}_z''$ or $\mathbf{E}_z'$ are incorrect, the results will be automatically corrected in the solution by negative values of A_z'' or A_z'. Using the right-hand rule for the relation between the directions of $\mathbf{E}$, $\mathbf{H}$, and the direction of propagation, we may find the directions of the magnetic fields $\mathbf{H}$, $\mathbf{H}''$, and $\mathbf{H}'$ for each of the three rays

Figure 277. Determination of the directions of the magnetic fields from the known electric field and the directions of propagation. The electric field is taken in the positive z direction.

as shown in Fig. 277. From the fourth and second boundary condition we obtain

$$(H + H'')\sin\phi = H'\sin\phi', \qquad (16.17)$$

and $$(-H + H'')\cos\phi = -H'\cos\phi'. \qquad (16.18)$$

From Eq. (13.43) in electromagnetic theory $\mathbf{H} = \sqrt{\epsilon}\mathbf{E}$. Thus $\mathbf{H} = n_1\mathbf{E}_z$, $\mathbf{H}'' = n_1\mathbf{E}_z''$, and $\mathbf{H}' = n_2\mathbf{E}_z'$. Thus in Eqs. (16.17) and (16.18) we may substitute the electric field strength $\mathbf{E}_z$ and indices of refraction n for the magnetic field strengths $\mathbf{H}$. Since, at the point of incidence on the boundary, x and y are zero, the oscillating field strengths $\mathbf{E}_z$ may be replaced by the amplitudes A_z. Thus we obtain from Eqs. (16.14), (16.17), and (16.18) three simultaneous equations for the boundary conditions

$$A_z + A_z'' = A_z' \qquad (16.19)$$

$$(A_z + A_z'')n_1\sin\phi = A_z'n_2\sin\phi' \qquad (16.20)$$

$$(A_z - A_z'')n_1\cos\phi = A_z'n_2\cos\phi'. \qquad (16.21)$$

If we eliminate A_z' and solve for A_z''/A_z, we obtain

$$\left(1 - \frac{A_z''}{A_z}\right) \frac{\cos \phi}{\sin \phi} = \left(1 + \frac{A_z''}{A_z}\right) \frac{\cos \phi'}{\sin \phi'} .$$ (16.22)

Replacing A_z''/A_z by the coefficient of amplitude reflection r_N, we obtain

$$\frac{1 - r_N}{1 + r_N} = \frac{\sin \phi \cos \phi'}{\cos \phi \sin \phi'} .$$ (16.23)

Solving for r_N, we obtain

$$r_N = \frac{-\sin (\phi - \phi')}{\sin (\phi + \phi')} .$$ (16.24)

Likewise, eliminating A_z'' from Eqs. (16.19), (16.20), and (16.21), we solve for the coefficient of amplitude transmission $t_N = A_z'/A_z$ and obtain

$$t_N = \frac{2 \sin \phi' \cos \phi}{\sin (\phi + \phi')} .$$ (16.25)

Case II. Electric field of the incident wave parallel to the plane of incidence. In this case the magnetic field is perpendicular to the plane of incidence and thus parallel to the boundary surface. Since **H** is parallel to the boundary we find it simpler to treat three equations for the **H** waves. Recalling that **H** = n**E**, we note that the amplitudes of the magnetic waves may be expressed in terms of nA. Thus

$$\mathbf{H}_z = n_1 A_z e^{j[\omega t - (2\pi/\lambda)(lx + my + pz)]}$$ (16.26)

$$\mathbf{H}_z = n_1 A_z'' e^{j[\omega'' t - (2\pi/\lambda)(l''x + m''y + p''z)]}$$ (16.27)

$$\mathbf{H}_z = n_2 A_z' e^{j[\omega' t - (2\pi/\lambda')(l'x + m'y + p'z)]},$$ (16.28)

where H_z, H_z'', and H_z' are the complex amplitudes of the incident, reflected, and refracted waves of the z component of the magnetic field. From the second boundary condition,

$$\mathbf{H}_z + \mathbf{H}_z'' = \mathbf{H}_z',$$ (16.29)

and

$$n_1 A_z e^{j[\omega t - (2\pi/\lambda)(lx + my + pz)]} + n_1 A_z'' e^{j[\omega'' t - (2\pi/\lambda)(l''x + m''y + p''z)]}$$
$$= n_2 A_z' e^{j[\omega' t - (2\pi/\lambda')(l'x + m'y + p'z)]}.$$ (16.30)

From Eq. (16.30) the proofs of the laws of reflection and refraction are identical to the proofs in Case I, and Eq. (16.30) becomes

$$n_1 A_z e^{j(2\pi/\lambda)(x \sin \phi - y \cos \phi)} + n_1 A_z'' e^{j(2\pi/\lambda)(x \sin \phi + y \cos \phi)} = n_2 A_z' e^{j(2\pi/\lambda')(x \sin \phi' - y \cos \phi')}.$$ (16.31)

We shall now determine the ratios A_z''/A_z and A_z'/A_z for the coefficients of reflection and transmission, respectively. Since the magnetic fields are taken in the positive z direction the electric fields are in the plane of incidence. Using the right-hand rule for the relation between the directions of **E**, **H**, and the direction of propagation, we may find the directions of electric fields **E**, **E″**, and **E′** for each of the three rays shown in Fig. 278. Using the third boundary condition, the continuity of the normal component of **D** across the boundary, and recalling that **D** $= \epsilon$**E** $= n^2$**E** when the medium is isotropic, we obtain

$$(\mathbf{E} + \mathbf{E}'')n_1^2 \sin \phi = n_2^2 \mathbf{E}' \sin \phi'.$$

(16.32)

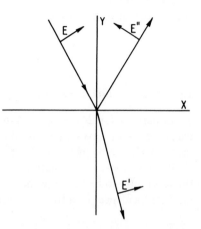

Figure 278. Finding the directions of the electric fields from known magnetic fields and the directions of propagation.

From the first boundary condition which expresses the continuity of the tangential electric field, we obtain

$$(E - E'') \cos \phi = E' \cos \phi'. \quad (16.33)$$

From Eq. (13.43) in electromagnetic theory, **H** $= \sqrt{\epsilon}$**E** $= n$**E**. Thus Eq. (16.29) for the second boundary condition may be expressed in terms of electric fields. Since, at the point of incidence on the boundary x and y are zero, the oscillating field strengths **E** may be replaced by amplitudes A. Thus we obtain from the three Eqs. (16.29), (16.32), and (16.33) three simultaneous equations for the boundary conditions

$$(A_z + A_z'')n_1 = n_2 A_z' \tag{16.34}$$

$$(A_z + A_z'')n^2 \sin \phi = n_2^2 A_z' \sin \phi' \tag{16.35}$$

$$(A_z - A_z'') \cos \phi = A_z' \cos \phi'. \tag{16.36}$$

If we eliminate A_z' and solve for A_z''/A_z, we obtain

$$\left(1 - \frac{A_z''}{A_z}\right) \frac{\cos \phi}{\sin \phi'} = \left(1 + \frac{A_z''}{A_z}\right) \frac{\cos \phi'}{\cos \phi}. \tag{16.37}$$

Replacing A_z''/A_z by the coefficient of amplitude reflection r_P, we obtain

$$\frac{1 - r_P}{1 + r_P} = \frac{\sin \phi' \cos \phi'}{\sin \phi \cos \phi}. \tag{16.38}$$

Solving for r_P, we obtain

$$r_P = \frac{\sin \phi \cos \phi - \sin \phi' \cos \phi'}{\sin \phi \cos \phi + \sin \phi' \cos \phi'}. \tag{16.39}$$

We shall retain for the problems the proof that Eq. (16.39) becomes

$$r_P = \frac{\tan(\phi - \phi')}{\tan(\phi + \phi')}.$$ (16.40)

Likewise, eliminating A_z'' from Eqs. (16.34), (16.35), and (16.36), we solve for the coefficient of amplitude transmission $t_P = A_z'/A_z$ and obtain

$$t_P = \frac{2 \sin \phi' \cos \phi}{\sin(\phi + \phi') \cos(\phi - \phi')}.$$ (16.41)

16.7 Interpretation of Fresnel's Equations

Equations (16.24), (16.25), (16.40), and (16.41) for the reflection and transmission of waves were found empirically by Fresnel before the development of electromagnetic theory and are known as *Fresnel's equations*. We shall collect these four equations, and interpret them for waves incident from the less dense to more dense medium. In the following section we shall treat internal incidence from the more dense medium. The collected equations are

$$r_N = \left(\frac{A''}{A}\right)_N = \frac{-\sin(\phi - \phi')}{\sin(\phi + \phi')}$$ (16.42)

$$r_P = \left(\frac{A''}{A}\right)_P = \frac{\tan(\phi - \phi')}{\tan(\phi + \phi')}$$ (16.43)

$$t_N = \left(\frac{A'}{A}\right)_N = \frac{2 \sin \phi' \cos \phi}{\sin(\phi + \phi')}$$ (16.44)

$$t_P = \left(\frac{A'}{A}\right)_P = \frac{2 \sin \phi' \cos \phi}{\sin(\phi + \phi') \cos(\phi - \phi')}.$$ (16.45)

For angles of incidence sufficiently close to zero that the cosines of ϕ and ϕ' may be considered equal to unity, we may express these four equations in terms of the indices of refraction by expanding the sine and cosine functions of the sums and differences of ϕ and ϕ', neglecting terms in the sine cubed compared to the first power of the sine, dividing the numerators and denominators by $\sin \phi'$, and replacing $\sin \phi / \sin \phi'$ by the ratios of indices of refraction n_2/n_1. Thus we obtain as normal incidence is approached

$$r_P = -r_N = \frac{n_2 - n_1}{n_2 + n_1},$$ (16.46)

and

$$t_P = t_N = \frac{2n_1}{n_2 + n_1}.$$ (16.47)

We made use of Eq. (16.46) in treating interference in thin films in Chapter VIII.

Here r_P becomes zero when $(\phi + \phi')$ is 90°. When $(\phi + \phi')$ is 90° the angle between the reflected and refracted rays is also 90°, which was Brewster's experimental condition for the complete polarization of the reflected ray. From electromagnetic theory we have shown, if the incident ray is randomly polarized, the reflected ray is polarized with the electric field perpendicular to the plane of incidence which is as we observed with microwaves.

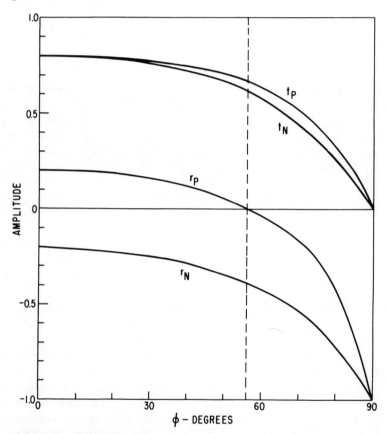

Figure 279. Graphs of r_N, r_P, t_N, and t_P plotted against the angle of incidence ϕ for $n = 1.5$.

The values of r_N, r_P, t_N, and t_P are plotted against the angle of incidence ϕ in Fig. 279 for the index of refraction 1.5. Note that r_N is always negative, indicating that the reflected wave which is polarized perpendicular to the plane of incidence has undergone π phase change upon reflection for all angles of incidence. By Eq. (16.43) the reflected wave, which is polarized with its electric field in the plane of incidence, undergoes no phase change upon reflection for values of ϕ less than Brewster's angle $\bar{\phi}$. For values of ϕ greater than $\bar{\phi}$ the reflected wave undergoes π change. We need to give special attention to the rule of signs for this case in which the electric field is in the plane of incidence. By the rule which has come out of the electromagnetic equations, *the two rays are in phase if their y components are in the same direction* and the x components are opposed just before and after reflection. Figure 280 shows the direction of the electric field at the boundary for angles of incidence greater and less than Brewster's angle. Note that this rule of signs is necessarily awkward when the angle of incidence is zero. The incident and reflected fields are opposite as ϕ approaches zero for electric fields either parallel or normal to the plane of incidence. At normal incidence this oppositeness of fields is expressed by a negative sign for $(A''/A)_N$ and a positive sign for $(A''/A)_P$.

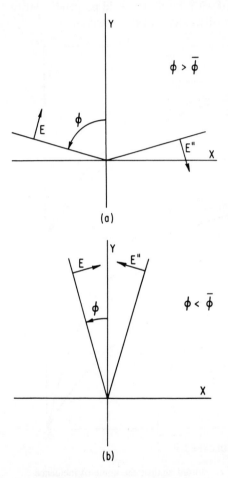

This awkwardness might be overcome by changing the sign of $\tan(\phi - \phi')/\tan(\phi + \phi')$ of Eq. (16.43). However, that would lead to an equally annoying conclusion at grazing incidence, so we shall retain the rule of signs which resulted from the solution of the electromagnetic theory.

As the angle of incidence approaches $90°$ the intensity of the refracted beam approaches zero and all the light is reflected. Even a black asphalt road becomes a good mirror at grazing incidence.

Figure 281 consists of four plots of intensity ratios r_N^2, r_P^2, t_N^2, and t_P^2 against ϕ for incidence from air to glass. At Brewster's angle, when the reflected light is totally polarized, 15 % of the incident radiation polarized perpendicularly to the plane of incidence is reflected. Thus only 7.5 % of the incident randomly polarized light is reflected at Brewster's angle for glass.

Since Eqs. (16.42)–(16.45) are for nonabsorbing media, we may check

Figure 280. Direction of the electric field at the boundary for angles of incidence (a) greater and (b) less than Brewster's angle.

them by use of conservation of energy. The power incident on the boundary equals the sum of the reflected and transmitted power leaving the boundary. The beams in the two media have different widths and different velocities, so that the intensity is not conserved. If P'' and P' are the reflected and refracted powers,

$$\frac{P''}{P} + \frac{P'}{P} = 1. \tag{16.48}$$

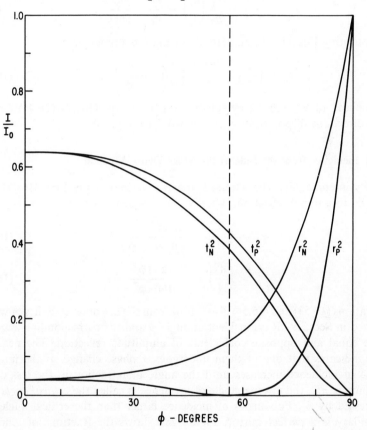

Figure 281. Graphs of intensity ratios r_N^2, r_P^2, t_N^2, and t_P^2, plotted against the angle of incidence ϕ for incidence from air to glass.

The power or rate of flow of energy in a medium is the product of the velocity of the wave, the energy density, and the cross-sectional area of the beam. The energy density is ϵE^2 as given by Eq. (13.44). The average values of E^2 are proportional to the amplitude A^2, so that Eq. (16.48) becomes

$$\left(\frac{A''}{A}\right)^2 + \frac{v_2 \epsilon_2}{v_1 \epsilon_1} \left(\frac{A'}{A}\right)^2 \frac{a_2}{a_1} = 1. \tag{16.49}$$

From solid geometry we may show that the ratio of the cross-sectional areas in the two media

$$\frac{a_2}{a_1} = \frac{\cos \phi'}{\cos \phi}. \qquad (16.50)$$

From electromagnetic theory and the definition of index of refraction,

$$\frac{v_2}{v_1} \frac{\epsilon_2}{\epsilon_1} = \frac{n_1}{n_2} \left(\frac{n_2}{n_1}\right)^2 = \frac{n_2}{n_1} = \frac{\sin \phi}{\sin \phi'}. \qquad (16.51)$$

Substituting Eqs. (16.50) and (16.51) in Eq. (16.49), we obtain

$$\left(\frac{A''}{A}\right)^2 + \frac{\sin \phi}{\sin \phi'} \left(\frac{A'}{A}\right)^2 \frac{\cos \phi'}{\cos \phi} = 1. \qquad (16.52)$$

The check of Eq. (16.52) by substitution from Eqs. (16.42)–(16.45) for the two directions of polarization is retained for the problems.

16.8 Incidence from the Side of the More Dense Medium

By interchanging the letters ϕ and ϕ', we may apply Eqs. (16.42) and (16.45) to internal reflection. These equations then become

$$r_N = \left(\frac{A''}{A}\right)_N = \frac{\sin (\phi - \phi')}{\sin (\phi + \phi')} \qquad (16.53)$$

$$r_P = \left(\frac{A''}{A}\right)_P = -\frac{\tan (\phi - \phi')}{\tan (\phi + \phi')}. \qquad (16.54)$$

Equations (16.53) and (16.54) also follow from the law of reversibility of waves treated in Sec. 2.9. Rays incident at angle ϕ and the corresponding angle ϕ' have equal and opposite coefficients of amplitude reflection. The negative sign indicates that one of them undergoes π phase change. If the internal angle of incidence increases until the angle of refraction in the less dense medium is $\pi/2$, the internal angle of incidence is called the *critical angle* and expressed by ϕ_c. For angles of incidence larger than the critical angle the boundary is a perfect mirror. Figure 282 shows the fractions of reflected intensity r_N^2 and r_P^2 plotted against the angle of incidence for the case in which the more dense medium is glass of index of refraction 1.5, and the less dense medium is air. We note that the curves for external reflection in the range $\phi = 0$ to $\pi/2$ are squeezed into the range 0 to ϕ_c for internal reflection. There is a polarizing angle, Brewster's angle for internal reflection when $\phi + \phi' = \pi/2$.

If the irregularities in the dielectric surface are small compared to a wavelength and the surface is kept clean, total internal reflection is more perfect than that from any metal mirror. Since the critical angle for glass is less than 45°, prisms like that of Fig. 283 are used as reflectors in view finders of cameras, binoculars, and other optical instruments. Bent rods of dielectric conduct light over crooked paths provided the radius of curvature is large enough so that the angle of incidence on the wall is always greater than ϕ_c. In a dielectric wave guide for microwaves the angle of incidence of the internal beam on the walls must be above ϕ_c.

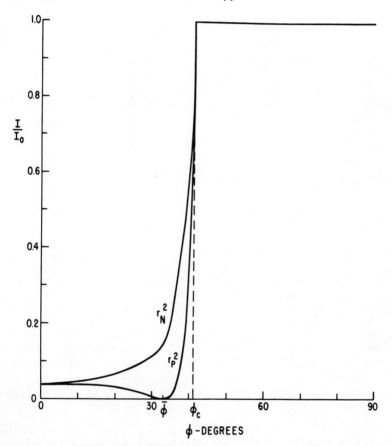

Figure 282. Fractions of reflected intensity r_N^2 and r_P^2 plotted against the angles of internal incidence less than the critical angle.

As they stand Eqs. (16.53) and (16.54) apply only for angles of incidence between zero and the critical angle. We may note some experimental facts about internal reflection that a more general equation must satisfy. If we move a dipole probe along line AB perpendicular to the reflecting surface of a wave guide for microwaves as in Fig. 284, we note that the wave extends outside the dielectric boundary with its amplitude decreasing exponentially

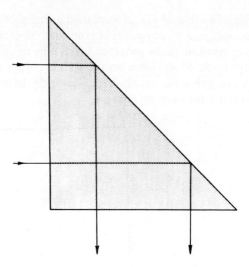

Figure 283. Totally reflecting prism.

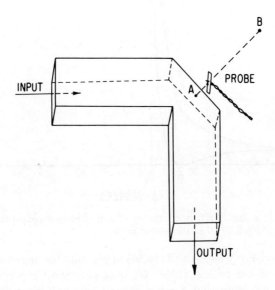

Figure 284. Probing the microwave field outside the dielectric wave guide.

in a direction perpendicular to the surface to less than 1 % at a distance of 1 wavelength.

The theoretical derivation of the equations for internal reflection must satisfy the following experimental observations: (1) The beam is totally reflected for angles of incidence greater than ϕ_c. (2) There is an exponentially decreasing wave in the x direction. (3) The traveling wave along the surface returns all its energy to the reflected beam. (4) For angles of incidence greater

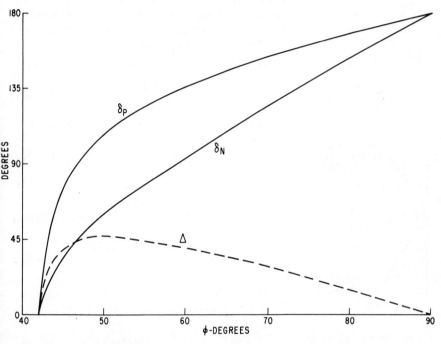

Figure 285. Plots of phase changes δ_P and δ_N and the phase difference Δ against the angle of incidence ϕ for $\phi > \phi_c$.

than the critical angle Snell's law does not apply, that is, the ratio of $\sin \phi'/\sin \phi$ is not a constant if $\sin \phi'$ can be said to be $\pi/2$. (5) Above the critical angle the phase lag of the reflected wave increases continuously from zero to π, as indicated in Fig. 285, for the electric field parallel and perpendicular to the plane of incidence. We note that the phase curves are not of the same shape, the greatest difference in phase being about 45°. Fresnel designed a rhomb, Fig. 286, grinding the reflecting surfaces by cut and try until the phase difference between the two waves was 90°. If the incident plane wave is polarized 45° to the plane of incidence, the wave may be considered to be divided into two components of equal amplitudes parallel and perpendicular to the plane of incidence. As we recall from Sec. 3.6 and Fig. 40, two coherent

waves of the same amplitude with vibrations at right angles to each other and
90° out of phase combine to give circular polarization.

In our treatment of reflection in Sec. 16.6 we did not insert an unknown
phase angle α in the exponents of Eqs. (16.11)–(16.13). Our only justification
in making this omission was in the experimentally observed fact that the
phase changes upon reflection were zero or π, and
could be contained in the signs of the constants
A for which we solved. It is possible to solve all
the experimentally known facts about internal
reflection for all angles of incidence.[9] However,
we shall take an empirical short cut.

At the critical angle of incidence ϕ_c,

$$\frac{n_2}{n_1} = \frac{\sin(\pi/2)}{\sin\phi_c} = \frac{1}{\sin\phi_c}. \qquad (16.55)$$

We shall define the relative index of refraction

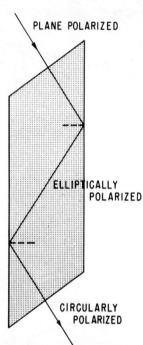

PLANE POLARIZED

ELLIPTICALLY
POLARIZED

CIRCULARLY
POLARIZED

Figure 286. Fresnel rhomb.

$$n_{12} = \frac{n_1}{n_2}. \qquad (16.56)$$

When $\phi > \phi_c$, $\sin\phi > n_{12}$ and $\sin\phi/n_{12} > 1$. If
we define ϕ' by Snell's law, $\sin\phi' = \sin\phi/n_{12}$,
where $\sin\phi$ is unity only when ϕ is the critical
angle.

$$\cos\phi' = \pm\sqrt{1 - \frac{\sin^2\phi}{n_{12}^2}}. \qquad (16.57)$$

Since the quantity under the radical is negative,
we shall express the complex value of $\cos\phi'$ by

$$\cos\phi' = -\frac{j}{n_{12}}\sqrt{\sin^2\phi - n_{12}^2}. \qquad (16.58)$$

The negative sign has been chosen because it makes the phase angle a
continuous function of ϕ near the critical angle of incidence. Since Eqs.
(16.53) and (16.54) contain $\cos\phi'$, the coefficients of amplitude reflection r_N
and r_P are complex, which means that the reflected waves undergo phase
changes upon reflection which vary with the angle of incidence ϕ. Thus

$$r_N = \left(\frac{A''}{A}\right)e^{j\delta_N} = \frac{\sin(\phi - \phi')}{\sin(\phi + \phi')} \qquad (16.59)$$

$$r_P = \left(\frac{A''}{A}\right)e^{j\delta_P} = -\frac{\tan(\phi - \phi')}{\tan(\phi + \phi')}, \qquad (16.60)$$

[9] B. Rossi, *Optics:* Reading, Mass., Addison-Wesley (1957) Sec. 8–7.

where δ_N and δ_P are the phase angles of the reflected waves polarized normally and parallel to the plane of incidence taken relative to the incident ray. The fraction of reflected intensity for the component polarized perpendicularly to the plane of incidence is

$$\left(\frac{I''}{I_0}\right)_N = \left|\left(\frac{A''}{A}\right)_N e^{j\delta_N}\right|^2 = \left|\frac{\sin(\phi - \phi')}{\sin(\phi + \phi')}\right|^2. \tag{16.61}$$

Substituting from Eq. (16.58) and $\sin \phi' = \sin \phi / n_{12}$, we obtain

$$\left(\frac{I}{I_0}\right)_N = \left(\frac{-j\sqrt{\sin^2 \phi - n_{12}^2} - \cos \phi}{-j\sqrt{\sin^2 \phi - n_{12}^2} + \cos \phi}\right)\left(\frac{j\sqrt{\sin^2 \phi - n_{12}^2} - \cos \phi}{j\sqrt{\sin^2 \phi - n_{12}^2} + \cos \phi}\right) = 1. \tag{16.62}$$

Similarly we may show that $(I/I_0)_P = 1$. Thus for values of

$$\phi > \phi_c, \qquad \left(\frac{A''}{A}\right)_N = \left(\frac{A''}{A}\right)_P = 1,$$

and

$$e^{j\delta_N} = \frac{\sin(\phi - \phi')}{\sin(\phi + \phi')}, \tag{16.63}$$

from which we may solve for δ_N. Substituting in Eq. (16.63) from Eq. (16.58) and replacing $\sin \phi'$ by $\sin \phi / n_{12}$, we obtain

$$e^{j\delta_N} = \frac{\cos \phi + j\sqrt{\sin^2 \phi - n_{12}^2}}{\cos \phi - j\sqrt{\sin^2 \phi - n_{12}^2}}. \tag{16.64}$$

Equation (16.64) is of the form

$$e^{j\delta_N} = \frac{v + jw}{v - jw}. \tag{16.65}$$

Expressing the numerator and denominator of Eq. (16.65) each in exponential form, we obtain

$$\begin{cases} v + jw = ze^{j\theta} \\ v - jw = ze^{-j\theta}. \end{cases}$$

Dividing, we obtain

$$\frac{v - jw}{v + jw} = e^{2j\theta}. \tag{16.66}$$

Thus $\delta_N = 2\theta$, and $\tan(\delta_N/2) = \tan \theta = w/v$, so that

$$\tan\left(\frac{\delta_N}{2}\right) = \frac{\sqrt{\sin^2 \phi - n_{12}^2}}{\cos \phi}. \tag{16.67}$$

In similar manner we may show that

$$\tan\left(\frac{\delta_P}{2}\right) = \frac{\sqrt{\sin^2\phi - n_{12}^2}}{n_{12}^2\cos\phi}. \tag{16.68}$$

Figure 285 consists of plots of δ_N and δ_P and of $\Delta = \delta_P - \delta_N$ against the angles of incidence between ϕ_c and $\pi/2$, for glass of index of refraction $n_{21} = 1.5$ ($n_{12} = 0.66$). Because the maximum value of Δ is more than $45°$, Fresnel was able to build the rhomb of Fig. 286 with which he could obtain by two reflections a phase difference in the two components of $90°$ and thus obtain circularly polarized light.

16.9 Reflection from Metals

Within the next few decades we may expect the study of reflection of electromagnetic waves from metals to (1) extend through the spectrum from soft x-rays to microwaves and (2) include all metal elements.

The greatest current motivation for the study of reflection of electromagnetic waves from metals comes from the field of solid state physics. The optical properties of metals are being correlated with crystal structure, electrical conductivity, and electron emission from surfaces.

The optical constants for a given metal vary for reflection from polished and evaporated surfaces. An essential technique of solid state physics is the art of growing crystals of pure metals such as copper, iron, germanium, and silicon. These crystals may be broken along cleavage planes in a vacuum and the optical properties of surfaces studied before they become oxidized.

A promising source of polarized radiation that is continuous throughout the spectrum is that from the centripetally accelerated electrons of the betatron and synchrotron.

The simplest of all cases of reflection from metals to be treated in the student laboratory is that of reflection of microwaves. Using the "universal" probe of Comely and Talham,[10] Fig. 287, we may study independently the intensity of radiation E^2 of the electric wave and B^2 of the magnetic wave. When each arm of the rectangular loop is 0.1 wavelength long, the loop is equally sensitive to both electric and magnetic waves and small enough not to disturb greatly the pattern that is being measured. When the loop is oriented as in Fig. 288(a), it links with the oscillating magnetic field. The crystal arm is perpendicular to the electric field. The loop detects only the intensity of radiation B^2 of the magnetic field. In the orientation of Fig. 288(b) the loop does not link with the magnetic field. The crystal arm is parallel to the electric field and only the intensity of radiation E^2 of the electric field is detected.

[10] R. E. Comley and R. J. Talham, *Am. J. Phys.*, **25**, 568 (1957).

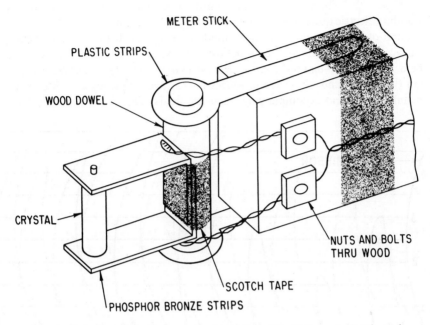

Figure 287. A probe for measuring intensities of radiation of electric and magnetic waves independently.

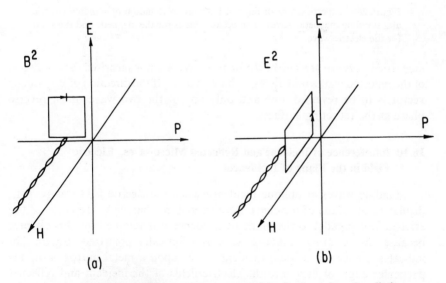

Figure 288. Orientation of probe for measuring the intensity of radiation (a) B^2 of the magnetic wave, (b) E^2 of the electric wave.

Figure 289 shows superposed recordings of intensities of radiation of standing electric and standing magnetic waves. The intensity curves approach a node of electric field and an antinode of magnetic field at the reflecting surface. At the "perfectly" conducting metal screen there can be no electric field. *The incident and reflected electric waves are π out of phase at the surface.* On the other hand, the wave produces microwave frequency currents in the metal surface and accompanying magnetic fields. *The incident and reflected*

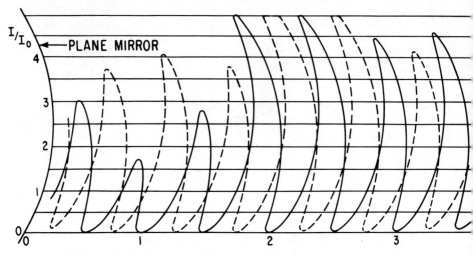

Figure 289. Superposed recordings of intensity of radiation of standing electric and standing magnetic waves. The broken line is for the magnetic and the solid for the electric wave.

magnetic waves are in phase at·the surface. We are not surprised that only one of the reflected waves undergoes π phase change. If the direction of Poynting's vector is to be reversed, one and only one of the two waves must reverse phase at the reflecting surface.

16.10 Interference of Incident and Reflected Microwaves. Electric Field in the Plane of Incidence

Standing waves at oblique incidence when the electric field was perpendicular to the plane of incidence were treated in Chapter V. The case of the electric field parallel to the plane of incidence was retained for this chapter because the resulting standing wave is elliptically polarized. Figure 290 indicates a microwave beam incident at 45° upon a metal mirror. For this particular angle of incidence the electric fields of the incident and reflected waves are perpendicular to each other. The electric dipole probe must be rotated about an axis which is perpendicular to the plane of incidence to record the major and minor axes of the ellipse. A plot of the square root of the recorded intensity of radiation E^2 on polar graph paper gives the elliptical shape of the variation of the electric field strength E. Interesting special cases of the ellipse are the circle and straight line. When the two waves are π out of phase as at the surface of the mirror, the ellipse becomes a straight line perpendicular to the surface as indicated in Fig. 290. The planes in which the polarization is perpendicular to the screen are separated by the distance

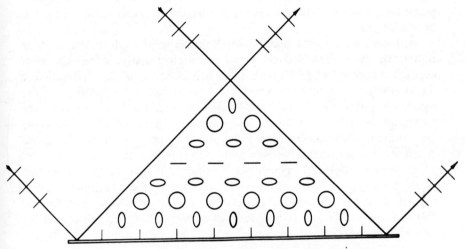

Figure 290. Resultant elliptically polarized electric wave where the incident and reflected waves interfere. Polarization in the plane of incidence.

$\lambda/(2 \cos \phi)$, and correspond to the nodal planes when the field is perpendicular to the plane of incidence as treated in Chapter V. At the distance $\lambda/(8 \cos \phi)$ from the surface the waves are $\pi/2$ out of phase, and the ellipse becomes a circle. At the plane distant $\lambda/(4 \cos \phi)$ the resultant electric field is parallel to the reflecting surface. We note that it is only the resultant electric field within the triangle ABC that is elliptically polarized. The reflected wave is plane polarized.

In Wiener's experiment of Fig. 65 the photographic film showed uniform blackening for this case in which the electric field lay in the plane of incidence, but showed standing waves when the electric field was perpendicular to the plane of incidence. This was further evidence that the oscillating electric field and not the magnetic field affects the photographic plate.

16.11 Optical Properties of Metals

The high reflectivity of metals compared to that of dielectrics is due to the free electrons that migrate between the atoms. These same free electrons make metals good conductors of heat and electricity. At the high frequencies of the ultraviolet and visible spectra molecular electrical dipoles take part in the high-frequency current. Indeed, in the ultraviolet, metals have transmission bands between the natural dipole frequencies very similar to those of dielectrics. For instance silver has a band of poor reflectivity corresponding to high transmission near 3200 A in the ultraviolet. The reflectivity of silver increases to over 95 % in the visible spectrum and still higher in the infrared where the free electrons play the major role in determining the optical properties of metals. Narrow absorption bands for alkali metals appear in the visible spectrum.

At longer wavelengths than 20,000 A in the infrared, the currents are so completely those of free electrons that a quantitative relation is found between the optical properties and the electrical resistivity of the metal. The fraction of the intensity that enters the metal and is absorbed is proportional to the square roots of the resistivities for all metals. Metals having high temperature coefficients of resistance display a temperature coefficient of reflectance in the far infrared. Constantan, named for its low temperature coefficient of resistance, has constant reflectivity with change in temperature.

The theory of electromagnetic waves in metals is more complex than that of electromagnetic waves in dielectrics because of the additional electron current in metals. Maxwell's expression of Ampere's laws must include electron currents as well as displacement currents. Thus Eq. (13.14) for the curl of **H** becomes

$$
\begin{cases}
j_x + \epsilon \dfrac{\partial E_x}{\partial t} = \dfrac{\partial H_z}{\partial y} - \dfrac{\partial H_y}{\partial z} \\[2mm]
j_y + \epsilon \dfrac{\partial E_y}{\partial t} = \dfrac{\partial H_x}{\partial z} - \dfrac{\partial H_z}{\partial x} \\[2mm]
j_z + \epsilon \dfrac{\partial E_z}{\partial t} = \dfrac{\partial H_y}{\partial x} - \dfrac{\partial H_x}{\partial y}.
\end{cases}
\tag{16.69}
$$

Maxwell's expression of Faraday's law of Eq. (13.21) is unaltered. Since there is no concentration of charge and the metal is nonmagnetic so that **H** replaces **B**, the divergence laws are the same as for dielectrics. Expressed in vector algebra,

$$\text{div } \mathbf{E} = 0, \tag{16.70}$$

and

$$\text{div } \mathbf{H} = 0. \tag{16.71}$$

The current density is dependent on the field strength E_x as expressed by

$$j_x = \sigma E_x,$$

where σ is the conductivity of the metal, the reciprocal of the resistivity.

We shall leave for the problems the proof that the wave equation of the x component of the electric field is

$$\mu_0 \sigma \frac{\partial E_x}{\partial t} + \mu_0 \epsilon \frac{\partial^2 E_x}{\partial t^2} = \frac{\partial^2 E_x}{\partial x^2} + \frac{\partial^2 E_x}{\partial y^2} + \frac{\partial^2 E_x}{\partial z^2} . \tag{16.72}$$

We shall not solve the wave equations and boundary conditions but merely note that the waves are reflected with phases other than zero and π, so that the amplitudes may be expressed as complex quantities and the index of refraction becomes complex. The complex index of refraction

$$\mathbf{n} = n(1 - j\kappa). \tag{16.73}$$

This is the combination of real quantities n the index of refraction and κ the index of absorption treated in Sec. 15.10.

The *amplitude reflectivity* at normal incidence on metals becomes

$$\frac{A''}{A} e^{-j\delta} = \frac{n(1 - j\kappa) - 1}{n(1 - j\kappa) + 1}, \tag{16.74}$$

where A'' and A are the amplitudes of the reflected and incident electric fields, and δ the phase change upon reflection. The *intensity reflectivity*

$$R = \frac{I''}{I_0} = \left| \frac{n(1 - j\kappa) - 1}{n(1 - j\kappa) + 1} \right|^2 . \tag{16.75}$$

Thus
$$R = \frac{(n - 1)^2 + \kappa n}{(n + 1)^2 + \kappa n} . \tag{16.76}$$

We note that the reflectivity of nonabsorbing dielectrics at normal incidence is a special case of the reflectivity of metals obtained by letting κ be zero.

There are striking similarities between reflection from metals and total internal reflection in dielectrics in addition to their high reflectivities. (1) The wave penetrates the metal damping to 1 % intensity in a fraction of a wavelength, just as the wave reflected by total internal reflection damps rapidly in the second medium as shown in Fig. 291. (2) The reflected waves from metals and totally internally reflected waves in dielectrics both undergo phase changes upon reflection that vary continually with angle of incidence ϕ. To express these phases we let the amplitude coefficients of reflection r_N and r_P be complex as expressed in Eqs. (16.59) and (16.60) of the previous section.

The treatment of reflection from metals is more complicated than that of transparent dielectrics, in that the metals are so highly absorbing that we can not measure their indices of refraction by transmission through a prism as we have done for dielectrics. We must determine the indices of refraction and absorption indirectly by measuring the *principal angle of incidence* $\bar{\phi}$, the value of ϕ when the coefficient of reflection r_P is a minimum as indicated in

Fig. 292, and the corresponding *principal azimuth angle* $\bar{\psi}$ of the reflected beam.

An azimuth angle is the angle which the electric field makes with the normal to the plane of incidence. In the measurement of optical constants of metals, the azimuth of the incident beam is made 45° so that the components E_P and E_N parallel and normal to the plane of incidence are equal. In the

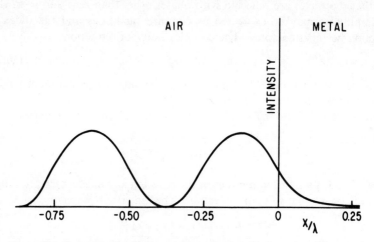

Figure 291. Intensity of wave in metal compared to the intensity of the standing wave on the side of the incident and reflected waves.

case of reflection from dielectrics, the reflected wave is plane polarized and the azimuth angle of the reflected ray is given by

$$\tan \psi = \frac{E_P''}{E_N''}, \tag{16.77}$$

as indicated in Fig. 293(a). Since the two components of the reflected wave from a metal vary differently in both amplitude and phase with the angle of incidence, the reflected wave is elliptically polarized as indicated in Fig. 293(b). The elliptical vibration may be thought of as made up of two simple harmonic motions of complex amplitudes $\mathbf{E}_P''$ and $\mathbf{E}_N''$. Figure 294 is a plot of the difference of phase change $\Delta = \delta_P - \delta_N$ of the two components upon reflection plotted against the angle of incidence ϕ. We note that at the principal angle of incidence $\Delta = \pi/2$. Even though these two vibrations are not in phase, we shall arbitrarily define the azimuth angle of the reflected wave by Eq. (16.77) using the absolute values $\mathbf{E}_P''$ and $\mathbf{E}_N''$.

The laboratory measurements of azimuth angle for reflections from dielectrics and metals are described by Valasek.[11] From the principal angle of

[11] J. Valasek, *Introduction to Theoretical and Experimental Optics:* New York, Wiley (1940) Experiments 20 and 21.

incidence $\bar{\phi}$ and the principal azimuth angle $\bar{\psi}$ we may compute approximately the index of refraction n and the index of absorption κ from the simultaneous equations[12]

$$n\sqrt{1 + \kappa^2} = \sin\bar{\phi}\tan\bar{\phi} \qquad (16.78)$$

$$\kappa = \tan 2\bar{\psi}. \qquad (16.79)$$

Tables of optical constants[13,14] of metals are recorded for a few metals

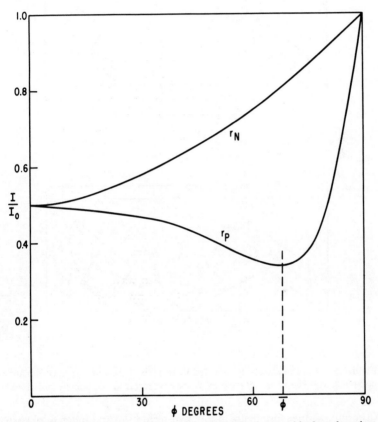

Figure 292. Reflectivities r_P and r_N of sodium light from gold plotted against angle of incidence. Note the minimum of r_P is not zero as it is for reflection from the surface of a dielectric.

over a range of wavelengths. The constants include the measured constants $\bar{\phi}$ and $\bar{\psi}$, the computed constants n and κ, the product $n\kappa$, and R the percentage

[12] R. W. Wood, *Physical Optics:* New York, Macmillan (1934) p. 554.
[13] *Handbook of Chemistry and Physics:* Cleveland, Ohio, Chemical Rubber Publishing Co.
[14] *International Critical Tables,* 5, 248–256.

reflection of intensity of radiation at normal incidence. An examination of the tables reveals a few generalizations. (1) The reflectivity increases with the index of absorption, being highest at resonance as illustrated by the 99% reflection from sodium metal at the sodium resonance frequency.

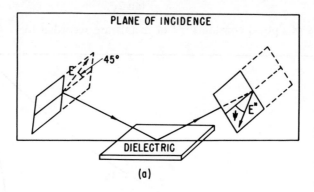

(a)

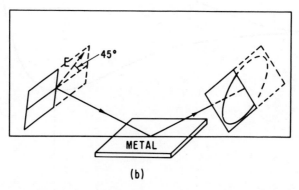

(b)

Figure 293. (a) The externally reflected wave from a dielectric surface is plane polarized. (b) The reflected wave from a metal surface is elliptically polarized.

(2) Although the measurements of index of refraction and index of absorption differ by a factor of several hundred for different metals and the same wavelength, the product $n\kappa$ differs by less than 50% for all measurements made on different metals reflecting the same wavelength. (3) The product $n\kappa$ is roughly proportional to the first power of the wavelength.

In Sec. 15.10 we derived the relation between the index of absorption κ and the coefficient of absorption μ,

$$\kappa = \left(\frac{\lambda}{4\pi}\right)\mu. \tag{16.80}$$

Throughout the range from 2000 A to 20,000 A, μ is of the order of 10^{-6} cm^{-1}, varying by less than a factor of two. This is in great contrast to the λ^3 law for the variation of the coefficient of absorption in the hard x-ray region.

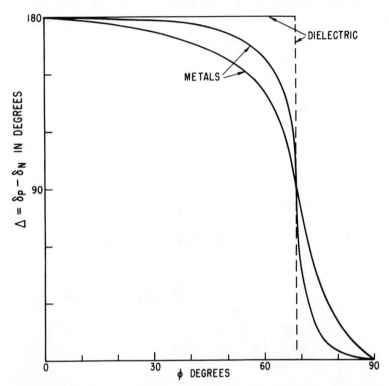

Figure 294. Difference of phase change $\Delta = \delta_P - \delta_N$ of the parallel and normal components of the electric field upon reflection from metals plotted against the angle of incidence ϕ. As the index of absorption approaches zero, the curve becomes that for a dielectric.

16.12 Selective Reflection

The most distinctive feature of the optical properties of metals compared to those of dielectrics is their high reflectivity throughout the low-frequency spectrum due to free electrons. However, even in the visible range certain metals such as gold and copper show color selectivity due to resonant molecular dipoles. If we watch a glass plate in a glass bell jar on which gold is being evaporated, the gold film is seen to reflect the yellow-red portion of the spectrum and transmit the blue-green. If we observe a white light source by multiple reflection from gold mirrors as in Fig. 295(a), the image of the source appears bright red by multiple selective reflection.

In the farthest infrared region of the spectrum selective reflectivity is used to locate narrow absorption bands for certain crystals such as quartz and the chlorides of alkali metals. The reflectivities are of the order of 90% in the narrow region, dropping to 10% on either side. Figure. 295(b) shows an arrangement for isolating these residual rays (*restrahlen*) and measuring their

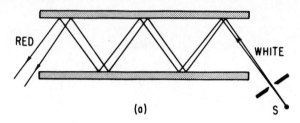

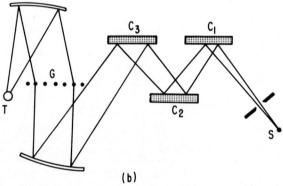

Figure 295. (a) Multiple reflections from gold give a red image of a white source. (b) Residual rays by reflection from the longest wavelengths of infrared from crystals reveal narrow absorption bands.

wavelength with a grating. The source S is a white-hot oxide which can not be oxidized further in air; C_1, C_2, C_3, and C_4 are reflecting surfaces of the crystal to be studied; G a wire grating; and T a thermopile. By this means wavelengths of absorption lines as long as 0.1 mm have been measured.

16.13 Polarization by Scattering

Scattering and polarization by scattering are observed throughout the electromagnetic spectrum. Looking through a disk of Polaroid at the blue sky in any direction perpendicular to the line from the observer to the sun as indicated in Fig. 296(b), and rotating the Polaroid about the axis of observation, we observe variation in intensity of the light.

Barkla's[15] study of scattering of x-rays revealed that x-rays are polarized and therefore transverse waves. Later refined measurements by Compton and Hagenow,[16] Fig. 296(a), confirmed J. J. Thomson's theory of scattering which had applied also to the scattering of sunlight.

Scattering of polarized microwaves from individual objects of known size and shape, Fig. 296(c), are used as a check upon theory and to reveal details of the nature of scattering. In other parts of the spectrum we study only cumulative scattering from many particles.

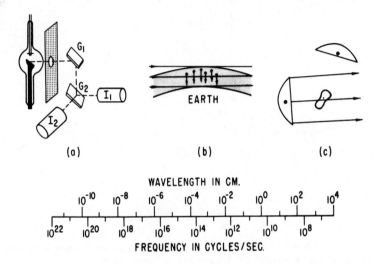

(a)   (b)   (c)

Figure 296. (a) The study of polarization of scattered x-rays revealed that x-rays are transverse waves. (b) Polarization by scattering of blue sunlight. (c) Scattering of microwaves from individual particles of different sizes and shapes.

We shall note geometrically that portion of Thomson's theory of scattering that reveals the dependence of the intensity of polarized light on the direction of scattering. Let the x axis of the coordinate system lie in the direction of propagation of the randomly polarized wave, with the origin S placed at the position of the scatterer. The scatterer contains many independent electrons or ions which the wave will cause to oscillate. The accelerated electrons will reradiate as described by Eq. (2.1). We wish to study the radiation along the surface of a cone which makes angle ϕ with the direction x of the incident beam, and has its vertex at the scatterer S, the origin. Here O is some point of observation on the cone. For convenience we shall rotate the y and z axes about the x axis until O lies in the xy-plane. The oscillations of the charges

[15] C. G. Barkla, *Proc. Roy. Soc. (London)*, **A77**, 247, (1906).
[16] A. H. Compton and C. F. Hagenow, *J. Opt. Soc. Amer.*, **8**, 487 (1924).

in the scatterer are all in the yz-plane, and the reradiated electric fields may be divided into equal components E_y and E_z. The component of E_y radiated in the direction OP is

$$E_P = E_y \cos \phi. \qquad (16.81)$$

The subscript P indicates a direction parallel to the *plane of reference*, which is the plane determined by the lines of the incident ray on the scatterer and

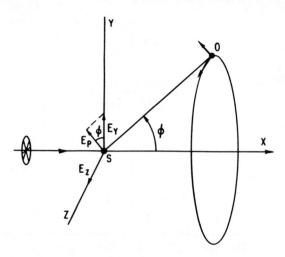

Figure 297. Showing the dependence of the degree of polarization by scattering upon the angle ϕ between the incident and scattered wave.

the scattered ray to the observer at O. Since E_y and E_z are equal and the intensities of radiation are proportional to the square of the amplitudes, an observer at O rotating a Polaroid disk as analyzer about axis SO will find the intensity I_P polarized parallel to the plane of reference to be less than I_N polarized perpendicularly to the plane of reference by the factor $\cos^2 \phi$. If we keep the distance SO constant and let ϕ vary from zero to π, the circle of Fig. 297 sweeps out a spherical surface. Anywhere on this surface the total intensity is

$$I = I_N + I_P = \text{const} (1 + \cos^2 \phi). \qquad (16.82)$$

When $\phi = \pi/2$, I_P is zero and the wave is polarized perpendicularly to the plane of reference.

In Barkla's study the x-rays were not completely polarized because of multiple scattering. By using thin graphite scatterers, Compton and Hagenow reduced the steps of scattering effectively to one and found complete polarization within the limits of experimental error when ϕ was $\pi/2$.

PROBLEMS FOR CHAPTER XVI

16.4.1. A microwave transmitter and intensity meter are aligned as in Fig. 269, and the meter rotated about axis AB to the position of maximum intensity I_0 when the antennas are parallel. The intensity meter is then rotated 90° to the position of extinction. A parallel-wire polarizing screen is then set with its plane perpendicular to the beam, and with the wires making an angle of 45° with the electric field. What will be the ratio I/I_0 of the intensity reading to the initial intensity?

16.5.2. Find Brewster's angle of incidence for white light on water of index of refraction 1.33.

16.5.3. Find Brewster's angle of incidence for microwaves on water for which the index of refraction is 9.0. Also find Brewster's angle for internal incidence.

16.6.4. Solve the three simultaneous Eqs. (16.19), (16.20), (16.21) for the coefficient of amplitude transmission t_N which is A'/A when the electric field is normal to the plane of incidence.

16.6.5. As one of the steps in the solution for the amplitude coefficient of reflection r_P prove that

$$\frac{\tan(\phi - \phi')}{\tan(\phi + \phi')} = \frac{\sin\phi\cos\phi - \sin\phi'\cos\phi'}{\sin\phi\cos\phi + \sin\phi'\cos\phi'}.$$

16.7.6. Find the amplitude coefficient of reflection of crown glass at normal incidence if its index of refraction is 1.54.

16.8.7. Make a drawing indicating how a fish sees the surrounding shores. The index of refraction of water is 1.33.

16.11.8. Derive the wave equation, Eq. (16.72), from Maxwell's differential equations of electricity and magnetism. Let Maxwell's differential equation for Ampere's law include both electron current and displacement current.

16.12.9. If in Fig. 295(b) 90% of the intensity of a line of wavelength 8 microns is reflected but the percentage reflection for the spectral region on either side is only 10%, compare the intensities of reflection of the line with that of the neighboring spectrum after reflection from three crystal surfaces.

chapter XVII

Double Refraction

17.1 Observation of Double Refraction in Calcite

Before making generalizations about double refraction (*birefringence*) in classes of crystals we shall recall our laboratory experience with a particular crystal. Because of its large size, the ease of cleaving large faces, and the wide separation which it gives of the two images of a point source, calcite, calcium carbonate in crystalline form, is used in introductory studies of double refraction.

If we place one of the cleavage surfaces of calcite over a black dot on a white paper and look vertically down into the crystal, we observe two images of the dot. If, with the crystal surface remaining on the paper, we rotate the crystal about a vertical axis, one of the images rotates about the other while the distance between them remains constant. One of the images remains at rest relative to the point source. This we shall call the *ordinary image*, and the ray from the source through it we shall call the *ordinary ray* because it behaves like the rays in isotropic substances such as glass and water. The other image which revolves about the real image we shall call the *extraordinary image*, and a ray from the source through that image an *extraordinary ray*. The ordinary image is raised more than the extraordinary image. Thus the index of refraction of the ordinary ray is higher than that of the extraordinary ray. We recall the theorem from elementary geometrical optics that the ratio of the depth of object to the depth of image below the refracting

428

surface when the observer is looking normally down on the surface is equal to the index of refraction. Thus the velocity of the ordinary ray in calcite is less than that of the extraordinary ray.

17.2 Definition of a Plane of Reference in the Calcite

There is one direction in which the velocity of light in calcite is the same for all rays of the same wavelength. This direction is called the *optic axis*. The optic axis of calcite is a line which makes equal angles with each of the three edges of a blunt corner, as indicated in Fig. 298(a). We note two blunt

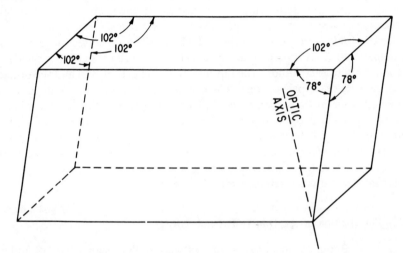

Figure 298(a). Calcite crystal. The optic axis makes equal angles with each of the edges of a blunt corner.

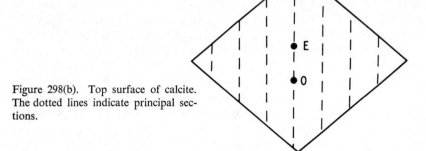

Figure 298(b). Top surface of calcite. The dotted lines indicate principal sections.

corners on each calcite crystal. Any line parallel to an optic axis is an optic axis. The optic axis is a direction rather than a single line in the crystal.

The optic axis is an axis of symmetry for many physical properties. For instance, if we grind a sheet of calcite with surfaces perpendicular to the optic axis, coat the surface with paraffin, and heat the calcite by a tight fitting wire through a hole perpendicular to the surface, we observe that the paraffin melts in an expanding circle around the wire. On any other plane surface of the calcite the molten paraffin would form an expanding ellipse. Of more immediate importance in optics is the fact that the optic axis is an axis of symmetry for the dielectric constants of calcite.

Any plane that contains an optic axis is a *principal plane*. For a given optic axis there are an infinite number of principal planes. If we are looking vertically downward on a cleavage plane at a point beneath the crystal, we are concerned only with vertical principal planes. The cross section cut by a principal plane that is perpendicular to a cleavage surface is called a *principal section*. Figure 298(b) shows the top surface of a calcite crystal and the dotted lines indicate principal sections. The ordinary and extraordinary images are observed to lie in the same principal plane. The ordinary and extraordinary rays always lie in a common principal plane. This reduces the study of double refraction by a calcite crystal to plane geometry. Just as we treated the plane of incidence as *plane of reference* when we studied polarization by reflection, so we shall consider a principal plane as plane of reference as we study the polarization of doubly refracted rays by calcite.

17.3 Polarization of the Doubly Refracted Rays

If we examine the two images with a Polaroid disk as analyzer, we find as we rotate the analyzer that the ordinary ray is polarized perpendicularly to the principal plane while the extraordinary ray is polarized parallel to the principal plane. The crystal resolves randomly polarized waves into two components of equal amplitude vibrating at right angles to each other, as indicated in Fig. 299. If we let plane-polarized light be incident upon the calcite, we may check the resolution into components. In Fig. 300, E indicates the direction of the amplitude of the electric field in the incident wave, and θ is the angle between E and the principal plane. The amplitude of the extra-ordinary wave polarized in the principal plane is $E \cos \theta$, and that of the ordinary wave polarized perpendicularly to the principal plane is $E \sin \theta$. The intensities of the extraordinary and ordinary rays are $E^2 \cos^2 \theta$ and $E^2 \sin^2 \theta$. Since none of the wave energy is absorbed, we are not surprised at the expression of equality of the sum of the intensities of the two rays to the intensity of the incident ray

$$E^2 \cos^2 \theta + E^2 \sin^2 \theta = E^2. \tag{17.1}$$

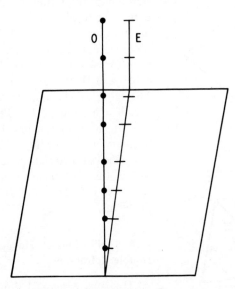

Figure 299. The crystal resolves randomly polarized light into two components vibrating at right angles to each other.

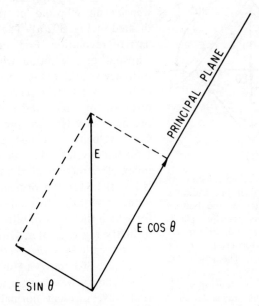

Figure 300. Resolution of the incident beam into components by the crystal.

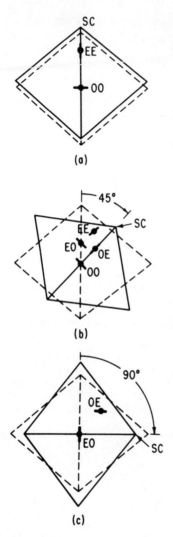

(a)

(b)

(c)

Figure 301. Stacked calcite crystals. The broken line indicates the top surface of the bottom crystal and its principal plane. The solid lines indicate the top surface of the top crystal and its principal plane. The letters SC indicate the sharp corner of the principal section toward which the extraordinary ray is deviated.

A good laboratory check of our understanding of resolution of vibrations into components is to place one calcite crystal on top of another. In Fig. 301 is indicated the observed dots and the directions of the vibrations for two stacked crystals when the angles θ between their planes are 0°, 45°, and 90°. The letter labels indicate the history of the ray. For instance, OE indicates that the ray was ordinary in the first crystal and extraordinary in the second. The sharp corner of the principal section is indicated by the letters SC on the bottom crystals. The cases of θ equal to 135° and 180° are retained for the problems.

17.4 Applications of Huygens' Principle to Double Refraction

Huygens explained double refraction on the basis of his principle of reradiation of secondary wavelets. In calcite the *ordinary wavelet* is a sphere and the *extraordinary wavelet* an ellipsoid of revolution, as indicated in Fig. 302(a). The optic axis is the axis of revolution. For a quartz crystal the ellipsoid of revolution which is the extraordinary wavelet fits inside the spherical ordinary wavelet. A crystal which has one direction in which the ordinary and extraordinary wavelets are propagated with the same velocity is called a *uniaxial crystal*. Uniaxial crystals like calcite, for which the index of refraction of the extraordinary ray is less than for the ordinary ray, are called *negative crystals*. Uniaxial crystals like quartz, for which the index of refraction of the extraordinary ray is greater than for the ordinary ray, are called *positive crystals*.

Figure 303 shows a Huygens construction of secondary wavelets for a randomly polarized wave incident normally on a cleavage surface of calcite. The figure is a principal section. The bounding rays of the ordinary and extraordinary beams are shown. The elliptical wavelets with minor axes parallel to the optic axis of the crystal explain the double refraction by calcite.

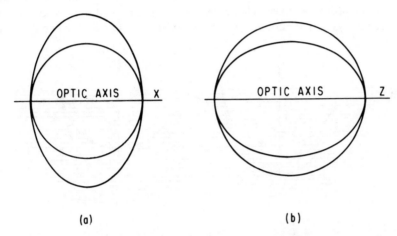

(a)   (b)

Figure 302. Huygens wavelets in (a) calcite and (b) quartz are spheres and ellipsoids of revolution. The axes of revolution are the optic axes.

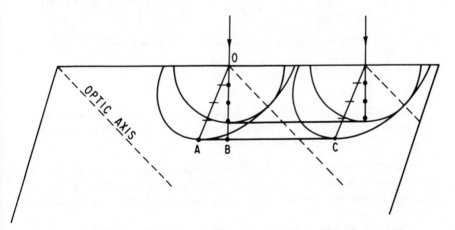

Figure 303. The construction of Huygens wavelets in calcite when a plane wave is incident normally on a cleavage surface.

We note two rules of the optics of ordinary rays that are applicable only to special cases of extraordinary rays. (1) Only those extraordinary rays which are parallel or perpendicular to the optic axis are perpendicular to the wave-front. (2) Only those extraordinary rays which are parallel or perpendicular to the optic axis obey Snell's law.

The Huygens constructions which we have made suggest two interesting experimental checks. If a special crystal of calcite is ground and polished with faces parallel to the optic axis, the ordinary and extraordinary rays are superposed as indicated in Fig. 304(a). The extraordinary image of a dot lies behind the ordinary image. However, by moving the head slightly to one side to receive rays that are not normal to the surface, we may see the two dots and

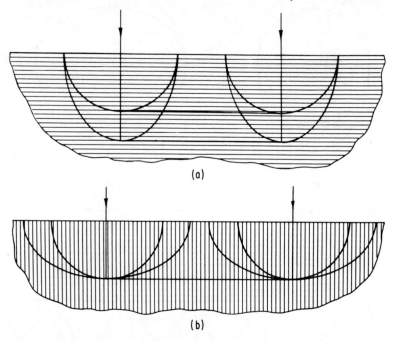

(a)

(b)

Figure 304. (a) Normal incidence on a calcite crystal with parallel surfaces ground parallel to the optic axis. (b) Normal incidence on a calcite crystal with parallel surfaces ground perpendicular to the optic axis.

determine their relative depths by parallax. If the two parallel ground surfaces are perpendicular to the principal axis, the ordinary and extraordinary rays are superposed again as indicated in Fig. 304(b) and only one image of the dot may be seen.

For all directions except parallel and perpendicular to the optic axis we must define two velocities for the extraordinary wave. (1) The *ray velocity* is proportional to the length of ray OA in Fig. 303. (2) The *normal velocity* is the velocity at which the wavefront moves normally to itself, and is proportional to distance OB. In Fig. 305 the broken line indicates the relative values of the *normal velocities*, found by constructing a series of tangents to the ellipse and a corresponding series of normals from the center to the tangent. The oval is drawn through the bases of the normals as a broken line. This *normal velocity surface* is an ovaloid of revolution lying outside the wave surface which is an ellipsoid of revolution for ray velocities.

For negative uniaxial crystals like calcite the only indices of refraction that are measured and recorded in physical tables are (1) the ordinary index of refraction n_O, which is also the largest index of refraction for the extraordinary wavelet, and (2) the smallest index of refraction of the extraordinary wave, which is the index of refraction n_E of the ray along the major axis of the ellipse. Here n_O and n_E are known as the *principal indices of refraction*.

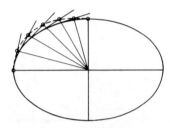

Figure 305. Construction method of determining normal velocities. The broken line is the normal velocity surface.

In a positive crystal like quartz the index of refraction is the same for both rays along the optic axis, but the index of refraction n_E for an extraordinary ray perpendicular to the optic axis is larger than n_O.

17.5 Measurement of Principal Indices of Refraction of Uniaxial Crystals

If the rays in the crystal are either parallel or perpendicular to the optic axis, the definition of index of refraction

$$n = \frac{\sin \phi}{\sin \phi'} \qquad (17.2)$$

is applicable to uniaxial crystals as it was to isotropic media. The most precise means of measuring indices of refraction for light waves is with a prism of the material and a spectrometer. We recall that when the angle of deviation is a minimum,

$$n = \frac{\sin \frac{1}{2}(\delta + A)}{\sin \frac{1}{2}A}, \qquad (17.3)$$

where δ is the minimum angle of deviation and A is the angle of the prism between the two refracting surfaces. If the prism is cut so that the rays are perpendicular to the optic axis as in Fig. 306(a), both indices of refraction can be measured with the use of one prism. In the prism of Fig. 306(b) the rays are perpendicular to the optic axis only when the prism is set for minimum deviation. The prism in Fig. 306(c) is interesting for comparison with the other two in demonstrations. Since its principal axis is parallel to the rays at minimum deviation, the ordinary and extraordinary rays will not be separated. The indices of refraction for sodium yellow are $n_O = 1.658$ and $n_E = 1.486$. For quartz the difference is much less, $n_O = 1.544$ and $n_E = 1.553$.

17.6 Polarizing Devices Made by Cutting and Splicing Uniaxial Crystals

By a cut-and-try process William Nicol in 1828 devised a means of cutting

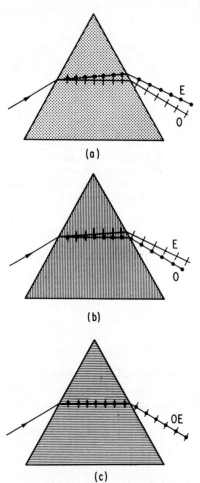

(a)

(b)

(c)

Figure 306. (a) Calcite prism cut so that the rays are always perpendicular to the optic axis. (b) Calcite prism cut so that the rays of minimum deviation are perpendicular to the optic axis. (c) Calcite prism cut so the rays are parallel to the optic axis.

a calcite crystal in two parts and cementing the parts together so that it would transmit only the extraordinary ray. Two *Nicol prisms* in series make up a polarizer and analyzer known as a *polarimeter*. When their principal planes are set perpendicularly to each other they give the most complete extinction of any polarizing device throughout the visible spectrum.

To form the Nicol prism, the long calcite crystal of which Fig. 307 is a principal section has had its ends cut in two parallel planes which make an angle of 68° with the long edges instead of the 71° formed by a cleavage plane. This crystal is cut into two equal parts by a plane which is perpendicular both to the small end surfaces and to the principal section. The pieces are cemented together by a layer of Canada balsam which is transparent to the visible spectrum and has an index of refraction intermediate between that of the ordinary and extraordinary rays for calcite, so that the ordinary ray is reflected at the first boundary of calcite and Canada balsam with total internal reflection and passes out of the side of the calcite to be absorbed in black paint. If the incident beam is too divergent, the extraordinary beam may become totally reflected on the one hand or the ordinary beam not totally reflected on the other, so that the greatest allowable divergence between the extreme rays of the beam is 28°.

Although the Polaroid sheets have the advantage of unlimited large aperture and may be used for widely divergent or convergent beams so as to be most convenient for classroom demonstrations, the more completely polarizing Nicol prism is still superior for many research purposes in the whole visible spectrum.

The Nicol prism can not be used in the ultraviolet because of absorption by the Canada balsam. Figure 308(a) shows a quartz prism designed by Rochon, and Fig. 308(b) one designed by Wollaston, each of which gives wide separation of the ordinary and extraordinary rays but does not eliminate

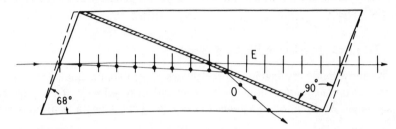

Figure 307. Nicol prism for transmitting only the extraordinary rays.

either. The two halves are cemented together by glycerine. Made either of calcite or quartz, these prisms may be used over a wavelength range from 2000 A in the ultraviolet to 10,000 A in the infrared. If unpolarized light enters the Rochon prism normally on the left, it travels along the optic axis in the first prism and undergoes double refraction as it is separated into two

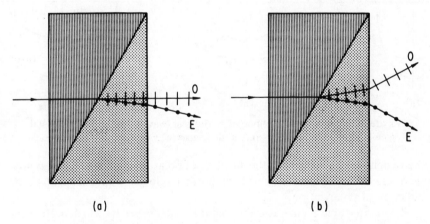

(a)   (b)

Figure 308. (a) Rochon prism of quartz. (b) Wollaston prism of quartz.

components at the boundary of the second. The ordinary ray is undeviated and achromatic. The extraordinary ray is deviated and the wavelengths dispersed. In the Rochon prism of quartz the ray should be incident from the left along the principal axis of the first crystal. Otherwise it will undergo rotary dispersion, a topic treated under *rotation of the plane of polarization.*

In the Wollaston prism the optic axes in the two halves are also at right angles to each other, and the triangular sections are also 30°–60° right triangles. The incident ray is perpendicular to the optic axis of the first crystal. When it enters the second crystal also perpendicular to the optic axis of that prism, both rays are deviated and the deviation is increased upon exit from the prism. The construction of ray diagrams and the direction of polarization in Rochon and Wollaston prisms of calcite will be reserved for the problems.

17.7 Huygens Wavelets in Biaxial Crystals

We may divide crystals into three classes, isotropic, uniaxial, and biaxial. In an *isotropic crystal* such as halite (rock salt) the velocity of the waves is independent of direction. In a *uniaxial crystal* there is one axis along which

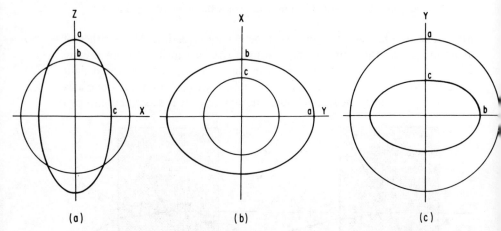

Figure 309. Three cross sections of a Huygens wavelet for a biaxial crystal taken at right angles to each other in the planes (a) $y = 0$, (b) $z = 0$, (c) $x = 0$.

the velocity is independent of the direction of polarization. In a *biaxial crystal* there are two directions in which the normal velocity is independent of the direction of polarization.

There are three planes at right angles to each other by which a Huygens wavelet in a biaxial crystal may be cut to yield a circle and an ellipse in each plane, as shown in Figs. 309(a), (b), and (c). Thus we shall use Cartesian coordinates in describing it. Although the three planes each intersect the Huygens wavelet in two curves, there is but one surface of wavelet with one equation. The inside surface passes continuously into the outside surface at four singular points. In Fig. 309(a) each curve is part inside and part outside. Thus we shall have no occasion to speak of an inside or outside wavefront.

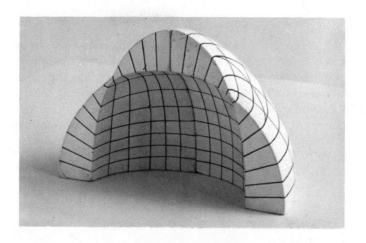

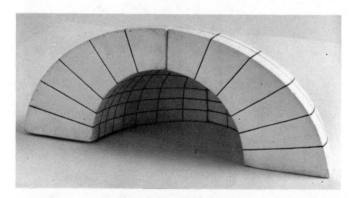

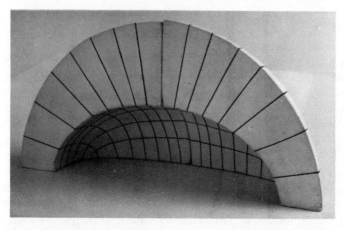

Figure 310. Plaster of Paris models of sections of the Huygens wavelet for a biaxial crystal. The faces correspond to the curves of Fig. 309 in the planes (a) $y = 0$, (b) $z = 0$, (c) $x = 0$.

Although the wavelet has three intercepts in the planes $x = 0$, $y = 0$, and $z = 0$ which are ellipses, it is not an ellipsoid. We shall omit the interesting study in analytic geometry[1] and treat the Huygens wavelet for biaxial crystals by construction methods. Figures 310(a), (b), and (c) are plaster of Paris models of portions of sections of the wavelets. The flat surfaces facing us are the planes $y = 0$, $z = 0$, and $x = 0$ for (a), (b), and (c), respectively, in the same order as in Fig. 309. Each of the three forms is made by fitting together the same pair of octants, which are mirror images of each other. Different faces of the octant are fitted in each of the three cases.

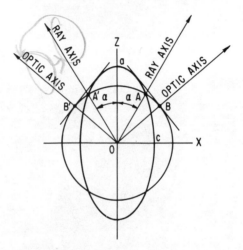

Figure 311. Cross section of the wavelet of a biaxial crystal in the plane $y = 0$ showing the ray axes and the optic axes.

In Fig. 311 rays OA and OA' are in directions in which the *ray velocities* of the circle and ellipse are the same. In all other directions there are two ray velocities. Here OA and OA' are called *ray axes*.

Figure 312 is a plaster of Paris model of the wavelet indicating a circle along which a plane is tangent to the wavelet. The tangent plane is a common wavefront for the circle and ellipse of Fig. 311, and OB represents the common normal velocity. We shall define OB and OB' as the *optic axes* of the biaxial crystal. If the angle α which the optic axis makes with the major axis of the ellipse is less than $45°$ the crystal is *positive*. If α is greater than $45°$ the crystal is *negative*.

For each of the three ordinary waves represented by three circles of radii a, b, and c in Fig. 309, Snell's law is obeyed. Thus we can measure the three corresponding indices of refraction by cutting three prisms such that the

---

[1] R. W. Ditchburn, *Light:* New York, Interscience Publishers, Inc. (1952) Chap. 16.

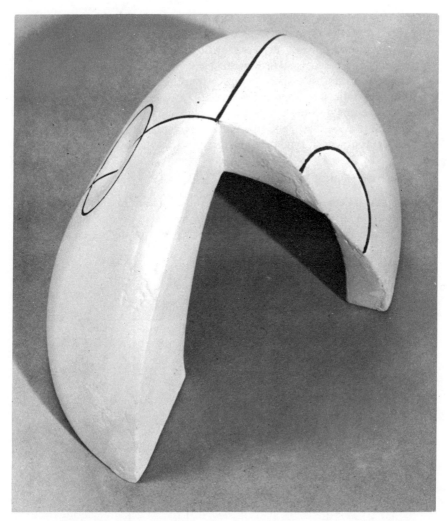

Figure 312. Plaster of Paris model of three octants of the Huygens wavelet of a biaxial crystal showing circles along which a plane is tangent to the wavelet.

triangular cross sections include one of the three planes $y = 0$, $z = 0$, and $x = 0$, and with one of the coordinate axes making equal angles with the two refracting surfaces. The three principal indices of refraction of the biaxial crystal are, respectively, in increasing order,

$$n_a = \frac{v}{a}, \qquad n_b = \frac{v}{b}, \qquad n_c = \frac{v}{c},$$

where v is the distance the wave travels in air while it is traveling distances *a*, *b*, and *c* in the coordinate planes of the crystal in decreasing order. Along the three axes the normal velocities equal the ray velocities. In all other directions normal velocity surfaces may be formed by the same constructions of tangents and normals as in Fig. 305.

Uniaxial crystals are special cases of biaxial crystals. In the limit as 2α between the optic axes approaches zero, the two optic axes and the two ray axes become one and the crystal is a positive uniaxial crystal. If the ellipse expands until $2\alpha = 180°$, the two optic axes and rays also become one and the crystal is a negative uniaxial crystal.

17.8 Internal Conical Refraction

We may make one generalization about uniaxial and biaxial crystals. They both divide an incident ray into two component rays polarized at right angles to each other. We must note one exception for biaxial crystals when

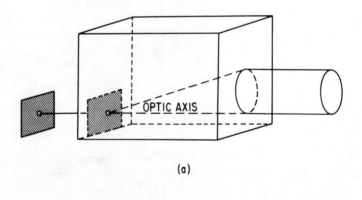

(a)

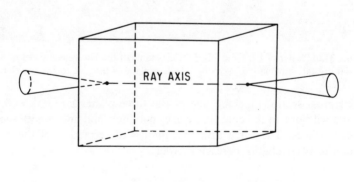

(b)

Figure 313. (a) Internal conical refraction. (b) External conical refraction.

the ray is incident so as to be refracted along either the ray axis or optic axis. Sir William Hamilton pointed out that, since the optical path lengths from the center of the Huygens wavelet to a circle of tangency are equal, light

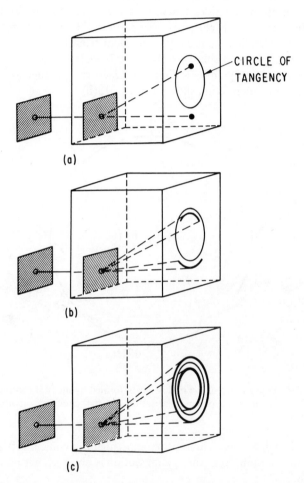

Figure 314. Observations in the transition from double refraction to internal conical refraction. (a) The incident ray undergoes the usual double refraction. (b) The arcs expand. (c) The arcs become concentric circles.

incident along the optic axis should follow all paths along the conical surface from the center to the circle of tangency. If a parallel plane section is cut with its surfaces perpendicular to the optic axis, a circle of tangency to the wave-front lies on the cut surface; and since all points on the circle are in phase, the hollow beam should proceed as a hollow circular cylinder outside the crystal as indicated in Fig. 313(a). This is called *internal conical refraction.*

Since the wavefront has an infinite number of tangent planes at the singularity (bottom of the dimple), an internal ray along the ray axis should, on striking points on all sides adjacent to the singularity, be refracted as a cone at a surface which is cut perpendicularly to the ray axis. From the law of reversibility, a hollow cone may be incident from the left on the parallel plane section cut perpendicularly to the ray axis so as to be refracted along the ray axis, and emerge again as a cone with each ray parallel to the original direction in the incident cone shown in Fig. 313(b).

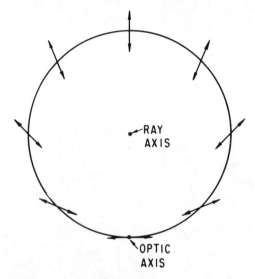

Figure 315. Polarization of the hollow beam formed by internal conical refraction. The directions of plane polarization on the circle are indicated by straight lines.

Collins[2] has described a laboratory experiment in conical refraction. The hollow beam emerging from the crystal section is observed with a micrometer microscope.

In Fig. 314(a) the incident ray undergoes the usual double refraction. To search for the direction of the ray which will produce internal conical refraction, we move one of the slits. In practice Collins turned the crystal about two axes at right angles to each other in order to obtain the desired angle of incidence. As the desired angle of incidence is approached, two arcs appear as in Fig. 314(b). By micrometer adjustment of the angle of incidence we may cause the arcs to expand until they are uniform concentric circles with

[2] J. R. Collins, *Am. Phys. Teacher,* **7,** 409 (1939).

a black band at the circle of tangency, as in Fig. 314(c). Givens and Discher[3] have explained with diagrams why the intensity is zero on the circle of tangency between the bright rings.

The polarization of the rings observed in the microscope may be studied with a Polaroid disk. The upper ray of Fig. 314(a) is polarized parallel to the principal plane, and the lower perpendicular to the principal plane. Figure 315 shows the direction of polarization around the circle. At points diametrically opposite, the polarizations are perpendicular to each other.

17.9 The Fresnel Ellipsoid

Fresnel found a simple way to explain double refraction in crystals, including the wave shapes for uniaxial and biaxial crystals. For every crystal there can be constructed an *ellipsoid of index of refraction*

$$\frac{x^2}{n_a^2} + \frac{y^2}{n_b^2} + \frac{z^2}{n_c^2} = 1, \qquad (17.4)$$

where n_a, n_b, and n_c are the principal indices of refraction the measurement of which was treated in Sec. 17.7. The distance from the center O to any point on the surface of the ellipsoid of Fig. 316 represents an index of refraction.

In Fresnel's theory these indices of refraction were determined by the shear modulus of elasticity and the density of the ether in the crystal. In electromagnetic theory these same indices of refraction are expressed in terms of permittivities by

Figure 316. Ellipsoid of index of refraction.

$$n_a^2 = \epsilon_a, \qquad n_b^2 = \epsilon_b, \qquad n_c^2 = \epsilon_c. \qquad (17.5)$$

The wave in the dielectric which corresponds to Fresnel's mechanical wave is a wave of the electric displacement **D**. Here **D** is not in the direction of **E** except when **E** is parallel to one of the three principal axes. For that special case

$$D_a = \epsilon_a E_a, \qquad D_b = \epsilon_b E_b, \qquad D_c = \epsilon_c E_c, \qquad (17.6)$$

where

$$\epsilon_a = n_a^2, \qquad \epsilon_b = n_b^2, \qquad \epsilon_c = n_c^2. \qquad (17.7)$$

For every direction of normal velocity in the crystal there are two waves of electric displacement **D** corresponding to two indices of refraction. Given any direction of propagation from center O in the ellipsoid of Fig. 317, we may construct a plane through O perpendicular to the direction of propagation. A plane through the center of the ellipsoid cuts the ellipsoid in an

[3] M. P. Givens and W. V. Discher, *Am. J. Phys.*, **22**, 379 (1954).

ellipse. We shall let n_1 be the index of refraction which is the minor axis of the ellipse, and n_2 that of the major axis. Any ray which has this direction upon entering the crystal at O will have its direction of oscillation of **D** resolved into two components parallel to these two axes. The plane of vibration of the wave of electric displacement $\mathbf{D_1}$ is the plane containing the minor axis and the ray. The plane of vibration of $\mathbf{D_2}$ contains the major axis

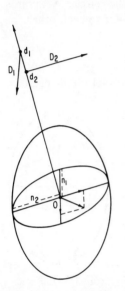

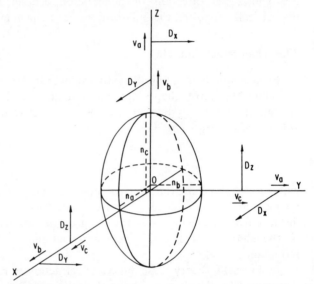

Figure 317. Use of the ellipsoid of index of refraction to determine the normal wave velocities and polarizations of waves of electric displacement traveling in a given direction.

Figure 318. Use of the ellipsoid of index of refraction to determine the velocities and polarizations of waves traveling along the principal axes.

and the ray. The normal velocities of the two rays are inversely as the two indices of refraction, so that in a given time the $\mathbf{D_1}$ wave corresponding to the smaller index of refraction travels the larger distance Od_1 while the $\mathbf{D_2}$ wave travels the shorter distance Od_2.

We may consider the special case of waves traveling along the three principal axes indicated in Fig. 318. The principal indices of refraction n_a, n_b, and n_c for electric displacements D_x, D_y, and D_z parallel to the x, y, and z axes are given relative sizes 2, 3, and 4. Actually the indices of refraction for biaxial crystals differ much less than this. The large differences of the diagram are used for clarity. The corresponding velocities are in the order $v_a > v_b > v_c$.

Corresponding to the smallest index of refraction n_a, the wave of D_x has the largest value v_a along the y and z axes. The middle-sized index of refraction yields the middle-sized velocity v_b of D_y along the x and z axes, and the large index of refraction n_c gives the smallest velocity v_c of D_z along the x and y axes. The wave of D_x has the velocity v_a in the yz-plane, the wave of D_y has the velocity v_b in the xz-plane, and the wave of D_z has the velocity v_b in the xy-plane. The three velocities correspond to three circular cross sections of radii a, b, and c of the Huygens wavelet shown in Fig. 309.

An ellipsoid whose principal axes are all different can be cut by only two planes through the center of the ellipsoid to give circles of intersection as indicated in Fig. 319. The common diameter of these two circles is the middle-sized axis of the ellipsoid which we chose as the y axis. The waves propagated along this axis have but one index of refraction corresponding to the radius of the circle, and thus only one normal velocity. These directions are the two *optic axes*, and must lie in the plane of the largest and smallest principal axes, the xz-plane.

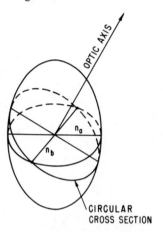

Figure 319. Determination of the optic axis from the ellipsoid of index of refraction.

If the middle-sized index of refraction is decreased until it equals n_a, the two circles of Fig. 319 become one in the xy-plane, the ellipsoid is an ellipsoid of revolution about axis z, and the crystal is a *positive uniaxial crystal* with optic axis in the z direction. If the middle-sized index of refraction is increased until it equals n_c, the two circles become one in the yz-plane, the index of refraction ellipsoid is an ellipsoid of revolution about the x axis, and the crystal is a *negative uniaxial crystal* with its optic axis in the x direction.

PROBLEMS FOR CHAPTER XVII

17.1.1. A microscope is focused on a dot on a table top. A calcite crystal 2.31 cm thick is then placed over the dot and the microscope moved vertically a distance of 0.76 cm to bring the ordinary image of the dot in focus. What is the ordinary index of refraction of calcite?

17.3.2. Determine the positions and polarizations of the images of a point source when two calcite crystals are stacked so that the angle between their principal sections is (a) 135°, (b) 180°.

17.5.3. What is the minimum deviation of an ordinary ray of sodium light by a 60° calcite crystal for which the index of refraction is 1.4864? If angles can be measured on the spectrometer to ±1.0″, to how many significant figures can the index of refraction be measured?

17.6.4. Construct ray diagrams and show the directions of polarization for Rochon and Wollaston prisms of calcite.

17.9.5. Construct to scale the cross sections of the wave surface for the biaxial crystal sulfur in the coordinate planes similar to those of Fig. 309, where $n_a = 1.95$, $n_b = 2.04$, $n_c = 2.24$.

chapter XVIII

Elliptical Polarization

18.1 Elliptical Oscillations of Electric Fields

Two superposed simple harmonic motions at right angles to each other yield a resultant elliptical motion. The shape of the ellipse depends on the relative amplitudes and phases of the components. In most of the cases we shall consider, the two amplitudes will be equal. In Fig. 40 we plotted the resultant ellipses corresponding to phase differences of 0°, 45°, 90°, 135°, and 180°. In Sec. 3.6 we derived the equation for the elliptical motion. We may represent the elliptically polarized electric wave passing a point by a rotating **E** vector with its tail at the center of the ellipse and the arrow revolving in the elliptical path. For the electric wave, Eqs. (3.9) and (3.10) become

$$E^2 = E_x^2 \sin^2(\omega t + \alpha) + E_y^2 \sin^2 \omega t, \tag{18.1}$$

and

$$\tan \theta = \frac{E_y \sin \omega t}{E_x \sin(\omega t + \alpha)}, \tag{18.2}$$

where E is the magnitude of the electric field, E_x and E_y are its components in the x and y directions, α is the phase of the x field relative to the y field, and θ is the angle which the resultant field makes with the positive x axis as indicated in Fig. 320.

449

18.2 Elliptically Polarized Microwaves

Microwaves provide a vivid introduction to elliptical polarization. Figure 321 shows an arrangement whereby two antennas are excited by the same source through two coaxial cables of the same length so that the two sources have the same phase and amplitude. This is the two-antenna adaptor

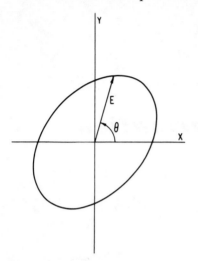

used for Young's experiment in interference. The relative phases of the two waves arriving at the intensity meter are determined by the path difference from the secondary sources. Figure 322 shows the two antennas set at right angles to each other and in the same plane together with the component and resultant electric fields.

The two-antenna adaptor may be made with twin lead of 300 ohms characteristic impedance commercially used for television. If care is taken not to hold the twin lead in the hand or let it lie along a metal surface, it will not radiate except at the antenna. The antennas are folded dipoles of phosphor bronze which clamp over the two pieces of upright meter stick as shown in Fig. 323.

Figure 320. Elliptical polarization of the wave of electric field.

We may rotate the intensity meter about axis AB of Fig. 321 and measure the maximum and minimum intensities of radiation. The square roots of the

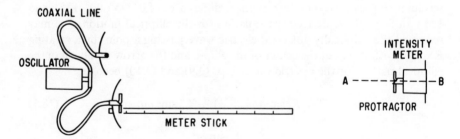

Figure 321. Two secondary-source antennas for production of elliptical polarization.

intensities or amplitudes may be checked by construction of the ellipse from Eqs. (18.1) and (18.2). For any angular setting of its antenna the intensity meter indicates a plane-polarized component of the elliptical oscillation. The phase difference of the x and y component waves is determined by

$$\alpha = \frac{2\pi d}{\lambda}, \tag{18.3}$$

where d is the path difference from the two sources to the intensity meter.

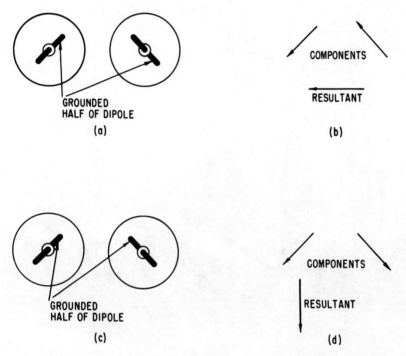

Figure 322. Orientations of dipole antennas showing the resulting polarization.

Figure 324 shows the resulting polarization corresponding to phase differences from 0° to 360° in steps of 45°.

18.3 Elliptical Polarization by Double Refraction

If a uniaxial crystal such as calcite is cut as a thin plate with faces parallel to the optic axis and a normally incident wave is polarized at 45° to the optic axis, the wave is divided into two components of equal amplitude upon entering the crystal. The two rays remain superposed and have the same geometrical path lengths. However, their *optical path lengths* are dependent on the indices of refraction so that the optical path difference is

$$\Delta = d(n_O - n_E),$$

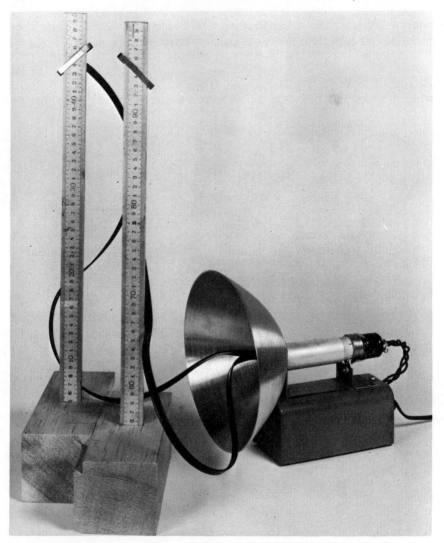

Figure 323. Experimental arrangement for demonstrating elliptical polarization of microwaves.

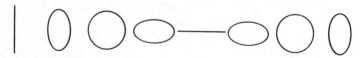

Figure 324. Elliptical polarization corresponding to phase differences from 0° to 360° in steps of 45°.

and the phase difference

$$\delta = \frac{2\pi d}{\lambda}(n_O - n_E),$$ (18.4)

where d is the thickness of the plate, and n_O and n_E are the principal indices of refraction.

Grinding and polishing of calcite surfaces which are not cleavage faces is an art. It is easier to produce the desired thickness of parallel faces of mica by peeling off layers with a razor blade. Mica is a biaxial crystal, but

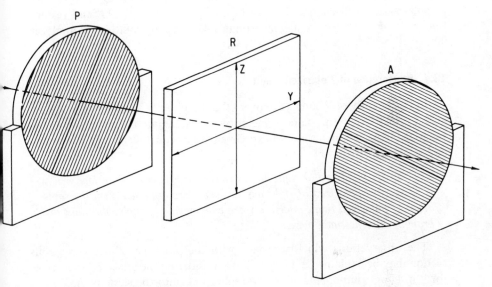

Figure 325. A polarimeter consisting of polarizer P and analyzer A. A retarding plate R is inserted.

fortunately it splits most easily along the yz-plane, the plane which includes the optic axes, so that the components of a normally incident wave travel in the same direction. The indices of refraction n_b and n_c of the two components in white mica, muscovite, are 1.590 and 1.594 for sodium light.

A useful retarding sheet is a *quarter-wave plate* which is of such thickness as to produce a phase difference of 90°, thus producing circularly polarized light. We note that a quarter-wave plate may be many wavelengths thick. Substituting $\delta = \pi/2$ in Eq. (18.4) and the values of n_b and n_c for muscovite, we obtain $d = 62\lambda$. Here 62 wavelengths of sodium light is about 0.0036 cm, thick enough so that its thickness can easily be adjusted to the desired value by peeling off layers of mica.

Figure 325 is a polarimeter made up of two Polaroid disks, the polarizer P

and the analyzer A, whose axes are crossed to give extinction before the retarding plate R is inserted. The retarding plate is inserted with its principal axes at 45° to the direction of polarization. The vibration of the ray entering the retarding plate is divided into two components, the z component with the index of refraction n_c and the y component with index of refraction n_b. If the retarding plate is a quarter-wave plate for sodium light, the transmitted light through the retarder is circularly polarized and we can not alter the intensity of the beam by rotating the analyzer.

If the retarder is a *half-wave plate* for sodium light, insertion of the plate between the crossed Polaroids with the principal axes at 45° to the direction of polarization will change the direction of polarization by 90° and restore full brightness. The beam may be extinguished again by rotating the analyzer 90°.

18.4 Interference of Polarized Light

Independently of Young's discovery that light is a transverse wave, Arago and Fresnel drew the same conclusion by studying the interference of polarized light. From a series of experiments they concluded what are known as the *Fresnel-Arago laws*:

I. *Two rays polarized at right angles to each other do not interfere.*
II. *Two rays polarized at right angles, which are obtained from the same beam of polarized light, interfere when components of their vibrations are brought into the same plane.*

The observations which we made with the polarimeter in the previous section may be explained equally well by considering the analyzer as a device for "bringing components of the two vibrations into the same plane," as in the language of Fresnel and Arago. We shall treat *plane polarizations only.*

Let the oscillations of the electric wave transmitted by the polarizer be vertical as in Fig. 326(a). If the y axis of the retarding plate makes an angle θ with the vertical direction of the incident oscillation, the crystal resolves the oscillation into y and z components

$$E_y = E \cos \theta, \qquad (18.5)$$

$$E_z = E \sin \theta, \qquad (18.6)$$

as indicated in Fig. 326(a). These waves pass through the crystal receiving a difference of phase

$$\delta = \frac{2\pi d}{\lambda} (n_O - n_E).$$

The horizontal components of these two amplitudes are $E \cos \theta \sin \theta$ and $E \sin \theta \cos \theta$, as shown in Fig. 326(b). The components at right angles to the polarization of the initial wave are always equal in magnitude. The vertical components are $E \cos^2 \theta$ and $E \sin^2 \theta$.

The *complex amplitudes* of the two horizontal components are

$$\mathbf{E}_1 = \mathbf{E} \cos \theta \sin \theta \qquad (18.7)$$

and

$$\mathbf{E}_2 = -\mathbf{E} \sin \theta \cos \theta \epsilon^{j\delta}, \qquad (18.8)$$

where $\mathbf{E}_1$ is taken as reference vector at any time. The negative coefficient in

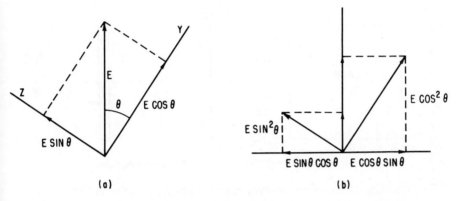

Figure 326. (a) The retarding plate divides the vibration of the incident wave into two components. (b) The horizontal and vertical components of the vibrations transmitted by the retarding plate.

Eq. (18.8) indicates the negative direction obtained upon resolution into components. The complex amplitudes of the two vertical components are

$$\mathbf{E}_3 = \mathbf{E} \cos^2 \theta, \qquad (18.9)$$

$$\mathbf{E}_4 = \mathbf{E} \sin^2 \theta \epsilon^{j\delta}. \qquad (18.10)$$

If the crystal is a half-wave plate, $\delta = \pi$, the resultant horizontal complex amplitude is

$$\mathbf{E}_H = \mathbf{E}_1 + \mathbf{E}_2 = \mathbf{E} \sin 2\theta, \qquad (18.11)$$

and the vertical complex amplitude is

$$\mathbf{E}_V = \mathbf{E}_3 + \mathbf{E}_4 = \mathbf{E}(\cos^2 \theta - \sin^2 \theta). \qquad (18.12)$$

If $\theta = 45°$ as in the preceding section,

$$\mathbf{E}_H = \mathbf{E} \quad \text{and} \quad \mathbf{E}_V = 0. \qquad (18.13)$$

The intensity of the horizontally polarized beam is

$$I_H = |\mathbf{E}_H|^2 = E^2.$$

If the axis of the analyzer is horizontal, the beam is transmitted by the polarimeter undiminished in intensity but the direction of polarization has been shifted by 90°. This is the same result we obtained when we treated elliptical polarization.

If the crystal is a quarter-wave plate and $\theta = 45°$,

$$\mathbf{E}_H = \mathbf{E}_1 + \mathbf{E}_2 = \frac{E}{2}(1 - j), \qquad (18.14)$$

and

$$\mathbf{E}_V = \mathbf{E}_3 + \mathbf{E}_4 = \frac{E}{2}(1 + j).$$

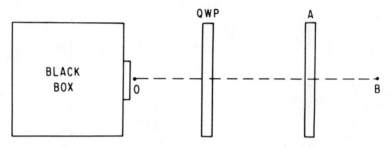

Figure 327. Arrangement for analysis of polarized light.

The intensity of the horizontally polarized light from the retarding crystal is

$$I_H = |\mathbf{E}_H|^2 = \frac{E^2}{2},$$

and the intensity of the vertically polarized beam is

$$I_V = |\mathbf{E}_V|^2 = \frac{E^2}{2}.$$

The intensity of transmission can not be altered by rotating the analyzer. This is the same conclusion we drew when we used the concept of elliptical polarization.

18.5 Simple Analysis of Polarized Light

If sodium light of unknown polarization is emitted by the "black box" of Fig. 327, we may make a quick analysis of the polarization with a quarter-wave plate QWP and an analyzer A mounted to rotate about axis OB. We shall treat some cases.

(1) If the light is *plane polarized*, it can be extinguished with the analyzer alone. (2) If the light is circularly polarized, a quarter-wave plate will render it plane polarized no matter what the direction of its optic axis. This is because circularly polarized light may be considered the resultant of any two simple harmonic motions of equal amplitude at right angles to each other in the plane of the circle, and 90° out of phase. The quarter-wave plate will

either increase the phase difference of the plane-polarized components to 180° or decrease it to zero. In either case we may extinguish the light with an analyzer. (3) If the beam is *randomly polarized* as from many atoms, a quarter-wave plate and analyzer arranged as in Fig. 327 give the same intensity no matter how they are rotated. (4) If the beam is a *mixture of plane- and randomly polarized light*, we observe varying intensity which never reaches zero when we rotate the analyzer alone. Also, if with the analyzer set for maximum intensity, we insert the quarter-wave plate with its optic axis parallel to the transmission axis of the analyzer, we obtain a maximum for the same position of the analyzer and no position of the analyzer gives zero intensity. (5) If the beam is a *mixture of circularly polarized and randomly polarized light*, we find no variation of intensity with rotation of the analyzer alone; but with the quarter-wave plate inserted we find a minimum but no zero of intensity when the analyzer is rotated. (6) If the beam is *elliptically polarized*, the intensity varies with rotation of the analyzer alone but does not become zero. We may think of the elliptical motion of Fig. 328(a) as composed of two plane vibrations along the principal axes and 90° out of phase. If we set the axis of the quarter-wave plate parallel to either the major or minor axis of the ellipse, in one case the relative retardation of the two vibrations is increased to 180° and in the other case decreased to zero. Vectors *a* and *b* of Fig. 328(b) represent the in-phase components with their resultant *c*. Vectors *a* and *b'* represent the

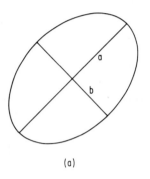

(a)

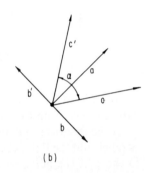

(b)

Figure 328. (a) Elliptical motion may be considered as composed of two plane vibrations along the principal axes and 90° out of phase. (b) Vectors **a** and **b** represent the in-phase components with their resultant **c**. Vectors **a** and **b'** represent the out-of-phase components with their resultant **c'**.

out-of-phase components with their resultant *c'*, α is the angle between these plane polarizations and also the angle between the two settings of the analyzer for extinction, and tan α/2 is the ratio of the axes of the ellipse.

18.6 Babinet Compensator

If we wish to measure the relative retardation by crystals, we may use the Babinet compensator or one of its modifications. It is commonly used as a null instrument balancing the relative retardation by other double-refracting crystals and devices.

Figure 329 indicates a cross section of a Babinet compensator made of two thin quartz wedges with their optic axes parallel and perpendicular, respectively, to the refracting edges. Quartz is used because it can be ground with durable optical surfaces. One wedge is held in a frame and the other slid over it with a micrometer screw. In passing from one wedge to the other an extraordinary ray becomes ordinary and the ordinary ray becomes extraordinary. At the line where the wedge thicknesses are equal, the difference in

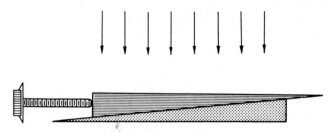

Figure 329. Babinet compensator.

retardation of the two rays is zero. The relative retardation varies linearly with distance from this central line.

If the polarizer and analyzer are set for transmission with their optic axes parallel, and the Babinet compensator placed between them with its axis at 45° to those of the polarizer and analyzer, white light will have an interference pattern with a white center like Young's interference pattern. In use the polarizer and analyzer are crossed so that the black line is at the center.

The Babinet compensator must be calibrated for each wavelength for which it is to be used. Under monochromatic light the black bands are equally spaced. Each black band counted from the center outward corresponds to relative retardations of $2n\pi$, where n is any integer including zero at the center. The light bands correspond to plane polarization parallel to the transmission axis of the analyzer. Between the dark and bright bands the polarization is elliptical as indicated in Fig. 330. The micrometer screw readings are graphically calibrated against angle of relative retardation δ as the centers of the black bands are moved in turn to the fixed cross hairs.

If we now wish to measure the retardation in a doubly refracting crystal such as a sheet of mica, the cross hair is first set at the center of the pattern. Then the crystal is inserted between the polarizer and compensator with its principal axes at 45° to the transmission axis of the polarizer. The band system will be seen to shift. The micrometer screw of the compensator is turned until the center of the shifted band is moved back to the cross hair and the relative retardation δ read from the compensator. From the thickness of crystal d we may determine the difference in indices of refraction

$$n_1 - n_2 = \frac{\delta\lambda}{2\pi d}. \qquad (18.15)$$

We shall find use for the Babinet compensator in measuring the relative retardation in the Kerr cell.

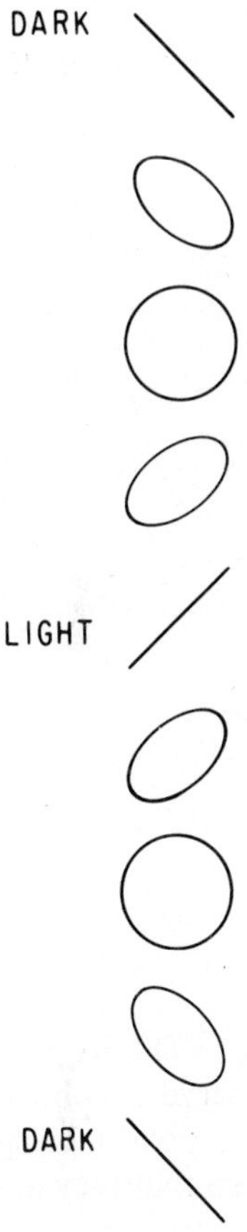

18.7 Kerr Effect

In 1875 John Kerr discovered that isotropic solids and liquids could be made doubly refracting in an electric field. We have discussed the use of the Kerr cell as an electro-optical shutter in measuring the velocity of light. Other uses are in studying the electric spark discharge between two balls during the first billionth of a second, showing that the discharge does not go from one ball to the other but starts in the middle and goes both ways; also fluorescence of minerals excited by light from the intense spark takes place in less than 10^{-8} sec.

Figure 331 is a diagram of a glass Kerr cell between two crossed Polaroids. The liquid in the field between the metal plates behaves like a uniaxial crystal with its optic axis parallel to the field. As the electric field strength E is increased, the relative retardation of the components of the wave of electric displacement D oscillating parallel and perpendicular to the field increases.

If we insert the Babinet compensator between the Kerr cell and the analyzer, we may measure the difference in retardation δ as a function of the electric field strength.

The component of the wave parallel to the field is slowed most, thus having the larger index of refraction n_P. If n_N is the index of refraction for polarization normal to the electric field,

$$n_P - n_N = \frac{\delta\lambda}{2\pi L}, \qquad (18.16)$$

where δ is the measured phase difference and L the length of path of the light beam between the plates. Kerr found that for liquids and isotropic solids

$$n_P - n_N = \lambda B E^2, \qquad (18.17)$$

where E is the strength of electric field and B a constant for the liquid called

DARK

LIGHT

DARK

Figure 330. The elliptical polarization between the dark and light bands of a Babinet compensator.

the *Kerr constant*. Since E is squared the effect is independent of the direction of the field between plates of the cell. Some of the larger Kerr constants at the wavelength of sodium light are for carbon disulfide 3.5×10^{-14}, water 5.2×10^{-14}, and nitrobenzene 244×10^{-14} m/volt^2. Nitrobenzene is generally used in electro-optical shutters.

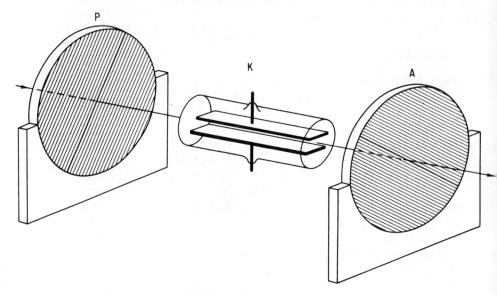

Figure 331. Kerr cell in a polarimeter.

The Kerr effect and its magnetic counterpart, the Cotton-Mouton effect, serve as a check upon molecular structure. The electric fields cause orientation of polar molecules and create electric dipole moments in nonpolar molecules so that they also become aligned.

18.8 Double Refraction by Mechanical Strain

Isotropic substances such as glass and plastics become doubly refracting under mechanical strain. A compressed block of glass is like a negative uniaxial crystal and one under tension is positive. Glass blowers study their products between two large sheets of Polaroid to determine if they are properly annealed.

Photoelastic stress analysis[1] is an important part of engineering design of buildings, machinery, and such simple components as the hook of a chain. Sample engineering sections in plastic are provided for classroom demonstrations by scientific supply companies. Projections with white light on a

---

[1] M. M. Frocht, *Photoelasticity:* New York, Wiley, Vol. I (1941), Vol. II (1947).

screen are most colorful, but for quantitative strain analysis sodium light is used. Figure 332 shows a plastic cylinder under compression between two planes.

High speed stroboscopic motion pictures reveal the stress waves moving through plastic materials as a result of impact. Thus photoelastic stress analysis is becoming a method of engineering dynamics as well as statics.

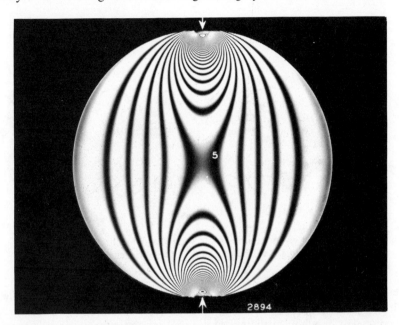

Figure 332. Double refraction in a plastic cylinder under compression. (From Frocht's *Photoelasticity* Vol. II, copyright 1948, John Wiley and Sons, Inc. Reprinted by permission.)

18.9 Dispersion by Double Refraction

The continuous change of the difference of index of refraction $(n_2 - n_1)$ with wavelength gives rise to color selection by thin doubly refracting films between crossed Polaroids. Sheets of mica, cellophane, or cellulose Scotch tape may be built in layers or cut in artistic figures. Cellophane has an axis in the direction in which it is drawn out when in production.

If the thin plate is set with its axis at 45° to that of the polarizer as in Fig. 325 and inserted in a beam of white light, a different elliptical polarization will be transmitted for each color and may be studied with the analyzer. If the plates are too thin the color will be white. We may increase the thickness of the plate until δ differs by 180° for the red and violet ends of the spectrum. Figure 333(a) indicates the polarization for different wavelengths. The crossed analyzer transmits the violet and decreasing components of the ellipses across the spectrum down to zero component for the red. If the analyzer is rotated 90°, the precise complement of the first color is transmitted. If the thickness of the double refracting plate is doubled, the elliptical polarization across the spectrum goes through two cycles as indicated in Fig. 333(b). The rotation of the analyzer from the crossed to parallel position with the polarizer always

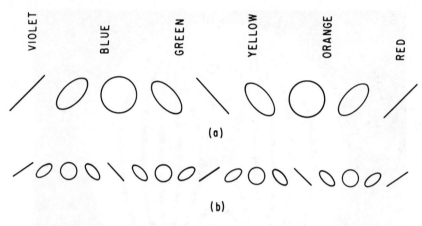

Figure 333. (a) A given retarding plate produces different elliptical polarization of different colors. (b) The thickness of the bifringent plate is twice that of case (a).

gives complements in color. The bands of transmitted color may be studied with the spectroscope. If the thickness of the plate is increased several times, the color will be white to the naked eye, but many uniformly spaced bands will be seen in the spectrometer. The uniform spacing indicates that δ varies almost linearly with wavelength.

18.10 Convergent Polarized Light in Crystals

If a calcite crystal plate cut with faces perpendicular to the optic axis is mounted between crossed Polaroids and observed by converging rays to the eye coming from an extended ground-glass screen illuminated with white light as in Fig. 334, we observe a black Maltese cross with brilliantly colored rings. With sodium light behind the ground glass the rings shown in Figs. 335(a) and (b) become so sharp that we can count hundreds with a microscope. As in the case of Newton's rings the diameters are as the square roots of the integers.

The highly convergent rays provide a means of obtaining a wide range of optical thickness from one plate. We have previously treated only parallel beams. For a ray propagated parallel to the optic axis in Fig. 336(a) the phase difference δ is zero because all vibrations perpendicular to the axis lie in a principal plane. The convergent rays are divided into ordinary and extraordinary components vibrating perpendicularly and parallel to the principal plane. Black ring number n counted from the center corresponds to $\delta = 2\pi n$. Between the center and ring n the polarization will have passed through the cycles of Fig. 324 n times. Figure 336(b) shows the face of the crystal toward the polarizer as it divides the electric field $\mathbf{E}$ into components,

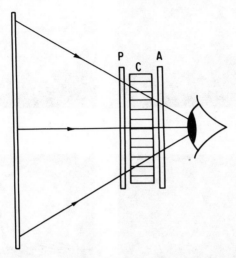

Figure 334. Observation of convergent polarized light through a crystal.

and AB indicates an end view of the principal plane of Fig. 336(a). The vertically polarized wave from the polarizer will be divided into an ordinary component

$$\mathbf{E}_O = \mathbf{E} \sin \theta, \tag{18.18}$$

and an extraordinary component

$$\mathbf{E}_E = \mathbf{E} \cos \theta, \tag{18.19}$$

where θ is the angle that the principal plane under consideration makes with the vertical.

If θ is zero, all the light is extraordinary and polarized vertically and extinguished by the analyzer. If θ is 90°, all the light is ordinary and again polarized vertically and extinguished by the analyzer. For angles near zero and 90° the elliptical vibrations are elongated and nearly plane, so that the extinction extends beyond those angles to form the Maltese cross commonly called *brushes*. When θ is 45°, the polarization along the path from the center outward alternates between horizontal and vertical with elliptical polarization between, so that the alternate rings are transmitted and stopped by the analyzer. The explanation may also be treated from the point of view of

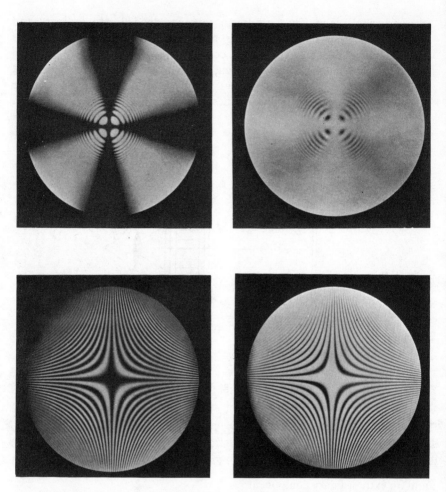

Figure 335. Patterns produced by calcite crystals in convergent polarized light. (a) Calcite cut perpendicular to the optic axis, crossed polaroids. (b) Calcite cut perpendicular to the optic axis, parallel polaroids. (c) Calcite cut parallel to the optic axis, crossed polaroids. (d) Calcite cut parallel to the optic axis, parallel polaroids. (Photographed by H. Hauswaldt, Magdeburg 1902. Plates loaned by M. W. Zemansky.)

interference of plane-polarized light as in Sec. 18.4. If the axis of the analyzer is set parallel to that of the polarizer, the light and dark portions will be interchanged.

Mineralogists use polarizing microscopes in which small plates of crystals may be placed in highly convergent light. They can determine if the crystal is biaxial or uniaxial, and what the directions of the axes are. Sample patterns are shown in Fig. 335.

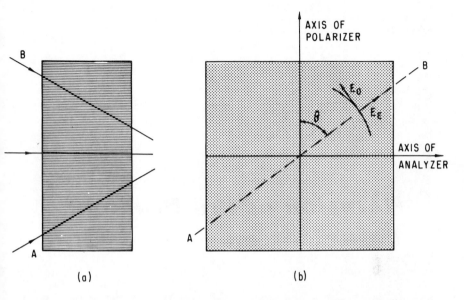

Figure 336. Determination of the components of the ordinary and extraordinary wave vibrations transmitted by a crystal in convergent light. (a) Cross section of the crystal including a principal plane and showing the converging rays. (b) The face of the crystal on the side toward the polarizer where the crystal divides the field E into components.

PROBLEMS FOR CHAPTER XVIII

18.2.1. What must be the path differences from the two secondary source antennas of Fig. 323 to the receiving antenna in order that the received wave be circularly polarized? Let $\lambda = 12$ cm.

18.3.2. How thick is a quarter-wave plate of calcite for sodium light, $\lambda = 5890$ A? The plate is cut with its surface parallel to the optic axis. The indices of refraction are $n_E = 1.486$ and $n_O = 1.658$. Note that it is too thin to be practical. Why is mica superior to calcite for making retardation plates?

18.4.3. If the y axis of a mica half-wave plate makes an angle of 30° with the vertically polarized incident sodium light, compare the amplitudes of the horizontal and vertical components of the vibrations transmitted by the plate.

18.6.4. A thin sheet of mica is inserted between a polarizer and a Babinet compensator causing the black bands to shift by 0.16 of the space between centers of black bands. What is the thickness of the mica? The indices of refraction are $n_b = 1.590$ and $n_c = 1.594$.

18.7.5. Determine the potential difference required between the plates of a Kerr cell that are 5.0 cm long and 0.20 cm apart in order to restore full brightness through the crossed Polaroids of the Kerr optical shutter.

chapter XIX

Rotation of the Plane of Polarization

19.1 Rotation of the Plane of Polarization by Liquids

Through the process of elliptical polarization by double refraction we were able to shift the direction of polarization of plane-polarized waves 90° with a relative retardation of 180° in phase. This was not a case of continuous rotation of plane polarization, but one of continuous change in the form of elliptical polarization for which two directions of plane polarization are special cases.

In 1811 Biot found that a continuous rotation of the plane of polarization was produced in the liquid turpentine, and in the same year Arago showed that plane-polarized light propagated along the optic axis of quartz also had its plane of polarization rotated. In both cases the angle through which the plane of polarization was rotated was proportional to the thickness of the substance in the direction through which the beam passed.

This ability of a substance to rotate the plane of polarization is called *optical activity*. Sugars in solution show optical activity. Since the angle of rotation is approximately proportional to the density of the substance in solution, provided the densities are not too high, optical activity is a means of quantitative chemical analysis. Chemical tables[1] give the *specific rotation* in

[1] *Handbook of Chemistry and Physics:* Cleveland, Ohio, Chemical Rubber Publishing Co.

466

degrees of rotation for 10 cm of length in a solution whose densities are expressed in grams per cubic centimeter of solution.

Dextrose and levulose are sugars of the same chemical formula $C_6H_{12}O_6$. The molecules are long chains containing multiples of the combination of 24 atoms expressed in the formula. These two molecules have their atoms arrayed in oppositely twisted chains to produce rotation in opposite directions. So important is the property of optical activity in their analysis that they have been named for the direction in which they rotate the plane of polarization.

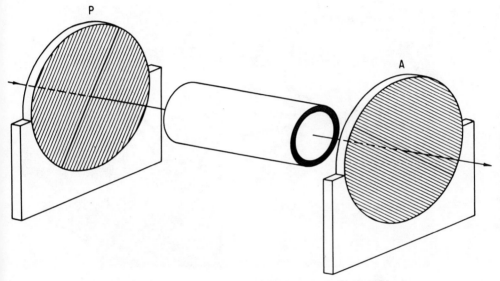

Figure 337. Polarimeter for measuring the rotation of the plane of polarization by optically active solutions.

Figure 337 shows a polarimeter of polarizer and analyzer with a cylinder of optically active solution between. In the sugar industry this special polarimeter is called a *saccharimeter*. If the direction of rotation of the plane of polarization as observed by a person looking into the analyzer is clockwise, the optically active substance is called *dextrorotatory* (right-handed). If the rotation relative to the observer is counterclockwise, the substance is called *levorotatory* (left-handed).

19.2 Rotation of the Plane of Polarization of Microwaves

In discussing rotation of the plane of polarization by sugar solutions or quartz crystals, the instructor often drives a nut along a bolt toward the class while the class notes the direction of rotation of the nut. If he then turns the opposite end of the bolt toward the class and again drives the nut toward the class, the direction of rotation is still the same relative to the observers. We thus note that if individual molecules rotate the plane of polarization, solutions of randomly oriented molecules also rotate the plane of polarization of a beam.

If microwaves are employed, then the individual rotator is large enough to be seen. If a parallel-wire screen is set between transmitter and intensity

Figure 338. "Spiral staircase" in a wave guide for producing rotation of the plane of polarization.

meter of Fig, 269 with its plane perpendicular to AB and the wires making an angle of 45° with the electric field, then the transmitted beam is plane polarized at right angles to the wires. However, only half the intensity is transmitted. If three parallel-wire screens are used with their planes separated by $\frac{1}{2}$ in., the wires of the first, second, and third screen from the source making angles of 105°, 120°, and 135°, respectively, with the electric field from the transmitter, the amplitude $\mathbf{u}$ of the transmitted beam relative to $\mathbf{u}_0$ of the incident beam is

$$\frac{\mathbf{u}}{\mathbf{u}_0} = (\cos 15°)^3 = 0.90.$$

If n such screens are used to rotate the beam through angle θ,

$$\frac{\mathbf{u}}{\mathbf{u}_0} = \left(\cos \frac{\theta}{n}\right)^n, \tag{19.1}$$

and the intensity I relative to I_0 of the incident beam is

$$\frac{I}{I_0} = \left(\cos\frac{\theta}{n}\right)^{2n}. \qquad (19.2)$$

If θ is less than $90°$ and n becomes large, I approaches I_0. The plane of polarization is rotated without loss in intensity.

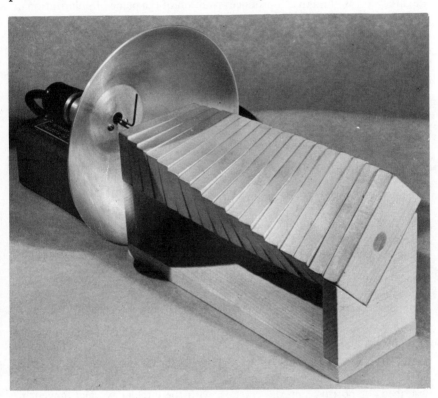

Figure 339. Twisted wave guide of wooden blocks painted with silver paint.

If a piece of cylindrical wave guide 0.7λ in diameter is employed (a tomato can will do), a series of $\frac{1}{8}$ in. diameter wires extending diametrically across the cylinder may replace the parallel-wire screens. Figure 338 is a photograph of such a rotator designed to rotate the beam through $60°$. If the opposite end of the wave guide is turned toward the observer it is still levorotatory.

We noted in the demonstration of Fig. 63 with rectangular wave guide that the wave was transmitted only when the electric field was parallel to the shorter edge. Rectangular wave guide is used in microwave circuits because it maintains the direction of polarization. Twisted rectangular wave guide is built to rotate the plane of polarization. Figure 339 is a twisted wave guide made of wooden blocks on a wooden dowel for demonstration purposes. The four walls of the wave guide are coated with silver paint.

19.3 Rotation of the Plane of Polarization by Quartz

If we cut a plate from a quartz crystal with its surfaces perpendicular to the optic axis, we find that it produces rotation of the plane of polarization of light transmitted along the optic axis. There are two kinds of quartz crystals, dextrorotatory and levorotatory. The natural faces of the two kinds of quartz crystals are observed to be mirror images of each other as indicated in Fig. 340.

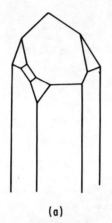 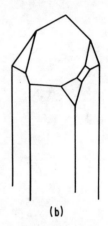

(a)   (b)

Figure 340. The natural faces of right- and left-handed quartz crystals are mirror images of each other. (a) Left-handed quartz. (b) Right-handed quartz.

The optical activity of quartz is a property of the crystal and not of its individual molecules. Fused quartz in which the molecules are randomly polarized shows no rotation of the plane of polarization.

The Huygens wavelets for quartz are not quite those which we have described for positive uniaxial crystals, with the circular wavelet tangent to the enclosed ellipse at the axis of rotation. For quartz the outer wavelet bulges slightly at the optic axis while the inner wavelet is compressed leaving a gap between the two. The gap shown in Fig. 341 is an exaggeration. The difference is too small to show in a scale drawing. The explanation of why the plane of polarization of light traveling along the optic axis of quartz is rotated was made by Fresnel.

19.4 Fresnel's Analysis of Optical Activity

Fresnel noted that linear simple harmonic motion may be treated as the resultant of two circular motions in opposite directions, as indicated in Fig. 342(a). The resultant of the horizontal components of the rotating vectors E_R

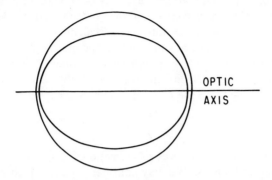

Figure 341. Huygens wavelets for a quartz crystal with the gap between the wavelets on the optic axis greatly exaggerated.

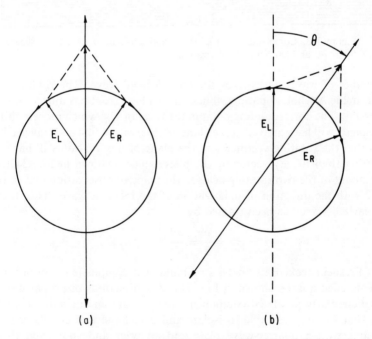

Figure 342. (a) Simple harmonic motion may be treated as the resultant of two circular motions in opposite directions. (b) If in a given plane E_R rotates more rapidly then E_L, the resultant plane polarization will be rotated to the right.

and E_L is zero. A plane-polarized wave may be thought of as the resultant of two circularly polarized waves, one right- and one left-handed. This is the case of transmission along the optic axis of calcite.

If a plane-polarized beam is incident on the quartz plate along the axis it is resolved into two circularly polarized components. If the right-handed component has a larger velocity and wavelength than the left-hand wave, the two waves emerging from the plate of thickness d have a phase difference

$$\delta = \frac{2\pi d}{\lambda} (n_L - n_R), \tag{19.3}$$

where n_L and n_R are the indices of refraction for the left- and right-hand circularly polarized waves. We may consider a plate which is some integer

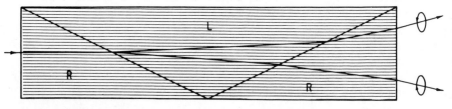

Figure 343. Composite prism of right- and left-handed quartz for separating the right- and left-handed polarizations.

number of wavelengths thick for the left-hand wave. The rotating field E_L has made N whole rotations while a given phase front has moved through the crystal. The corresponding point in the wave of E_R, which moves with higher velocity, will have arrived at the plane of observation first and traveled beyond, so that the rotating vector E_R in the plane of observation will have rotated farther than the E_L vector by the phase angle δ shown in Fig. 342(b). The resultant of the two rotating fields in the plane of observation makes an angle $\delta/2$ with the direction of polarization of the incident wave. Thus the plane-polarized wave has been rotated by

$$\theta = \frac{\delta}{2} = \frac{\pi d}{\lambda} (n_L - n_R). \tag{19.4}$$

Fresnel checked his analysis by building a composite prism of right- and left-handed quartz, shown in Fig. 343. The directions of propagation of the two circularly polarized components were separated angularly at each step, so that Fresnel was able to isolate and detect the two circularly polarized beams with a quarter-wave plate and analyzer and show that they were oppositely polarized.

The 60° quartz prisms for ultraviolet spectroscopy are so designed that the ray will be along the optic axis at minimum deviation. In this case the two oppositely circularly polarized waves of sodium light are separated by only $\frac{1}{2}'$. In the ultraviolet the separation is much greater. To bring the two components back together, Cornu built a quartz prism of two crystals, one left- and one right-handed, as shown in Fig. 344. The Cornu prism is commonly used in ultraviolet spectrographs.

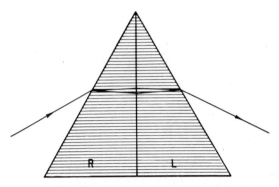

Figure 344. Cornu prism.

19.5 Rotatory Dispersion

Rotation of the plane of polarization is strongly dependent on wavelength. This method of separating wavelengths is called *rotatory dispersion*. The rotation by a given thickness of quartz crystal or optically active solution satisfies the form of Eq. (15.1) which Cauchy found for the dispersion by refraction through transparent materials. The specific rotation

$$\alpha = A + \frac{B}{\lambda^2}, \tag{19.5}$$

where A and B are constants for the material. For quartz, α is the rotation in degrees per millimeter of thickness.

Figure 345 is a plot of the specific rotation of quartz against wavelength. If a quartz plate 1 mm thick, cut with its faces perpendicular to the optic axis, is placed in the polarimeter of Fig. 325, bands of color of the visible spectrum may be observed in turn from red to violet as the axis of transmission of the analyzer is rotated in either direction from the position parallel to that of the polarizer.

If the rotations of two colors differ by 180°, they will be transmitted together by the analyzer and may be seen as bands in a spectroscope. For instance, we note from the graph of Fig. 345 that, if the thickness of the quartz plate were increased to 5 mm, the red and violet would be transmitted together. Turning the analyzer through 90° we observe the complement of this mixture of colors. As the thickness of the quartz plate increases, the number of bands of visible spectrum transmitted by the analyzer increases.

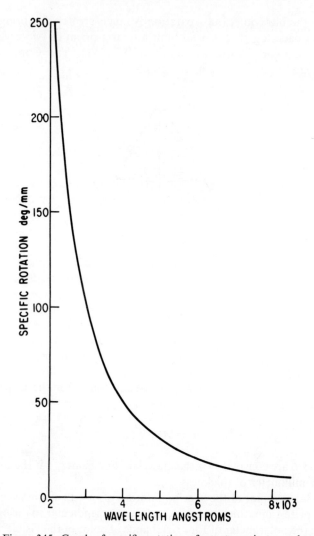

Figure 345. Graph of specific rotation of quartz against wavelength.

19.6 The Faraday Effect

We recall from Chapter I that Faraday searched for 20 years for some effect of electric or magnetic fields on light. In 1845 he discovered that when a beam of plane-polarized light was passed through a piece of lead glass in a direction parallel to the lines of force of the magnetic field, the plane of polarization was rotated. Faraday observed that when the light was reflected back along the same path through the magnetic field the direction of rotation was the same. By producing multiple reflections and obtaining angles of rotation in proportion to the number of times of transit, Faraday discovered a similar *temporary optical activity* for other solids and liquids in the field.

This is quite different from a beam reflected back along the optic axis of a quartz crystal, undergoing two rotations in opposite directions so that they cancel.

The angle of rotation in the Faraday effect is

$$\theta = VHL, \tag{19.6}$$

where H is the magnetic field strength, L the length of path in the magnetic field, θ the angle of rotation, and V Verdet's constant.

If the direction of rotation of the plane polarization is the same as the direction of a conventional current that would produce the magnetic field, V is a positive constant. Diamagnetic materials have positive Verdet constants, while paramagnetic and ferromagnetic substances have negative Verdet constants.

Because of the high internal magnetic fields, thin films of nickel, iron, and cobalt exhibit a strong Faraday effect. For these materials the intensity of magnetization I must replace the field strength H.

A century after its discovery the Faraday effect is finding its first engineering application in the microwave region of the spectrum.

19.7 The Faraday Effect of Microwaves

Until recent years all materials with high magnetic permeability have been electric conductors which were reflectors of waves, and permitted appreciable penetration to only a fraction of a wavelength. Thus the Faraday effect was observed only in thin films of iron.

Recently there have been developed several ceramics by intimately mixing combinations of nickel, zinc, manganese, magnesium, or cobalt oxide with iron oxide. The mixture is pressed to the desired shape and fired. These nonconducting magnetic materials are called *ferrites*. The resulting crystal structure is the same as that of the natural magnetite.

If a rod of permeable ferrite is placed along the axis in a cylindrical wave guide and an electromagnet wound around the wave guide, the strong magnetic field in the ferrite causes the plane of polarization of the microwaves to be rotated.[2] As in the case of the Faraday effect for light waves, the direction of rotation is independent of propagation of the waves.

This independence of the direction of rotation from the direction of propagation permits us to design a section of wave guide which is unidirectional for microwaves and thus an *isolator*. The wave from the source enters the isolator by a rectangular wave guide as shown on the left side of Fig. 346, and thence to the circular wave guide with a cylinder F of ferrite lying in the

[2] P. S. Epstein, *Revs. Mod. Phys.*, **28**, 3 (1956).

magnetic field along the axis. We may adjust the strength of the field so that the plane of polarization of the microwaves will be rotated 45°, and thus be transmitted through the rectangular wave guide on the other end which is set to transmit that polarization. Thence the wave may go to a load, to measuring

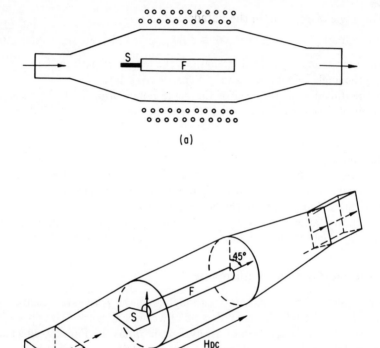

Figure 346. (a) Microwave isolator employing the Faraday effect in a ferrite rod F in the field of an electromagnet. (b) The microwaves entering on the left have their plane of polarization rotated 45° in the ferrite so that they pass through the rectangular wave guide on the right. Reflected waves are rotated another 45°, a total of 90°, and absorbed by sheet S.

equipment, or through a horn into free space. In each of these cases there will be reflections including those from objects in free space. The reflected waves pass through the magnetic field again and are rotated another 45° so that they can not be transmitted by the wave guide to the source. This wave is absorbed by a sheet S which is impregnated with carbon and set parallel to the electric field of the reflected wave.

We may illustrate the use of the isolator in microwave diffraction measurements of Chapter XII. When a metal sheet is inserted in the microwave beam, it may reflect back a sufficiently intense wave to the source to react on the oscillator and cause a readable change in the plate current of the oscillator tube and a serious change in output power of the oscillator. The isolator renders the output power of the source independent of the diffracting objects in the field.

The Faraday effect is the result of the spin momenta of electrons about axes through their centers as affected by the constant axial magnetic field and the high-frequency magnetic field at right angles to it. The spin momenta of electrons in the ferrite align with the constant magnetic field parallel to the axis of the ferrite rod. The weaker high-frequency field is at right angles to the spin momentum of an electron, and will thus produce a torque on the electron at right angles to both the constant and alternating magnetic field. When a torque acts on a body at right angles to its angular momentum it is caused to precess. If the frequency of the microwave beam is much higher than the frequency of precession the effects of the alternating fields cancel. However, if the microwave frequency is close to the frequency of precession, the angular momentum of the electron is tipped in its precession from the direction of the constant field. The rate of precession may be adjusted to the microwave frequency by altering the strength of the constant magnetic field. The spinning electrons are magnetic dipoles. Their high-frequency precession yields a corresponding high-frequency permeability, and thus index of refraction.

As in treating the wave along the axis of a quartz crystal, we may divide the plane-polarized wave incident on the ferrite into two circularly polarized waves rotating in opposite directions. The one that rotates with the precession of the electrons will be retarded. The index of refraction of the wave rotating in the opposite direction will be unaffected by the magnetic field. The direction of rotation of the plane-polarized wave is the same as the direction of rotation of the higher velocity circularly polarized component.

PROBLEMS FOR CHAPTER XIX

19.2.1. A plane-polarized beam of microwaves passes through two parallel-wire screens in series $\frac{1}{2}$ in. apart and set with their planes at right angles to the beam. The wires of the first and second screens make angles of 60° and 30°, respectively, with the initial incident beam. What fraction I/I_0 of the intensity is transmitted?

19.4.2. Determine the difference in the two indices of refraction n_L and n_R for the two circularly polarized components of light at 6000 A traveling parallel to the optic axis of quartz. Use the graph of Fig. 345.

19.5.3. Find the constants of Eq. (19.5) for quartz in the visible region from values of the specific rotation at 4000 A and 5000 A given in the graph of Fig. 345.

Differential Equation of Longitudinal Waves

ON THE basis of Newton's second law and Hooke's law we shall show that, if the pressure varies with distance in a particular direction in a solid or liquid, a longitudinal displacement wave or pulse will be propagated in the medium along the direction of the pressure variation. We shall derive a differential equation which will describe the propagation of waves in a continuous medium extending in all directions without boundaries. The density ρ of the medium will not vary effectively with pressure. Thus the equation we derive will not apply to gases. We shall confine our attention to a long region of rectangular cross section A perpendicular to the x axis of the coordinates indicated in Fig. 347. Let the pressure on the left-hand side of the element of thickness dx exceed that on the right-hand side. The force on the left-hand face is pA. That on the right-hand face is $A(p - (\partial p/\partial x)\,dx)$, and the resultant force f on the elemental section of volume $A\,dx$ is

$$f = A\frac{\partial p}{\partial x}\,dx. \tag{A1}$$

From Newton's second law,

$$f = \rho A\,dx\,\frac{\partial^2 \mathbf{u}}{\partial t^2}. \tag{A2}$$

The elemental mass is $\rho A\ dx$. The displacement of its center of gravity in the x direction we shall call **u**. From Hooke's law we obtain

$$p = B\frac{\partial \mathbf{u}}{\partial x}.$$ (A3)

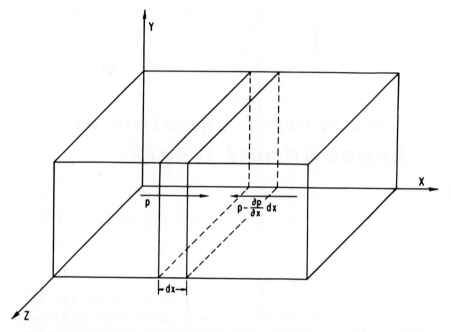

Figure 347. Section of a continuous medium in which the pressure varies in the x direction.

The pressure p is the *stress*, the displacement per length $\partial \mathbf{u}/\partial x$ is the *strain*, and B the bulk modulus of elasticity. Combining Eqs. (A1) and (A2), we obtain

$$\frac{\partial p}{\partial x} = \rho\frac{\partial^2 \mathbf{u}}{\partial t^2}.$$ (A4)

Taking the partial derivative of p with respect to x in Eq. (A3), we obtain

$$\frac{\partial p}{\partial x} = B\frac{\partial^2 u}{\partial x^2}.$$ (A5)

The subtraction of Eq. (A5) from Eq. (A4) yields

$$\frac{\partial^2 u}{\partial t^2} = \frac{B}{\rho}\frac{\partial^2 \mathbf{u}}{\partial x^2}.$$ (A6)

We may show that the descriptive, or kinematical, wave equation of Sec. 2.4 satisfies the differential equation, Eq. (A6), derived from the dynamical laws of mechanics. For a longitudinal wave the kinematical wave equation may be expressed as

$$u = Re^{(j2\pi/\lambda)(vt - x)}. \tag{A7}$$

Taking the second partials of the displacement **u** with respect to position x and time t, we obtain the simultaneous equations

$$\frac{\partial^2 \mathbf{u}}{\partial x^2} = -R \frac{4\pi^2}{\lambda^2} e^{(j2\pi/\lambda)(vt - x)} \tag{A8}$$

$$\frac{\partial^2 \mathbf{u}}{\partial t^2} = -R \frac{4\pi^2 v^2}{\lambda^2} e^{(j2\pi/\lambda)(vt - x)}. \tag{A9}$$

Eliminating the common factors from Eqs. (A8) and (A9), we obtain

$$\frac{\partial^2 \mathbf{u}}{\partial t^2} = v^2 \frac{\partial^2 \mathbf{u}}{\partial x^2}. \tag{A10}$$

The proportionality constant v^2 in this kinematics equation is equal to the constant B/ρ in the dynamics equation. Thus we may express the velocity of the wave in terms of the physical properties of the medium,

$$v = \sqrt{\frac{B}{\rho}}. \tag{A11}$$

Equation (A7) is a special solution of the differential equation of wave motion. The general solution of the second-order partial differential equation, Eq. (A10), is beyond the scope of this textbook. However, we might generalize somewhat more by showing that, if u is any function of $(vt - x)$, expressed by

$$\mathbf{u} = F(vt - x), \tag{A12}$$

this equation also satisfies the differential equation of wave motion. Taking the second partials of **u** with respect to x and t and expressing the second derivative of F by a double prime, we obtain

$$\frac{\partial^2 \mathbf{u}}{\partial x^2} = F''(vt - x) \tag{A13}$$

$$\frac{\partial^2 \mathbf{u}}{\partial t^2} = v^2 F''(vt - x). \tag{A14}$$

Eliminating the common factors, we obtain again Eq. (A10).

If the wave is periodic and the particles of the medium are undergoing longitudinal simple harmonic motion, the acceleration may be expressed in terms of the displacement as in Eq. (2.4),

$$\frac{\partial^2 \mathbf{u}}{\partial t^2} = -\left(\frac{2\pi}{T}\right)^2 \mathbf{u}. \tag{A15}$$

Substituting for the acceleration $\partial^2 u/\partial t^2$ from Eq. (A15) in Eq. (A10), and noting that $vT = \lambda$, we obtain

$$\frac{\partial^2 \mathbf{u}}{\partial x^2} = -\left(\frac{2\pi}{\lambda}\right)^2 \mathbf{u}. \tag{A16}$$

For simplicity we may replace $2\pi/\lambda$ by the constant k, and Eq. (A16) becomes

$$\frac{\partial^2 \mathbf{u}}{\partial x^2} = -k^2\mathbf{u}. \tag{A17}$$

This is another form of the differential equation of a plane wave traveling in the x direction. By letting the pressure p vary in the directions y and z as well as x, we could have derived a more general differential equation of wave motion

$$\frac{\partial^2 \mathbf{u}}{\partial x^2} + \frac{\partial^2 \mathbf{u}}{\partial y^2} + \frac{\partial^2 \mathbf{u}}{\partial z^2} = -k\mathbf{u}. \tag{A18}$$

Derivation of Kirchhoff's Formulation of Fresnel's Theory of Diffraction

FROM Green's theorem which is derived in textbooks of mathematics,[1,2]

$$\iint \left(\mathbf{u} \frac{\partial \mathbf{v}}{\partial n} - v \frac{\partial \mathbf{u}}{\partial n} \right) d\sigma$$

$$= \iiint \left[\mathbf{u} \left(\frac{\partial^2 \mathbf{v}}{\partial x^2} + \frac{\partial^2 \mathbf{v}}{\partial y^2} + \frac{\partial^2 \mathbf{v}}{\partial z^2} \right) - \mathbf{v} \left(\frac{\partial^2 \mathbf{u}}{\partial x^2} + \frac{\partial^2 \mathbf{u}}{\partial y^2} + \frac{\partial^2 \mathbf{u}}{\partial z^2} \right) \right] d\tau. \quad \text{(A19)}$$

The surface integral is taken over a closed surface and the volume integral throughout the volume enclosed by that surface. The elements of surface and volume are represented by $d\sigma$ and $d\tau$. The outward normal to the surface is represented by the vector n. The scalar functions $\mathbf{u}$ and $\mathbf{v}$ together with their first and second derivatives must be single valued and continuous throughout the space inside the closed region.

[1] C. H. Page, *Physical Mathematics:* New York, Van Nostrand (1955) Secs. 1–7.
[2] F. B. Hildebrand, *Advanced Calculus for Engineers:* Englewood Cliffs, N.J., Prentice-Hall (1952) Sec. 6.13.

We shall choose the functions **u** and **v** so that they satisfy the wave equation, Eq. (A18).

$$\frac{\partial^2 \mathbf{u}}{\partial x^2} + \frac{\partial^2 \mathbf{u}}{\partial y^2} + \frac{\partial^2 \mathbf{u}}{\partial z^2} + k\mathbf{u} = 0 \tag{A20}$$

$$\frac{\partial^2 \mathbf{v}}{\partial x^2} + \frac{\partial^2 \mathbf{v}}{\partial y^2} + \frac{\partial^2 \mathbf{v}}{\partial z^2} + k\mathbf{v} = 0. \tag{A21}$$

If there are no sources inside the closed surface, **u** and **v** satisfy Poisson's equation which is expressed

$$\frac{\partial^2 \mathbf{u}}{\partial x^2} + \frac{\partial^2 \mathbf{u}}{\partial y^2} + \frac{\partial^2 \mathbf{u}}{\partial z^2} = 0 \tag{A22}$$

$$\frac{\partial^2 \mathbf{v}}{\partial^2 x^2} + \frac{\partial^2 \mathbf{v}}{\partial y^2} + \frac{\partial^2 \mathbf{v}}{\partial z^2} = 0, \tag{A23}$$

and Green's theorem becomes simply

$$\iint \left(\mathbf{u}\,\frac{\partial \mathbf{v}}{\partial n} - \mathbf{v}\,\frac{\partial \mathbf{u}}{\partial n} \right) d\sigma = 0. \tag{A24}$$

We shall use this special case of Green's theorem to find the complex amplitude at a point P inside the closed surface due to a source at point S outside by integrating the effects of all longitudinal wave disturbances arriving at point P from the surface.

Let **v** be the wave function

$$\mathbf{v} = \frac{e^{-jkr}}{r}, \tag{A25}$$

in which r is measured from P and k is $2\pi/\lambda$. Note that time is omitted from the phase expression. The factor $e^{j2\pi t/T}$ would cancel from each term of Eq. (A18).

The function **v** of Eq. (A25) has a singularity at P where r becomes zero. In order that **v** may satisfy the conditions of continuity required in Green's theorem, we shall exclude a small region around P from the original volume by a spherical surface with its center at P. The resulting volume to which Green's theorem applies lies between the small spherical surface and the original surface, this volume being represented by the shaded portion of Fig. 348.

We shall find the value of the integral Eq. (A24) over the surface of the sphere in the limit as the radius of the sphere approaches zero. The element of surface area may be expressed in terms of the radius and the corresponding element of solid angle $d\omega$ subtended by $d\sigma$ at the center by the expression $d\sigma = r^2\, d\omega$. Over the surface of the sphere the outward normal from the shaded region of Fig. 348 is opposite to the radius so that $\partial/\partial n = -\partial/\partial r$ and the integral over the sphere becomes

$$\iint_{\text{sphere}} \left(-\mathbf{u}\frac{\partial \mathbf{v}}{\partial n} + \mathbf{v}\frac{\partial \mathbf{u}}{\partial r} \right) r^2 \, d\omega$$

$$= \iint_{\text{sphere}} \left(\mathbf{u}rjke^{-jkr} + \mathbf{u}e^{-jkr} + re^{-jkr}\frac{\partial \mathbf{u}}{\partial n} \right) d\omega. \quad \text{(A26)}$$

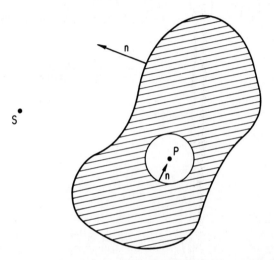

Figure 348. Green's theorem applies to the shaded volume. The outward normals are indicated for the outer surface and the spherical surface about P.

We shall let $\mathbf{u}$ be a spherical wave function

$$\mathbf{u} = \frac{e^{-jkr_S}}{r_S},$$

in which r_S is measured from the source S. On the surface of the sphere $\mathbf{u}$ and $\partial \mathbf{u}/\partial r$ are finite. Thus in the limit as r approaches zero the first and third terms become zero, and e^{-jkr} becomes unity. Also as the sphere becomes small the amplitude $\mathbf{u}$ inside the sphere becomes constant and we shall call it $\mathbf{u}_P$. Thus the integral over the sphere becomes

$$\mathbf{u}_P \iint_{\text{sphere}} d\omega = 4\pi \mathbf{u}_P. \quad \text{(A27)}$$

The integral over the two surfaces now becomes

$$4\pi \mathbf{u}_P + \iint \left[\mathbf{u}\frac{\partial}{\partial n}\left(\frac{e^{-jkr}}{r} \right) - \frac{e^{-jkr}}{r}\frac{\partial \mathbf{u}}{\partial n} \right] d\sigma = 0. \quad \text{(A28)}$$

The differential in the first term of the integral may be expressed

$$\frac{\partial}{\partial n}\left(\frac{e^{-jkr}}{r}\right) = e^{-jkr}\frac{\partial}{\partial n}\left(\frac{1}{r}\right) - \frac{jk}{r}e^{-jkr}\left(\frac{\partial r}{\partial n}\right). \tag{A29}$$

Substituting this result in Eq. (A28) and solving for $\mathbf{u}_P$, we obtain

$$\mathbf{u}_P = \frac{1}{4\pi}\int\int\left\{\frac{e^{-jkr}}{r}\left(\frac{\partial \mathbf{u}}{\partial n}\right) - \mathbf{u}e^{-jkr}\frac{\partial}{\partial n}\left(\frac{1}{r}\right) + \frac{jk\mathbf{u}e^{-jkr}}{r}\left(\frac{\partial r}{\partial n}\right)\right\}\,d\sigma. \tag{A30}$$

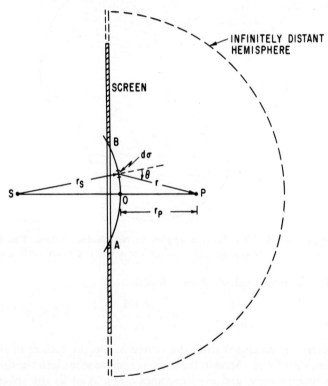

Figure 349. The surface of integration includes the absorbing screen, the wave front AOB, and the hemisphere of infinite radius.

This formulation by Kirchhoff is of general use in treating diffraction of longitudinal waves. We may now give physical interpretation to $\mathbf{u}$ and $\mathbf{u}_P$. The function $\mathbf{u}$ is the complex amplitude of the wave arriving at the surface element $d\sigma$ from source S. The surface integral is the summation of wavelets arriving at P from elements of surface $d\sigma$.

Kirchhoff's formulation may also be employed to determine the amplitude and phase of transverse electromagnetic waves when the source S and point of observation P both lie on the axis of a circular aperture in an opaque screen. For this special case indicated in Fig. 349, the amplitude and phase are independent of the direction of polarization and Eq. (A30) is identical for sound and electromagnetic waves. The surface of integration includes the portion of spherical wave front AOB of Fig. 349, the absorbing screen, and a hemisphere of infinite radius on the opposite side of the screen from the source. The contributions from the screen and infinitely distant hemisphere are zero, so that the integration is made only over the portion of the wave front AOB bounded by the edge of the circular aperture.

Every point of the wave on the remaining wave front is of the same amplitude and phase so we shall represent it by the constant

$$\mathbf{u_0} = \frac{e^{-jk_S}}{r_S},$$

where r_S is the distance from the source S to the surface element $d\sigma$. The partial $\partial r/\partial n$ is equal to the cosine of the angle between the outward normal n to the closed surface and the direction of r from P to the surface element. In optics we are more concerned with an equal and opposite angle θ, which is between the direction of the incident ray to the element of surface and the reradiated ray from the element to P. Thus $\partial r/\partial n = \cos\theta$. Substituting in Eq. (A30), we obtain

$$\mathbf{u}_P = \frac{\mathbf{u_0}}{4\pi} \int\int \left\{ \frac{e^{-jkr}}{r} \left[\left(jk + \frac{1}{r_S} \right) + \left(jk + \frac{1}{r} \right) \cos\theta \right] \right\} d\sigma. \qquad (A31)$$

If we wish to let the wavelet from the point O on the wave front be the reference wavelet, the phase angle may be changed to

$$\alpha = k(r - r_P),$$

where r_P is the distance OP. For this special case that is applicable to optics, Kirchhoff's equation becomes

$$\mathbf{u}_P = \frac{\mathbf{u_0}}{4\pi} \int\int \left[\frac{j2\pi e^{-j\alpha}}{\lambda r} (1 + \cos\theta) + \frac{e^{-j\alpha}}{rr_S} + \frac{e^{-j\alpha}\cos\theta}{r^2} \right] d\sigma. \qquad (A32)$$

TABLE I. FRESNEL INTEGRALS

v	Real	Imaginary	v	Real	Imaginary
0.0	0.0000	0.0000	2.6	0.3890	0.5500
0.1	0.1000	0.0005	2.7	0.3925	0.4529
0.2	0.1999	0.0042	2.8	0.4675	0.3915
0.3	0.2994	0.0141	2.9	0.5624	0.4101
0.4	0.3975	0.0334	3.0	0.6058	0.4963
0.5	0.4923	0.0647	3.1	0.5616	0.5818
0.6	0.5811	0.1105	3.2	0.4664	0.5933
0.7	0.6597	0.1721	3.3	0.4058	0.5192
0.8	0.7230	0.2493	3.4	0.4385	0.4296
0.9	0.7648	0.3398	3.5	0.5326	0.4152
1.0	0.7799	0.4383	3.6	0.5880	0.4923
1.1	0.7638	0.5365	3.7	0.5420	0.5750
1.2	0.7154	0.6234	3.8	0.4481	0.5656
1.3	0.6386	0.6863	3.9	0.4223	0.4752
1.4	0.5431	0.7135	4.0	0.4984	0.4204
1.5	0.4453	0.6975	4.1	0.5738	0.4758
1.6	0.3655	0.6389	4.2	0.5418	0.5633
1.7	0.3238	0.5492	4.3	0.4494	0.5540
1.8	0.3336	0.4508	4.4	0.4383	0.4622
1.9	0.3944	0.3734	4.5	0.5261	0.4342
2.0	0.4882	0.3434	4.6	0.5673	0.5162
2.1	0.5815	0.3743	4.7	0.4914	0.5672
2.2	0.6363	0.4557	4.8	0.4338	0.4968
2.3	0.6266	0.5531	4.9	0.5002	0.4350
2.4	0.5550	0.6197	5.0	0.5637	0.4992
2.5	0.4574	0.6192			

TABLE II | BESSEL INTEGRALS 489

TABLE II. BESSEL INTEGRALS

y	$\int_0^y J_0(t)\,dt$	$\int_0^y Y_0(t)\,dt$	y	$\int_0^y J_0(t)\,dt$	$\int_0^y Y_0(t)\,dt$
0.0	0.0000	0.0000	5.2	0.6865	0.1355
0.2	0.1993	−0.3457	5.4	0.6713	0.0681
0.4	0.3947	−0.5095	5.6	0.6699	0.0004
0.6	0.5822	−0.5993	5.8	0.6819	−0.0652
0.8	0.7583	−0.6379	6.0	0.7062	−0.1260
1.0	0.9197	−0.6371	6.2	0.7416	−0.1798
1.2	1.0636	−0.6049	6.4	0.7863	−0.2247
1.4	1.1875	−0.5478	6.6	0.8382	−0.2593
1.6	1.2898	−0.4716	6.8	0.8951	−0.2825
1.8	1.3694	−0.3814	7.0	0.9546	−0.2938
2.0	1.4258	−0.2822	7.2	1.0144	−0.2930
2.2	1.4591	−0.1787	7.4	1.0719	−0.2804
2.4	1.4703	−0.0753	7.6	1.1251	−0.2570
2.6	1.4607	0.0242	7.8	1.1719	−0.2239
2.8	1.4323	0.1162	8.0	1.2107	−0.1827
3.0	1.3876	0.1977	8.2	1.2402	−0.1352
3.2	1.3293	0.2662	8.4	1.2594	−0.0834
3.4	1.2606	0.3200	8.6	1.2678	−0.0294
3.6	1.1847	0.3578	8.8	1.2653	0.0245
3.8	1.1050	0.3790	9.0	1.2523	0.0763
4.0	1.0247	0.3837	9.2	1.2295	0.1239
4.2	0.9471	0.3725	9.4	1.1980	0.1655
4.4	0.8750	0.3467	9.6	1.1593	0.1997
4.6	0.8110	0.3078	9.8	1.1150	0.2252
4.8	0.7572	0.2580	10.0	1.0670	0.2413
5.0	0.7153	0.1997			

Answers to Alternate Problems

Chapter II

2.3.3. $y = R$.

2.5.5. The amplitude of the resultant wave is 4.4 cm and it lags the wave of 2 cm amplitude by 37°.

2.7.11. Power_A: Power_B: Power_R = 3.9: 2.4: 6.1. Since B lags A by 90°, $P_R = P_A + P_B$.

2.8.13. 0.24 newton.

Chapter III

3.3.1. If we let $\mathbf{u}_2$ lead $\mathbf{u}_1$ by α, then the resultant

$$\mathbf{u} = \left(2u_1 \cos \frac{\alpha}{2}\right)\left[\cos\left(\omega t + \frac{\alpha}{2}\right) + j \sin\left(\omega t + \frac{\alpha}{2}\right)\right].$$

3.6.5. 90° lead.

Chapter IV

4.2.1. 1.86×10^5 miles/sec.

4.3.3. 18 miles/sec.

Chapter V

5.1.1. $y = 2Y \cos \dfrac{2\pi x}{\lambda} \sin \dfrac{2\pi t}{T}$.

5.7.5. 19; 3.

Chapter VI

6.1.3. 0.37; 0.21.

6.1.7. If we measure from source one to source two, points of phase opposition occur at $x = (2n + 1)\lambda/4$ or 0.25λ, 0.75λ, 1.25λ, and so forth.

6.1.9. 4; 2; 1.33; 1.
6.2.13. 0.1λ.
6.3.15. Intensities 1.8; 0.66.
6.7.19. 2λ (nearest integer).

Chapter VII

7.3.1. 3.89×10^5.
7.4.3. 103.
7.8.5. 2.04×10^3.
7.10.7. 6.0×10^4 m.

Chapter VIII

8.4.5. $r_{\text{glass}} = 0.20$; $r_{\text{water}} = 0.14$.
8.4.7. 0.85.
8.6.9. 3.0; 1 cm.
8.7.11. 6000 A.

Chapter IX

9.3.3. 0.96; 0.83.
9.4.5. 0.40.
9.5.7. 1.2 A.
9.5.9. 14.7 m.
9.7.11. 6.

Chapter X

10.4.9. 500.
10.7.11. 3.2°.

Chapter XI

11.2.1. $1 + \cos\theta$ is 2.0 for all r/λ. $(\lambda\cos\theta)/2\pi r$ is 1.59, 0.159, and 0.0159 when r/λ is 0.1, 1.0, and 10, respectively.
11.6.9. 0.69 cm.
11.7.11. 0.047 cm.

Chapter XII

12.2.1. 1.1λ.
12.8.3. λ and 614λ.

Chapter XIII

13.3.3. Magnetomotive force $= \left(\dfrac{\partial H}{\partial z} - \dfrac{\partial H}{\partial x} \right) dx\, dz$.
13.8.9. $S = E \times H$.

Chapter XIV

14.3.1. The blue light is scattered 4.4 times as much as the red.
14.4.3. 8.7.

Chapter XV

15.8.5. 9×10^{-3}.

Chapter XVI
16.4.1. 0.25.
16.5.3. 83.7°; 6.3°.
16.8.7. Shore is seen at an angle of 48.7° with the normal.
16.12.9. The line is 729 times as intense as the surrounding spectrum.

Chapter XVII
17.1.1. 1.49.
17.5.3. 36°00′. 5 significant figures.

Chapter XVIII
18.2.1. 3.0 cm.
18.4.3. The horizontal amplitude is 1.73 times the vertical.
18.7.5. 4.1 × 10³ v.

Chapter XIX
19.2.1. 0.56.
19.5.3. $A = -50°/mm$.
       $B = 4.0 \times 10^5 \, A$ deg/mm.

Index

Main references are given in boldface type